INTRODUCTION TO
Electronic Analogue Computers

BY

C. A. A. WASS

formerly Superintendent of
the G. W. Dynamical Analysis Division,
Royal Aircraft Establishment, Farnborough, Hants

AND

K. C. GARNER

Lecturer in Control and Simulation,
Department of Electrical and Control Engineering,
The College of Aeronautics, Cranfield, Beds.

SECOND REVISED
AND ENLARGED EDITION

PERGAMON PRESS

OXFORD · LONDON · EDINBURGH · NEW YORK
PARIS · FRANKFURT

Pergamon Press Ltd., Headington Hill Hall, Oxford
4 & 5 Fitzroy Square, London W.1

Pergamon Press (Scotland) Ltd., 2 & 3 Teviot Place, Edinburgh 1

Pergamon Press Inc., 122 East 55th St., New York 22, N.Y.

Pergamon Press GmbH, Kaiserstrasse 75, Frankfurt-am-Main

First edition 1955
Second revised and enlarged edition 1965

Library of Congress Catalog Card No. 65–12670

2139

CONTENTS

v

FROM THE PREFACE TO THE
FIRST EDITION

This monograph is based on the ideas and experience of a group of workers at the Royal Aircraft Establishment, Farnborough, Hants. This group was formed in 1945 under the leadership of W. R. Thomas, then at R.A.E., who adopted and developed computing techniques employed at the Telecommunications Research Establishment, Malvern (now part of the Radar Research Establishment) by a team which included F. C. Williams, F. J. U. Ritson, R. J. Lees, R. Aspinall and H. Sutcliffe. The R.A.E. group has grown continuously since that time, both in numbers of staff and number and complexity of computers, until it is now one of the largest groups of its kind in the country.

Substantial contributions to the work of this group have been made by: D. W. Allen, E. G. C. Burt, W. A. Elfers, J. J. Gait, O. H. Lange, F. R. J. Spearman, H. T. Ramsay, M. Squires, W. R. Thomas. The names of members of the group associated with particular developments are mentioned where appropriate, although references are not always given because the relevant reports have not been published.

Many inventions and improvements have been made by other workers, both in Britain and abroad, and acknowledgements are made on the text. I offer my apologies for any inadvertent omissions.

I am particularly indebted to two of my friends and colleagues: J. J. Gait, for his careful and helpful reading of the manuscript and proofs, and K. C. Garner, who undertook the considerable task of preparing the diagrams and made a number of valuable suggestions.

Without sustained encouragement and assistance from my wife this monograph would not have been completed.

I have to thank the Chief Scientist, Ministry of Supply, for permission to publish this monograph.

Farnborough   C. A. A. Wass

PREFACE TO THE SECOND EDITION

THIS book is a revised version of the book with the same title that I wrote in 1955. The revision is almost entirely the work of my friend and former colleague Mr. K. C. Garner, of the College of Aeronautics, Cranfield.

Sheffield   C. A. A. WASS

AT the time when the first edition of this book appeared the analogue computers then in use were nearly all special-purpose machines, designed for the solution of particular military problems, often with little or no thought for versatility or for convenience for the user. Since that time there has been an enormous widening of the range of problems solved by analogue computers, and this now covers activities as diverse as civilian air-crew training [128] and the blood circulation system in the foetus of a lamb [129]. Furthermore, whereas it was customary for the intending user to design, and often build, his own machine, there is now an extensive selection of commercially-built computers and ancillary apparatus available, offering every facility for the solution of a wide range of problems. There has also been considerable improvement in the ease and convenience of using analogue computers, especially in such matters as setting up a problem and observing and recording the solution, and the introduction of transistorized computers promises further advances in this respect.

On the theoretical side, the application of network synthesis methods has developed to the point where it is theoretically possible to find a suitable network to simulate any rational transfer function using only a single operational amplifier. This has great significance for both analogue computing technique and for control system compensation network design.

Perhaps the most interesting developments have been concerned with hybrid computing techniques, where the dividing line between

ix

analogue and digital becomes diffuse. Computers using such techniques will eventually remove the main disadvantages of the pure analogue computer, namely, the restriction to time-integrals, and will facilitate in a straightforward manner the solution of systems of partial differential equations, and many other groups of linear and non-linear equations.

The foregoing are some of the new analogue computing topics which have merited inclusion in this revised edition. I have endeavoured to retain the character of the original work, which has won a well-deserved reputation, and to introduce new material in sufficient depth not to be too superficial, while retaining all the discussion on basic principles.

In content and level of discussion, the book should amply meet all the requirements for graduate examination syllabi of the professional engineering institutions and of the engineering degree courses of most universities, and it is hoped it will continue, as it has in the past, to be a useful reference work for both users and designers of simulation equipment and analogue control systems. Some acquaintance with the capabilities of electronic circuits and equipment is assumed, together with a mathematical background including simple differential equations.

Many inventions and improvements have been made by workers, both in Britain and abroad, to whom reference and acknowledgement is made in the text. I offer apologies on behalf of Dr. Wass and myself for any inadvertent omission or error.

I have to thank the following for permission to reproduce figures

> The College of Aeronautics, Cranfield.
> Solartron Electronic Products Ltd.
> Short Bros. and Harland Ltd.
> General Precision Systems Ltd.
> General Controls Ltd.
> Electronics Associates Ltd.
> Bryans Ltd.

Lastly, may I say that I am greatly indebted to Dr. Wass for allowing me the honour of associating with him in this work, and for his very patient co-operation and valuable advice throughout.

Cranfield   K. C. GARNER

CHAPTER 1

ELECTRONIC CALCULATION

FOR more than 20 years there has been a great interest in calculating machines which depend for their operation on electronic devices such as thermionic valves and, latterly, transistors. In the first part of this period solutions were required for the numerous complex mathematical problems which had arisen in the design of military equipment, particularly in the fields of ballistics, aeronautics, and guided missiles. In the latter 5 or 10 years the demand for the solution of difficult mathematical problems arising in academic and commercial fields has been accelerated by the increasing application of automatic control, and by a general tendency to apply a more scientific, and less empirical, method of design in many spheres of industry. Concurrently, electronic techniques have been developed which have permitted the construction of calculating machines of various kinds which can assist with the solution of these problems. None of these machines can perform mathematical operations other than those which a competent mathematician with paper and pencil can perform, but their capacity and speed is such that with their help it is practical to undertake the solution of problems which would involve prohibitive expenditure of labour by mathematicians and computors using the less costly and more familiar slide rule and desk calculating machine. The desk machine and also the mechanical differential analyser based on the "ball and disc" integrator have, of course, been known for many years. The present work is concerned only with developments in machines and techniques which are wholly or largely electronic.

The electronic machines tend to fall mainly into two broad classes, the "digital" machines and the "analogue" machines, with a developing "hybrid" class which is intended to exploit the better features of the former two types.

The following paragraphs present the main features of electronic machines in such a way as to emphasize the differences between the digital and analogue types. The analogue machine is in no sense a

1

replacement or substitute for the digital machine, and indeed it is rare to find problems which can be solved equally well by either type, and hence the present-day effort being put into the development of hybrid machines. The two main types, however, have features which fit them for different fields of application, and which make them attractive in different degrees to mathematicians, physicists, engineers, accountants, and many other users.

1.1. DIGITAL MACHINES

The digital machines form a fairly well-defined class which has received some popular recognition under the name of "electronic brains", and they are usually fairly elaborate and costly devices, using a few hundred or a few thousand valves or transistors. They are basically arithmetic machines, the quantities they handle being represented as integral numbers of electrical pulses, and the fundamental operations which they can perform comprise addition, subtraction and discrimination, i.e. the determination of which of two given numbers is the larger. To perform more complex operations they must be provided with a "programme" of instructions in which multiplication, division, integration, etc., have been broken down into a series of additions and other simple operations. Continuous changes in the values of variables cannot be represented exactly, because the number of pulses representing a quantity cannot change by less than a single pulse; for calculations involving integration or differentiation the methods of the calculus of finite differences must be used. However, the effective number of pulses representing a quantity is often of the order of a million, so that a sufficiently close approximation to continuous variation is usually possible. This large number of pulses means also that high precision can be achieved, and even allowing some loss of accuracy from rounding-off errors, the results are often accurate to better than a part in 10^4 or 10^5, depending on the complexity of the problem.

The simple arithmetic operations can be carried out in a few microseconds, and more complicated operations, for example the calculation of the sine of an angle by summing a sufficient number of terms of a series, can be carried out in a small fraction of a second. Nevertheless, in computations which involve great numbers of steps the total time for a single computation may be as long as half an hour. For certain classes of problems digital machines are much slower than analogue machines [1, 2].

A feature of the digital machine is that it needs a central set of equipment for pulse generating, etc., which does not alter rapidly in size as the capacity of the machine changes, and whose size cannot usefully be reduced below a certain minimum. The machine cannot be smaller than this central equipment allows, and it is usually economical to make it considerably larger. "Size" is a relative word, however, and in this context it is meant to convey the number of operating devices and not the individual physical size of each device. Thus recent developments in micro-miniaturization are making possible the construction of special-purpose digital computers which weigh no more than 15 lb.

1.2. ANALOGUE MACHINES

The analogue machines cover a wider range of size than the digital machines, from simple "hook-ups" using perhaps only half a dozen valves to machines which are larger, both in number of valves and in physical size, than the large digital machines. The common feature of analogue machines is that the various quantities in the problem to be solved are represented by corresponding physical quantities in the machine. Thus, in the slide rule, which is one of the simplest analogue devices, the numbers in a problem are represented by lengths proportional to the logarithms of the numbers. Lengths on the rule are used as the analogue quantities whatever the nature of the quantities in the problem. In the electronic analogue machines the analogue quantities are commonly voltages which correspond in some predetermined manner with the quantities in the problem. Analogue machines are generally much less accurate than digital machines. Errors are within 0·1 per cent on present-day commercial equipment and some even claim 0·01 per cent, although such accuracy is not achieved without considerable care and expense in the design. Errors of up to 1 per cent are not unusual in less costly installations, and they may be as large as 5 per cent to 10 per cent. This is in striking contrast with the performance of digital machines. However, there are a great many problems where extreme precision is unnecessary. For example, in some aerodynamic or chemical process calculations the parameters may not be known to better than, say, 10 per cent, and it would often be uneconomical to use more expensive equipment in order to reduce errors in calculation to less than the order of 1 per cent or 2 per cent.

The difference between the precision attainable by the two classes of machine arises from fundamental differences in the two methods of computation. In the digital machine the errors can be decreased without theoretical limit by increasing the number of pulses used to represent a quantity. In the analogue machine the total error is contributed by errors in the measurement of the physical quantities, such as voltage, and to variations in the characteristics of electronic components and valves; and although much can be done both to improve the accuracy of measurement and to reduce the effects of variations in characteristics the analogue machine cannot compete with the digital machine for calculations of the highest accuracy.

Analogue machines need no central set of equipment corresponding to the pulse-generating equipment of the digital machine, and it is economical and practicable to build quite small machines and extend these later if required.

Electronic analogue machines can perform addition, subtraction and some other operations directly, and can deal with continuously-varying quantities. In particular they can perform integration directly, provided that the independent variable is time.

Methods have been devised for integrating with respect to other variables, and particularly over the last few years these techniques are being consolidated into the so-called hybrid machines and digital differential analysers (DDA's). Most of these machines utilize digital techniques internally, but externally they are organized as if they were analogue computers. For the true analogue computer, this restriction on integration with time as the independent variable is a serious disadvantage of electronic analogue machines regarded as general-purpose calculators, when they are compared with digital machines, or with mechanical differential analysers based on the "ball and disc" integrator.

Besides limiting the usefulness for solving ordinary differential equations, this restriction makes it very difficult to solve partial differential equations. In the study of kinematic and dynamic systems, however, including aerodynamics and electrodynamics, this restriction is unimportant, and it is in this field that electronic analogue machines have found widest application. When the analogue machine is used in this way the variables and constants in the machine, and the way these quantities react on each other, often present a close parallel with the behaviour of the actual system being studied, so that the machine is effectively a model of the system, i.e. a simulator. This feature often appeals to development engineers and experimental physicists, who are able to get a better "feel" of the problem in this way than if they have to present their problem in a formal manner for solution on a digital machine, probably via an intermediary mathematician.

An attractive facility of analogue machines is that parts of the actual dynamic system being studied may be included as part of the analogue calculating machine (Section 10.4). This is useful when the system contains some non-linear elements whose behaviour cannot be described in simple terms. If the dynamic system includes a man, say as a pilot or operator, the man can be included in the analogue computer, provided he can be presented with a satisfactory "display" of information. Machines of this type are now highly developed as flight simulators, nuclear reactor control simulators, and missile training equipment.

The restrictions imposed by having no alternative to time as the nidependent variable are not quite as narrow or as complete as might at first be imagined. A differential equation containing derivatives of y with respect to x, where both y and x are independent of the time t, can sometimes be solved by replacing x temporarily by t, finding a solution for y in terms of t and substituting for t in the solution. Also, some problems in systems which are not normally regarded as dynamic systems can be solved by means of an analogue computer. A suggestion for solving problems in geometrical optics in this manner is made later (Section 10.1).

One final sub-group which may be included under analogue machines are those which are specifically used to solve field problems. Most of these are essentially laboratory-style instruments, utilizing the properties of the electrolytic tank, resistance sheet, or resistance net, and their description is specialized [3] and not included in this work.

1.3. DIFFERENTIAL ANALYSERS AND SIMULATORS

The class of analogue machines which are wholly or mainly electronic, and which form the subject of the present work, can be subdivided in several different ways. In the next two chapters a distinction will be drawn between machines which are used as "differential analysers" and machines which are used as "simulators". Formally, a differential analyser is a device for solving differential equations, whereas a simulator may be defined for the present purpose as an electrical or electro-mechanical model of a dynamic system, so designed and arranged that measurement on the model gives useful information about the system. The difference between these definitions might suggest considerable differences between the two types of calculator, but in fact they have much in common. They use the same kinds of basic computing elements, and such differences as do exist are mostly in the way they are used, and in the attitude of mind of the user. This will become clearer in later chapters, but it can perhaps be illustrated by considering the different ways in which two men—a mathematician and an engineer—might attack some problem concerning a dynamic system. The mathematician would examine the system, write down the differential equations of motion, and then build—or have built for him—a differential analyser to solve the equations. The engineer would examine the system and would then build a model of it, which he would call a simulator. He could then obtain solutions of his problem, perhaps without ever having written down the full set of equations of motion. Thus both men would obtain the required solutions, by somewhat different thought processes, but quite possibly the two calculating machines would be identical.

The term "simulator" is sometimes restricted to machines which work in "real" time, i.e. on a one-to-one time scale (see Section 10.1). This restriction will not be observed in the present work, and any machine which satisfies the foregoing definition will be referred to as a simulator, irrespective of the time scale in which it works.

1.4. ELEMENTS OF ELECTRONIC ANALOGUE COMPUTING

Electronic analogue machines generally use varying potential differences to represent the variables in the problem being studied and it will be assumed that this is so unless otherwise stated. The expression "voltage at a point" will be understood to mean the potential difference between the point and earth, measured in volts.

The voltages may be alternating, in which case the peak or r.m.s. values of a set of alternating voltages of constant frequency change in accordance with the variations of the variable quantities in the problem, or they may be what are loosely called "d.c. voltages", in which case it is the instantaneous value of each voltage which corresponds to some variable. The "d.c." machine is the more common, and in what follows this type will be assumed unless the contrary is stated.

The most important element of such machines is the high-gain directly-coupled amplifier, represented diagrammatically in Fig. 1.1. Ideally, the output voltage V_O should be an exact magnified image of the input voltage V_1, whether V_1 is constant or varying, and the

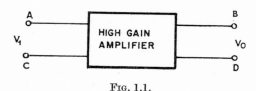

FIG. 1.1.

degree of magnification should approach infinity. In practical designs there is a reversal of phase through the amplifier so that V_1 and V_O are of opposite sign. The performance of the amplifier can therefore be represented by the equation

$$V_O = - M V_1 \qquad (1.1)$$

where M is a very large positive constant. The shortcomings of practical amplifiers will be ignored for the present, and it will be assumed that amplifiers are available which obey equation (1.1) from "d.c." up to some frequency much higher than any frequency occurring in the problem, with values of M so high that they are effectively infinite. The input and output impedances of the amplifier proper will be taken to be respectively infinity and zero. It will further be assumed that the amplifier is single-ended (i.e. not push–pull) so that terminals C and D in Fig. 1.1 are both connected to earth, and they will not be shown in later diagrams.

The most important applications of the high-gain d.c. amplifier are in the sign-reversing amplifier, the summing amplifier and the integrator. In principle some computations involving addition and integration can be performed without the need for high-gain amplifiers, but the loss in convenience and flexibility is so great that most analogue machines use amplifiers. For the present, attention will be confined to machines of this type, although some further reference will be made to this matter later (Chapter 6).

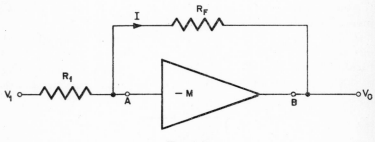

FIG. 1.2.

The sign-reversing amplifier is simply a high-gain d.c. amplifier with two resistors, an "input" resistor and a "feedback" resistor, shown respectively as R_1 and R_F in Fig. 1.2. Since the input impedance of the amplifier proper is infinite, the net current at terminal A is zero, so that currents in R_1 and R_F are equal; i.e. if the voltage at A is V_A, then

$$\frac{V_1 - V_A}{R_1} - \frac{V_A - V_O}{R_F} = 0$$

Also, $$V_O = -M V_A$$

Eliminating V_A,

$$R_F\left(V_1 + \frac{V_O}{M}\right) = -R_1\left(V_O + \frac{V_O}{M}\right)$$

$$\frac{V_O}{V_1} = -\frac{R_F M}{R_F + R_1(1 + M)} \tag{1.2}$$

And if M is very large,

$$\frac{V_O}{V_1} = -\frac{R_F}{R_1}, \text{ very nearly.}$$

In practice, if $R_F = R_1$, $V_O = -V_1$, and the output voltage is equal in magnitude to the input voltage, but of opposite sign.

Obviously this arrangement, besides being used as a sign-reverser, can be used to multiply V_1 by a constant other than -1 if R_F and R_1 are given unequal values.

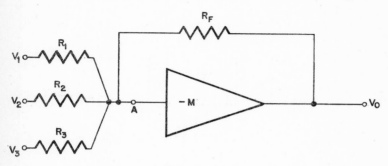

FIG. 1.3 a.

The summing amplifier is similar to the sign-reversing amplifier except that there are several input resistors, as shown in Fig. 1.3 a. The net current at A is again zero, so that

$$\frac{V_1 - V_A}{R_1} + \frac{V_2 - V_A}{R_2} + \frac{V_3 - V_A}{R_3} + \frac{V_O - V_A}{R_F} = 0 \qquad (1.3)$$

and

$$V_A = -\frac{V_O}{M}$$

Hence

$$\frac{V_1}{R_1} + \frac{V_2}{R_2} + \frac{V_3}{R_3} = V_O \left\{ -\frac{1}{R_F} - \frac{1}{M}\left(\frac{1}{R_1} + \frac{1}{R_2} + \frac{1}{R_3} + \frac{1}{R_F}\right)\right\}$$

$$(1.4)$$

If M is very large, then, very nearly,

$$V_O = -R_F\left\{\frac{V_1}{R_1} + \frac{V_2}{R_2} + \frac{V_3}{R_3}\right\} \qquad (1.5)$$

or

$$V_O = -(a_1 V_1 + a_2 V_2 + a_3 V_3)$$

where a_1, a_2, a_3 are positive constants equal to R_F/R_1, R_F/R_2, R_F/R_3, respectively.

If

$$R_1 = R_2 = R_3 = R_F,$$

then

$$V_O = -(V_1 + V_2 + V_3)$$

2*

Thus the summing amplifier with equal resistors gives an output voltage which is the negative of the sum of the input voltages. If suitable unequal values of resistance are used, each voltage can be multiplied by a constant before the addition takes place. In either case there is no restriction to three input resistors; any number can be used, so that any number of voltages can be summed.

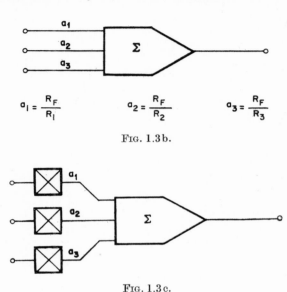

$$a_1 = \frac{R_F}{R_1} \qquad a_2 = \frac{R_F}{R_2} \qquad a_3 = \frac{R_F}{R_3}$$

FIG. 1.3b.

FIG. 1.3c.

In the preparation of diagrams of machines containing summing amplifiers it is often convenient to be able to indicate the gain between each input terminal and the output terminal, i.e. the values of a_1, a_2, etc., without showing the resistors specifically. Two devices will be used for this purpose; in the first the value of the gain is written beside each input lead, and in the second the gain values are assumed to be always unity, and the coefficients are introduced by inserting "multiplier boxes" at points in the leads before they enter the amplifier. These devices are illustrated in Figs. 1.3b and 1.3c, for both of which the gains are the same as for Fig. 1.3a. The $\sum$ sign indicates that the amplifier is being used for summing, and the pentagonal block includes the high-gain amplifier and the input and feedback impedances.

If, in equation (1.3), V_A is set equal to zero, then equation (1.5) appears at once. This is consistent with the assumption of an effectively infinite value for M, since if the amplifier has infinite gain but a finite output voltage then the input voltage must be zero. This device of assuming the voltage V_A to be zero is sometimes useful in making a quick estimate of the characteristics of a high-gain amplifier circuit.

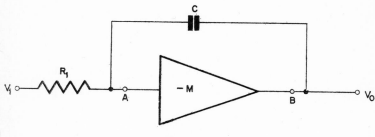

FIG. 1.4 a.

The circuit of the integrator is shown in Fig. 1.4 a, which is similar to Fig. 1.2 except that the feedback resistor R_F has been replaced by a feedback capacitor C. This arrangement is often called the "Miller" integrator, for a reason which will be mentioned later (Section 6.2). The current at A is zero, as before, and the current reaching A via the capacitor is equal to

$$C \frac{\mathrm{d}}{\mathrm{d}t} \left(V_O - V_A \right)$$

so that

$$\frac{V_1 - V_A}{R_1} + C \frac{\mathrm{d}}{\mathrm{d}t} \left(V_O - V_A \right) = 0$$

Again,

$$V_A = - \frac{V_O}{M}, \quad \text{giving}$$

$$V_1 + \frac{V_O}{M} + R_1 C \frac{\mathrm{d}}{\mathrm{d}t} \left(V_O + \frac{V_O}{M} \right) = 0 \qquad (1.6)$$

and if M is very large,

$$V_1 = - R_1 C \frac{\mathrm{d}V_O}{\mathrm{d}t}$$

Integrating,

$$V_O = -\frac{1}{R_1 C}\int_0^t V_1 \mathrm{d}t + V_{OO}$$

where V_{OO} is the value of V_O at $t = 0$.

The question of initial conditions will be taken up later (Section 8.2), and for the moment it will be assumed that $V_{OO} = 0$, so that

$$V_O = -\frac{1}{T_1}\int_0^t V_1 \mathrm{d}t \qquad (1.7)$$

where $T_1 = R_1 C$ is called the "time constant" of the integrator. Thus the arrangement of Fig. 1.4 a produces a voltage V_O proportional to the time-integral of an input voltage V_1.

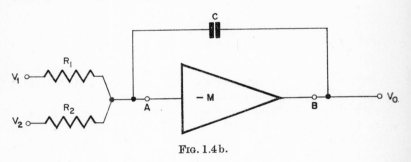

Fig. 1.4 b.

An integrator can be used to provide the sum of the integrals or the integral of the sum of two or more quantities, without using a separate summing amplifier, by adding extra input resistors, as in Fig. 1.4 b. For this arrangement it is easily shown that

$$V_O = -\frac{1}{T_1}\int_0^t V_1 \mathrm{d}t - \frac{1}{T_2}\int_0^t V_2 \mathrm{d}t = -\int_0^t \left(\frac{V_1}{T_1} + \frac{V_2}{T_2}\right)\mathrm{d}t$$

where $T_1 = R_1 C$, $T_2 = R_2 C$, and $V_{OO} = 0$.

When an integrator is shown in a block diagram the time constant may be indicated by writing the value inside the integrator block, or, alternatively, it is often convenient to assume that the time constant is unity and to perform the necessary level changes by means of "multiplier boxes" as for amplifiers.

By combining elements of these three types—reversing and summing amplifiers and integrators—in suitable ways, solutions can be obtained for linear differential equations with constant coefficients. The facility is not, of course, of great practical importance if the equations are of low order and only a few solutions are required, and if the disturbing function is of a simple form, such as a step function. The advantage of using such combinations is that large numbers of solutions, with different coefficients and different initial conditions, of equations of almost any order, can be obtained quickly and with comparatively little labour, and there is no restriction to simple disturbing functions.

It has already been mentioned that analogue computers tend to fall into two classes, *viz.* analysers and simulators, and these will be treated separately in the following two chapters. The segregation of the two types of machine is convenient for the present purpose, and corresponds to very real differences, not only in the block diagrams, but also in the way the machines are set up and used. Nevertheless, is should be appreciated that the description of a particular machine as an analyser does not necessarily mean that the machine is restricted to what will be called "analyser methods", and similarly, machines which may be called simulators can usually be used as differential analysers.

CHAPTER 2

DIFFERENTIAL ANALYSERS

A DIFFERENTIAL analyser is a device for solving differential equations. The name is not at all descriptive of the function of the device, and indeed, as van der Pol has pointed out [4], the way in which a differential analyser operates would make the title "integrating synthesizer" more appropriate. Furthermore, the description of the analyser as a device for solving equations requires some qualification, because the manner in which the solutions are represented differs from the usual "paper" presentation, in that the differential analyser can produce only particular solutions to differential equations. There is no possibility of producing general solutions containing arbitrary constants which can be evaluated later from consideration of initial conditions; the initial conditions must be set into the machine before a solution can be obtained. In the study of dynamic systems the solution commonly takes the form of an indication of the manner in which some variable in the system changes its value with time in response to some stimulus, such as an impressed force. The stimulus must be specified exactly, though it may be of a formal character, such as a step or impulse function. In electronic differential analysers the solution usually appears as a voltage varying with time, which can be fed into a suitable recorder to produce a graph.

There is, of course, no practical advantage in using a differential analyser to solve simple equations, but it will help in understanding both the principles and some practical points if one or two simple equations with well-known solutions are considered first. Take, for example

$$\frac{\mathrm{d}x}{\mathrm{d}t} - b = 0 \tag{2.1}$$

This may be regarded as a kinematic equation which says that the velocity of a particle (assumed to be moving in a straight line) is equal to b. The solution, whether it is obtained by analytical methods or by means of an analogue computer, will give x as a function of time, i.e. it will show how the position of the particle varies with time.

For solution of the differential equation by a differential analyser the initial condition must be known, so assume for the present that $x = 0$ when $t = 0$. Equation (2.1) may be written:

$$x = \int_0^t b \, \mathrm{d}t$$

Equation (1.7), which represents the behaviour of the integrator of Fig. 1.4 a, is

$$V_O = - \frac{1}{T_1} \int_0^t V_1 \, \mathrm{d}t \qquad (1.7)$$

Thus, ignoring the negative sign for the moment, if V_1 is made constant, to correspond with a constant value of b, then V_O will vary with time in the same manner as x. To establish a quantitative correspondence, suppose that V_1 is made proportional to b, and when b has a value of one foot per second V_1 has a value σ_1 volts. Then $V_1 = \sigma_1 b$, and σ_1 is a "scale factor" having the dimensions of volts per foot/second. Suppose also that $V_O = -\sigma_2 x$, where σ_2 is another scale factor, having the dimensions of volts per foot; the reason for the negative sign will appear below. The dimensions of σ_1 and σ_2 differ by the dimension of T_1, a time constant.

Substituting for V_1 and V_O,

$$\sigma_2 x = \frac{\sigma_1}{T_1} \int_0^t b \, \mathrm{d}t$$

or, if

$$\sigma_1 = \sigma_2 T_1,$$

$$x = \int_0^t b \, . \, \mathrm{d}t$$

which is identical with the original equation.

Assuming a constant value of b, the procedure for solving equation (2.1) by means of the differential analyser, which in this case consists only of the integrator of Fig. 1.4 a, is now straightforward.

A convenient way of satisfying the condition $x = 0$ when $t = 0$ is to assume that the velocity is zero for all negative time and increases instantaneously to the value b at $t = 0$. This assumption requires that in the arrangement of Fig. 1.4a

$$V_1 = 0, \qquad t < 0$$
$$V_1 = \sigma_1 b, \qquad t \geqslant 0.$$

These conditions can easily be reproduced by means of a changeover switch which connects the V_1 terminal to earth until $t = 0$ and then suddenly switches the connection to a battery of voltage $\sigma_1 b_1$, as shown in Fig. 2.1. For $t < 0$ there is no input to the amplifier, so $V_O = 0$ also. At $t = 0$, the integrator operates on V_1, and V_O changes in a manner representing x, thus giving the required solution. It is not strictly true to say that V_O is proportional to x, since the two quantities are of opposite sign. The negative sign would be less obvious if a scale factor σ_2' of opposite sign were used, giving

$$V_O = \sigma_2' x, \quad \text{where} \quad \sigma_2' = -\sigma_2,$$

but this would not alter the fact that as x becomes more positive with increasing t, so V_O becomes more negative. It is generally more

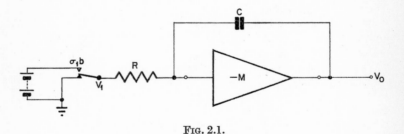

Fig. 2.1.

convenient to keep all the scale factors positive. If it is desired to produce a voltage $V_2 = \sigma_2 x$, of the same sign as x, a reversing amplifier can be connected after the circuit of Fig. 2.1.

The use of the integrator for solving equation (2.1) is of no practical value when b is constant, since the solution is already well known, but it may be useful when the value of b varies with time. Equation (1.7) shows that V_O is the time integral of V_1 (assuming $V_O = 0$ at $t = 0$ and again ignoring the minus sign) and this result is not dependent on V_1 being constant, so that V_1 may vary in any manner with time and V_O will always represent the time integral. Thus, if a particle begins to move in a straight line at $t = 0$, then provided a voltage can be produced which is at all times proportional to the velocity of the particle, a second voltage can be produced by the integrator of Fig. 1.4a which represents, at any instant, the position of the particle relative to its initial position. This is true whether the velocity of the particle is constant or varying, and independent of whether the variation is ordered or erratic. The last case is one which cannot be solved by a straightforward "paper" solution of equation (2.1).

Although the assumption of a step function of velocity is a convenient and common means of satisfying the condition that $x = 0$ at $t = 0$ it is only acceptable if interest is confined to the period after $t = 0$. The statement of the problem implies that the particle has been travelling along the straight line with velocity b for all time since $t = -\infty$ and that it will continue to do so until $t = +\infty$. However, for positive values of t there is no difference between the positions of this ideal particle and another particle which starts from rest at $t = 0$ and then travels along the line with velocity b, provided the rest position of the second particle is at the point on the line through which the ideal particle passes at $t = 0$. The identity between the two particles for positive values of t is sufficient justification for the use of the step function in practical problems. It is of interest to note that the circuit of Fig. 2.1 can give a close parallel to the motion of the ideal particle, although of course infinite values of t and x cannot be accommodated. For suppose that the switch is in the upper position, but the capacitor has been charged to a high voltage, so that V_O has a value corresponding to a high negative value of x. This condition corresponds to some instant a long time before $t = 0$, but the integrating action will proceed, and V_O will move near to zero and at some instant will pass through zero. If at this instant the clock measuring t is started, the conditions $V_O = 0$ at $t = 0$, and hence also $x = 0$ at $t = 0$, are satisfied. From $t = 0$ the conditions are exactly the same as if the circuit had been quiescent, with the switch in the lower position, until $t = 0$ and the switch had then been thrown to the upper position. If the clock were started at some other instant the value of x at $t = 0$ would not be zero. This suggests a method of introducing a non-zero initial condition which will be discussed more fully in a later chapter (Section 8.2).

2.1. USE OF FEEDBACK

Consider now the equation

$$\frac{\mathrm{d}x}{\mathrm{d}t} + cx = e \tag{2.2}$$

and for the present assume that c is a constant and e is an input disturbance in the form of a step function. Assume also that $t = 0$ when $x = 0$. Here again the solution is well known, but solution by means of a differential analyser introduces the important concept of feedback, which is necessary for all but the very simplest of differential equations.

It will be necessary to provide an input voltage V_1 to represent e, and the solution will appear in the form of a voltage V_O representing x. For simplicity assume that the same scale factor can be used for both these voltages, then

$$e = \sigma V_1$$

and

$$x = \sigma V_O$$

These relations can be used to substitute for e and x in equation (2.2) giving the corresponding voltage equation

$$\frac{\mathrm{d}V_O}{\mathrm{d}t} + cV_O = V_1 \tag{2.3}$$

Remembering that the desired output is the voltage V_O it is reasonable to rewrite this equation in the form

$$V_O = \frac{1}{c}\,V_1 - \frac{1}{c}\,\frac{\mathrm{d}V_O}{\mathrm{d}t}$$

Now the voltage V_1 is already available as the input voltage, and if there is also available a voltage V_2 proportional to $\mathrm{d}V_O/\mathrm{d}t$ then sign-reversing and summing amplifiers can be arranged to combine the two voltages so as to produce V_O. The multiplication by $1/c$ can be achieved by adjusting the values of amplifier input and feedback resistors. The two voltages are to be subtracted, so it is necessary to reverse the sign of one of them before adding, and since a reversal will occur in the summing amplifier the V_1 voltage is passed through the reversing amplifier. A block diagram of the arrangement is shown in Fig. 2.2, and this will provide the desired solution if means can be found to produce the voltage V_2. For simplicity it is assumed in the diagrams that the factor of proportionality between V_2 and dV_O/dt is unity. The triangular block containing " -1 " indicates a sign-reversing amplifier, including input and feedback resistors.

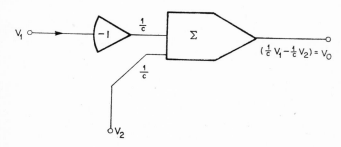

FIG. 2.2.

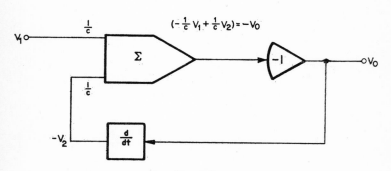

FIG. 2.3.

A computing element giving an output voltage proportional to the time-derivative of the input voltage, i.e. a differentiator, gives the desired V_2 when fed with V_O as input. Assuming that the differentiator, like some other computing elements, introduces a reversal of sign, the block diagram appears as Fig. 2.3, in which the position of the reversing amplifier has been changed so as to compensate for the reversal in the differentiator. For reasons which will appear later the use of differentiators is avoided wherever possible, and they were not included among the basic computing elements described earlier. Nevertheless, although the arrangement of Fig. 2.3 is not to be recommended as a practical analyser it is of value because it introduces the idea of feedback loops, by which a voltage appearing at one point in the circuit is tapped off and reintroduced at some earlier point.

The problem still remains of finding an arrangement for the solution of equation (2.2) which requires only amplifiers and integrators. A possible beginning is to assume that a voltage V_2 is available which is proportional to $\mathrm{d}V_O/\mathrm{d}t$, as before, but to use this as the input to an integrator which will give V_O as an output voltage. This will give the desired solution if V_2 can be provided, and this can be done by making use of the relation

$$V_2 = \frac{\mathrm{d}V_O}{\mathrm{d}t} = (V_1 - cV_O)$$

This leads to the block diagram shown in Fig. 2.4. A reversing amplifier in the feedback connection gives the required negative sign for $-V_O$, and the coefficient c is introduced by using an input resistor of value $1/c$ relative to the feedback resistor in the sum-

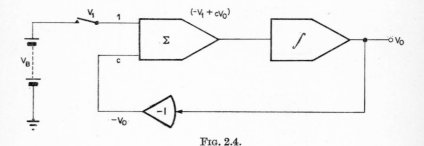

Fig. 2.4.

ming amplifier. The pentagonal block with the integral sign ($\int$) represents an integrator, including high-gain amplifier, input resistor, and feedback capacitor. The reversal introduced by the summing amplifier is cancelled by the reversal in the integrator.

In the arrangement of Fig. 2.4 the dependence of the output voltage V_O on the input voltage is given by equation (2.3). If V_1 is varied with time in the same manner as e, then the consequent variation of x will be reproduced as variation of V_O and hence the equation will be solved.

On first acquaintance with closed loops such as that in Fig. 2.4 doubt is sometimes felt as to the soundness of the arrangement, on the grounds that the solution cannot be computed until the answer is known, i.e. the second voltage required for the input to the summing amplifier cannot be produced until the output voltage from the integrator is available. Two considerations help to dispel this paradox. First, the usual procedure of describing the sequence of events in Fig. 2.4 is sometimes taken to mean that there really is a sequence, in the sense that events happen one after another, with a small time interval between, say, the appearance of the two voltages at the input of the summing amplifier and the appearance of the sum voltage at the output. In fact, of course, with the present assumptions of ideal amplifiers, etc., there is no such interval, and the output voltages appear instantaneously. The second helpful point is that although it is certainly necessary for the voltage V_O to be present before the second input to the summing amplifier can be produced it is only the instantaneous value of V_O which is needed, and not the complete "answer".

The question is also sometimes raised as to whether such loops as Fig. 2.4 are always stable. The answer is that if the analyser loop is unstable then, assuming that the analyser has been correctly set up with perfect computing amplifiers, the dynamic system represented by the differential equation under consideration is also unstable.

Understanding of the mechanism of Fig. 2.4 is improved by examining more closely the consequences of applying a step function by closing the switch. The voltage V_1 immediately rises to a steady value V_B, and since V_O is zero at this instant the output of the summing amplifier is $- V_B$. This voltage appears instantaneously when the switch is closed, and the integrator immediately begins to integrate. This means that the output voltage of the integrator begins to rise at the instant of closing the switch, so that the second input to the summing amplifier begins to increase from zero as soon as the switch is closed. The two input voltages are of opposite sign, so that the magnitude of the net input voltage to the integrator immediately begins to fall. The output of the integrator therefore continues to rise, but at a decreasing rate, and this continues until, after a theoretically infinite time interval, the output voltage of the analyser reaches a value equal to V_B/c. Then the output voltage from the summing amplifier will be zero, and the integrating action will stop. Expressed more briefly, this means that a step function input voltage at V_1 will cause the output voltage of the integrator to rise exponentially towards a value proportional to the magnitude of the step.

The question of scale factors has been deliberately simplified in this example, but in practice the determination of a convenient and consistent set of values for scale factors, input and feedback resistors and integrator time constants is an important part of the setting-up procedure for an analogue computer, and more attention will be given to this topic later (Chapter 8).

2.2. A SECOND-ORDER PROBLEM

As a further example, consider the simple dynamic system of Fig. 2.5. A mass m resting on a rough horizontal table, with coefficient of friction μ, is attached to a spring as shown. In the unstressed

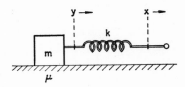

Fig. 2.5.

condition the turns of the spring are well separated, so that it can be both compressed and extended. When the mass is moving there is a frictional force proportional to the velocity. Let the positions of the free and attached ends of the spring be respectively x and y, relative to the initial positions, at which the spring is unstressed, and let the tension in the spring be $k(x-y)$. Then if the system is disturbed by displacing the free end of the spring horizontally there will be a force $k(x-y)$ acting on the mass due to the spring, and also a frictional force $-m\mu \, dy/dt$. The force on the mass will therefore be

$$m\frac{d^2y}{dt^2} = k(x-y) - m\mu \frac{dy}{dt}$$

whence

$$\frac{d^2y}{dt^2} + \mu \frac{dy}{dt} + \frac{k}{m} y = \frac{k}{m} x \qquad (2.4)$$

A skeleton diagram of a differential analyser for the solution of this equation is shown in Fig. 2.6. No scale factors are shown, but the quantities represented by the voltages at various points are given. This arrangement is derived by first assuming that there is available a voltage representing the highest-order derivative, in this case d^2y/dt^2. Then voltages representing dy/dt and y can be obtained by the use of two integrators.

Rewriting the above equation in the form

$$\ddot{y} = \frac{k}{m}x - \mu\dot{y} - \frac{k}{m}y$$

where the dots indicate differentiation with respect to time, it appears that a voltage representing $\ddot{y}$ can be produced by combining voltages representing x, $\dot{y}$, and y. The x voltage is provided from

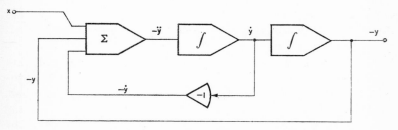

FIG. 2.6. Second-order Differential Analyser.

some external source, and the $\dot{y}$ and y voltages from the integrator outputs. A sign-reversing amplifier is needed to give the appropriate sign for the $\dot{y}$ voltage, and the three voltages are combined by the summing amplifier whose output voltage, representing $\ddot{y}$, is used as the input signal to the first integrator.

Thus the output voltage of the second integrator in Fig. 2.6 represents the variation in y corresponding to any variation x. As before, x can be the usual step function or any other function of time, provided that there is available a voltage proportional to x at all times.

The scheme of Fig. 2.6 can be extended to solve higher-order equations, and in principle there is no limit. Figure 2.7 shows an

3 EAC

arrangement for solving

$$a_4 \frac{d^4 y}{d t^4} + a_3 \frac{d^3 y}{d t^3} + a_2 \frac{d^2 y}{d t^2} + a_1 \frac{d y}{d t} + a_0 y = x \qquad (2.5)$$

Apart from the addition of two more integrators and their connections the only change is a second summing amplifier in place of the sign-reversing amplifier. Both dy/dt and $d^3 y/dt^3$ must have their signs reversed before combining with x, and it would be satisfactory in principle to use two sign-reversing amplifiers. It is more economical, however, to use a single summing amplifier to change both signs.

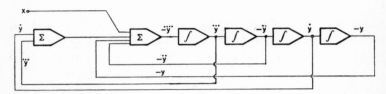

FIG. 2.7. Fourth-order Differential Analyser.

In the foregoing examples, it was assumed that y and all the derivatives of y were zero at $t = 0$. The method is not restricted to this set of initial conditions, and means for taking account of other initial values will be described later (Section 8.2).

2.3. DERIVATIVES OF THE INPUT QUANTITY

The examples have all referred to equations containing no function of x other than x itself. However, some equations which arise in the study of dynamic systems involve derivatives of x, and the solution of such equations by means of a differential analyser raises a new difficulty. Methods are available which largely overcome this difficulty, but they are little used in practice because the "simulator" approach is generally preferred. Two examples will be given of dynamic systems which lead to equations which contain derivatives of x, but the analyser method of solution for the second example is tedious and will be given in an appendix. The simulator method for both cases will be described in the next chapter.

As a simple example consider first the dynamic system shown in Fig. 2.8. This is similar to that of Fig. 2.5, but the table is now assumed smooth, and friction between the mass and the table is replaced by friction in the "dash-pot" connected between the ends of the spring. The frictional force, instead of being proportional to

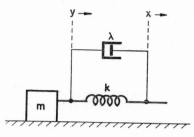

FIG. 2.8.

the velocity of the mass relative to the table, is now proportional to the relative velocity of the ends of the spring, i.e. the frictional force is equal to

$$\lambda \frac{\mathrm{d}(x-y)}{\mathrm{d}t}$$

In place of equation (2.4) there now appears the equation

$$\frac{\mathrm{d}^2 y}{\mathrm{d}t^2} + \frac{\lambda}{m} \frac{\mathrm{d}y}{\mathrm{d}t} + \frac{k}{m} y = \frac{k}{m} x + \frac{\lambda}{m} \frac{\mathrm{d}x}{\mathrm{d}t} \tag{2.6}$$

If a differentiator were available as a computing element the solution of this equation could be obtained by means of an analyser as shown in Fig. 2.9, which is similar to Fig. 2.6, but has a differen-

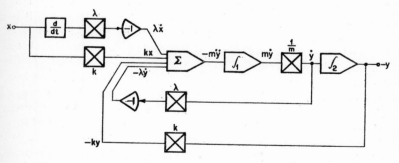

FIG. 2.9. Possible Analyser for System of Fig. 2.8.

3*

tiator added to produce the voltage representing dx/dt. It is assumed in this diagram that the differentiator gives a reversal of sign, so a sign-reversing amplifier is also added. In practice a second summing amplifier would be used in place of the two reversing amplifiers, the two voltages representing dx/dt and dy/dt being fed in through separate input resistors. The equation for the summing amplifier in Fig. 2.9 is

$$m\ddot{y} = kx - ky + \lambda\dot{x} - \lambda\dot{y}$$

However, as already mentioned, it is inadvisable to use differentiators, and a method of solution is therefore required which uses only amplifiers and integrators. In this particular case such a method

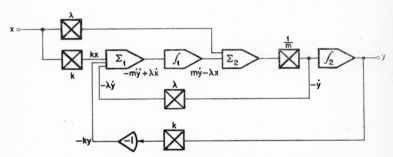

FIG. 2.10. Alternative Analyser for System of Fig. 2.8.

can be derived, and the first step in the derivation is to observe that the x voltage which is fed into the differentiator in Fig. 2.9 is passed on, after differentiation, through a summing amplifier and then, together with other voltages, through an integrator. The two operations on the x voltage effectively cancel each other, and it is natural to enquire whether they can both be omitted. To test this suppose that the $\dot{x}$ voltage is disconnected from the input to the summing amplifier. This changes the output voltage to $(-m\ddot{y} + \lambda\dot{x})$, and the output of the first integrator becomes $(m\dot{y} - \lambda x)$. The deficiency λx can be removed by adding a voltage obtained directly from the input voltage, as shown in Fig. 2.10, where a second summing amplifier has been provided to perform the addition. There is now available a voltage proportional to $\dot{y}$, which provides one of the feedback voltages and also the input to the second integrator. The remainder of the circuit is unaltered except for the transfer of the reversing amplifier from one feedback line to the other, because of the reversal of signs of the $\dot{y}$ and y voltages. This method can be extended to higher-order equations, though as will be seen in Appendix I the procedure is not so simple if derivatives of x higher than the first are present.

Arrangements similar to that shown in Fig. 2.10 can be derived by application of an interesting theorem due to Burns [5], although in the form he gives the method would be restricted to input disturbances which can be expressed in fairly compact mathematical form, whereas for electronic computers there need be no such restriction.

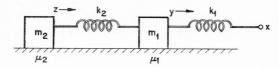

FIG. 2.11.

A more complicated equation involving derivatives of the input quantity arises from the dynamic system shown in Fig. 2.11. This is a "coupled" system, comprising two masses and two springs, and the assumptions are generally the same as for Fig. 2.5. For the sake of generality unequal masses, friction coefficients, and spring constants are assumed.

The tensions in the springs of Fig. 2.11 are:

$$T_1 = k_1(x - y)$$
$$T_2 = k_2(y - z)$$

and equating the total forces acting on m_1 to the product of mass and acceleration

$$m_1\ddot{y} = -m_1\mu_1\dot{y} + T_1 - T_2$$

Substituting for T_1 and T_2,

$$m_1\ddot{y} + m_1\mu_1\dot{y} + k_1y + k_2y = k_1x + k_2z \qquad (2.7)$$

For m_2,

$$m_2\ddot{z} + m_2\mu_2\dot{z} + k_2z = k_2y \qquad (2.8)$$

From equations (2.7) and (2.8) y or z can be eliminated, giving expressions for z in terms of x, or for y in terms of x. These expressions involve fourth-order derivatives and for convenience here and subsequently d/dt will be replaced by s, d^2/dt^2 by s^2, etc. Thus, eliminating z gives

$$as^4y + bs^3y + cs^2y + dsy + ey = fs^2x + gsx + hx \qquad (2.9)$$

where $a, b, \ldots, h,$ are functions of $k_1, k_2, m_1, m_2, \mu_1, \mu_2$ (see Appendix I).

This equation has first- and second-order derivatives of x, and solution would be possible in principle by an analyser similar to that shown in Fig. 2.7 with the addition of two differentiators. However, in view of the objections to the use of differentiators such an arrangement is not practical, and for an analyser solution one of the methods given in the Appendix I must be used. A preferable alternative is to discard the "analyser" approach and use the method given in the next chapter.

CHAPTER 3

SIMPLE SIMULATORS

SIMPLE simulators can be built up with the same basic elements as have been used so far in differential analysers, and it is instructive to build up the block diagrams for simulators to solve the same problems as were used as examples for differential analysers. This will show the difference in approach already mentioned, and although the block diagram for a simulator to represent a given simple dynamic system will be seen to differ little from the corresponding analyser, there are considerable divergences when more complicated systems are considered. Some advantages of simulators, as compared with analysers, will be demonstrated.

3.1. THE MASS–SPRING–FRICTION PROBLEM

The first problem concerns the mass and spring shown in Fig. 2.5. The tension in the spring is equal to

$$T = k(x - y)$$

and the acceleration of the mass is related to the tension and frictional force by the equation

$$ms^2y = T - \mu msy \tag{3.1}$$

The next step in the normal method of solution would be to eliminate T between these two equations. However, it is a feature of the "simulator method" that simulation of the equations should begin at as early a stage as possible, so that the problem involves the solution of a number of equations of low order rather than a single equation of higher order.

As a first step in setting up the block diagram, assume that there is available a voltage representing s^2y. If this is fed into two integrators in cascade, two voltages representing $-sy$ and y will be

29

produced. The s^2y voltage can be produced by feeding into an amplifier voltages representing $\mu\,msy$ and T, and a suitable voltage for the first of these is available from the output of the first integrator. A voltage representing T can be produced by adding voltages representing kx and $-ky$ in a second summing amplifier, giving the block diagram shown in Fig. 3.1. This arrangement is not very different from that shown in Fig. 2.6, and in fact if it is not required to observe the variation in tension T the second summing amplifier and the reversing amplifier in the feedback connection

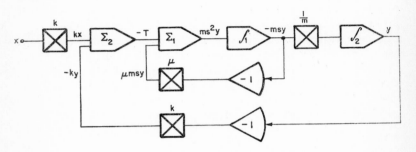

FIG. 3.1. Simulator for System of Fig. 2.5.

from the second integrator can both be removed, giving a diagram basically identical with Fig. 2.6. However, although the block diagrams may be similar, there is some difference in significance between the two arrangements. Thus, in Fig. 3.1 the voltage fed back from the output of the first integrator now quite obviously represents the frictional force, and the level of the feedback can be changed to represent different values of friction coefficient. This facility is, of course, available in the arrangement of Fig. 2.6, but the connection between the physical effect and the corresponding voltage is somewhat less direct. The voltage representing spring tension does not appear at all in Fig. 2.6, and although there would be no difficulty in providing it if it were required this would mean an extra step, whereas by the simulator approach it appears quite naturally.

For the system of Fig. 2.8, with the friction force between the ends of the spring instead of between the mass and table, the first step in the application of the simulator method is to write down the equations in the simplest form, *viz.*

$$T = k(x - y)$$
$$F = \lambda s(x - y)$$
$$ms^2 y = F + T = \lambda s(x - y) + k(x - y)$$

where T is the tension in the spring and

F is the frictional force.

Assuming as usual that there is available a voltage representing $ms^2 y$ at the output of amplifier 1 in Fig. 3.2, voltages representing

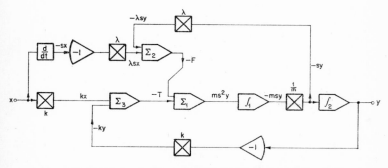

Fig. 3.2. Simulator for System of Fig. 2.8 using a Differentiator.

sy and y can be obtained by two integrators. (Here and elsewhere, for brevity, "amplifier" is used instead of "summing amplifier" when there is no likelihood of ambiguity.)

According to the above equation the input voltages to the amplifier 1 must represent F and T, and assuming for the moment that a differentiator is available, these voltages can be obtained as shown, in accordance with the above equations for F and T. If it is not required to observe the forces F and T explicitly the arrangement can be simplified by performing all the additions in a single amplifier, and the arrangement then reverts to that of Fig. 2.9.

The differentiator in Fig. 3.2 can be removed and the deficiency made up as before by inserting an x voltage after the first integrator, as in Fig. 3.3, which is similar to Fig. 2.10 except that a voltage representing T is still available at the output of amplifier 3.

A further possible modification consists in disconnecting the sy input of amplifier 1 (Fig. 3.3), and correcting the deficiency by

adding a voltage proportional to y after the first integrator giving the
arrangement shown in Fig. 3.4. Amplifier 3 of Fig. 3.3 is no longer
needed. If desired, the λx and $-\lambda y$ voltages could be combined in
a separate summing amplifier before being fed into amplifier 2. The
output of this additional amplifier would be proportional to F/s,

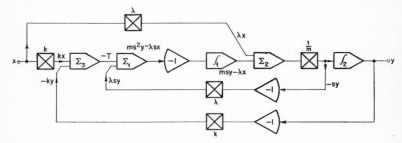

Fig. 3.3. Alternative Simulator for System of Fig. 2.8.

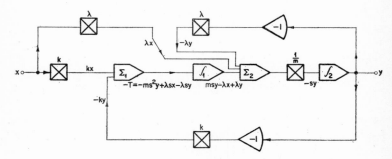

Fig. 3.4. Modification of Fig. 3.3.

which might be a useful quantity to observe. Also, since both the
λ multipliers would be in the input leads to this amplifier it would
only be necessary to vary the gain of this one amplifier to allow for
changes in the value of λ.

The arrangements of Figs. 3.3 and 3.4 do not provide such a complete model of the dynamic system as in the case of Fig. 3.1 and the
system of Fig. 2.5. This is the penalty of avoiding the use of
differentiators. Nevertheless, this simulator gives a slightly better
insight into the dynamic problem than the analyser of Fig. 2.10.

If in the dynamic system of Fig. 2.8 a rough table is substituted
for the smooth table, so that two forms of friction are present, the

appropriate change in the simulator can be made very easily. All that is necessary is to tap off a voltage representing $-msy$, multiply by μ, and feed the resulting voltage, representing $-\mu msy$, into the first summing amplifier, in either Fig. 3.3 or Fig. 3.4.

3.2. COUPLED MASS-SPRING-FRICTION SYSTEM

The mild advantages offered by the arrangement of Figs. 3.1, 3.3 and 3.4 appear much more strongly when the simulator method is applied to the more complicated problem of Fig. 2.11. The relevant equations are:

$$\text{Tension in spring } 1 = T_1 = k_1(x - y) \tag{3.2a}$$

$$\text{Tension in spring } 2 = T_2 = k_2(y - z) \tag{3.2b}$$

$$m_1 s^2 y = (T_1 - T_2) - \mu_1 m_1 sy \tag{3.2c}$$

$$m_2 s^2 z = T_2 - \mu_2 m_2 sz \tag{3.2d}$$

In the "analyser" treatment the tensions T_1 and T_2 were first eliminated, but for the simulator method the block diagram is built up immediately from these four equations. The procedure follows the same lines as before. Starting with equation (3.2d), which is identical in form with equation (3.1), assume that there is available, at the output of amplifier 2 in Fig. 3.5 a voltage proportional to

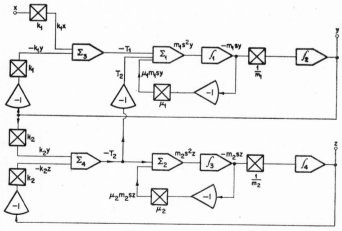

FIG. 3.5. Simulator for System of Fig. 2.11.

$m_2 s^2 z$. Proceeding as for Fig. 3.1 leads to the arrangement shown in the lower part of Fig. 3.5, which gives an output voltage representing z when the input is a voltage representing y. It is easily seen that the amplifiers 2 and 4 perform the additions indicated in equations (3.2 d) and (3.2 b).

For equation (3.2 c) a similar procedure is followed, starting with the assumption that a voltage proportional to $m_1 s^2 y$ is available, at the output of amplifier 1 (Fig. 3.5). The inputs required for this amplifier include a voltage proportional to T_2, and this is obtained as shown, from the output of amplifier 4 in the lower part of the diagram. Apart from this connection the two parts of the diagram are identical in form.

The arrangement of Fig. 3.5 has a number of attractive features. The voltages correspond directly to physical quantities in the dynamic system, and changes in coefficients can easily be made. The simulator includes no derivatives higher than the second, and it gives simultaneous solutions for both y and z in a natural manner. In contrast, the form of equation (2.9) suggests strongly that solution by the "analyser" method would involve representation of the third- and fourth-order derivatives, which have been introduced into equation (2.9) in a rather artificial way through elimination of z. Also, equation (2.9) has coefficients which are complicated functions of the masses, spring constants, and friction coefficients, which means that changes of these quantities would not be made so easily in the analyser. Lastly, a separate analyser, or at least a rearrangement of the analyser, would be necessary if solutions for both y and z were required. Besides these advantages Fig. 3.5 gives an excellent picture of the system being studied. The lower part of the diagram represents a second-order system, similar to that of Fig. 2.6, in which the only disturbance is the $k_2 y$ voltage coming from the upper part of the diagram. This corresponds with the left-hand part of the dynamic system (Fig. 2.11), in which the second spring and mass constitute a second-order system in which the only disturbance is due to the movement of the end of the spring attached to mass m_1. Similarly, the upper part of the diagram represents again a self-contained second-order system, but here in addition to the disturbance due to x there is also the effect of the tension T_2, or $k_2(y - z)$, which corresponds exactly with the conditions in the real system. If it is not required to observe the tensions T_1 and T_2 explicitly the arrangement may be simplified, with some saving in amplifiers, by feeding the appropriate x, y and z voltages directly into amplifiers 1 and 2 instead of carrying out a preliminary combination in amplifiers 3 and 4 (Fig. 3.6). The T_2 voltage feeding into amplifier 1 in Fig. 3.5 is allowed for by changing the y voltage from $k_1 y$ to $(k_1 + k_2) \, y$ and providing an additional input voltage to amplifier 1 representing $k_2 z$. As a result of the

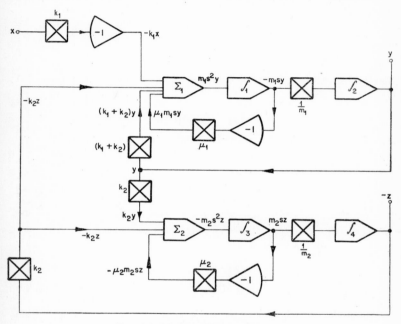

FIG. 3.6. Modified Form of Fig. 3.5.

omission of some amplifiers the signs of the quantities in the lower part of Fig. 3.6 are reversed compared with Fig. 3.5. The reversals can be cancelled by means of extra amplifiers if desired.

Although the system of Fig. 3.5 or 3.6 is capable of giving satisfactory solutions of the double mass and spring problem, it is of no great practical importance so long as all the coefficients are constant and x is some simple function of time, such as a step or impulse, or a sinusoidal variation. In such cases it would not generally be economic to build a simulator for this purpose only, since the required solutions can be obtained analytically. The attraction of a simulator increases, however, if the problem becomes more complex. Thus, suppose a third mass and spring is added to the system of Fig. 2.11. This raises the corresponding differential equation to the sixth order, but the extension of the simulator of Fig. 3.5 to include the third mass and spring involves no new principle. If the mass, spring factor, and friction coefficient are m_3, k_3, μ_3, and the position of the mass from its initial position is w, the tension in the third spring is

$$T_3 = k_3(z - w)$$

and for the third mass,

$$m_3 s^2 w = -\mu_3 m_3 s w + T_3$$

The equations for the second mass and spring are now changed to

$$T_2 = k_2(y - z)$$
$$m_2 s^2 z = -\mu_2' m_2 s z + (T_2 - T_3),$$

and for the first spring and mass there is no change:

$$T_1 = k_1(x - y)$$
$$m_1 s^2 y = -\mu_1 m_1 s y + (T_1 - T_2)$$

The extension to Fig. 3.5 would therefore involve the provision of an additional second-order loop for w, and additional connections between the loops to allow for the interactions of the different tensions. Any number of loops can be added by repeating this process.

3.3. COUPLED SYSTEM WITH "DASH-POT FRICTION"

Another modification of Fig. 2.11 is shown in Fig. 3.7, in which the friction due to the rough table has been replaced by dash-pot friction. The equations of motion are:

$$F_1 = \lambda_1 s(x - y)$$
$$F_2 = \lambda_2 s(y - z)$$
$$T_1 = k_1(x - y)$$
$$T_2 = k_2(y - z)$$
$$m_1 s^2 y = F_1 + T_1 - F_2 - T_2$$
$$= T_1 - F_2 - T_2 + \lambda_1 s x - \lambda_1 s y$$
$$m_2 s^2 z = F_2 + T_2$$
$$= T_2 + \lambda_2 s y - \lambda_2 s z$$

A simulator for this system can be built up using the same procedures as before. Assuming initially that a voltage representing y will be available, the block diagram for the part of the system comprising m_2, k_2, and λ_2 can be drawn immediately, since it is identical in form with Fig. 3.3 which simulates Fig. 2.8. It is shown in the lower part of Fig. 3.8. For the part of the simulator representing m_1, k_1, and λ_1 the normal procedure would be to assume that there is available, at the output of summing amplifier 2, a voltage proportional to ms^2y, but the above equations show that this would require as one of the inputs a voltage proportional to $\lambda_1 sx$,

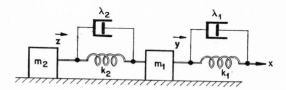

FIG. 3.7. Coupled System with "Dash-pot" Friction.

and this would need a differentiator. Assume, therefore, that the output of the amplifier represents $m_1 s^2 y - \lambda_1 s x$, and remove the unwanted x term as before after the first integrator. The remaining inputs are all available, and may be combined as shown. Since both sy and sz appear explicitly it is possible in this case to produce a voltage proportional to F_2, and this is shown in the upper part of the diagram as one of the inputs to summing amplifier 2. If desired this voltage can also be used as one of the inputs to amplifier 6 in the lower part of the diagram, as shown in Fig. 3.9. This gives some small economy in computing elements, and it also means that the only points in the simulator where the coefficient λ_2 appears are in the input leads to amplifier 4. Thus a change in the value of λ_2 can be accommodated simply by changing the gain of this amplifier. In a similar way the gains of amplifiers 1 and 5 can be changed to represent changes in the values of k_1 and k_2. Changes in the values of m_1 and m_2 require changes in the multipliers following amplifier 3 and integrator 3 respectively, and in practice this could be done by changing gains or time constants. A change in the value of λ_1 requires changes in two multipliers, one in the "feed forward" of x and the other in the feedback of sy.

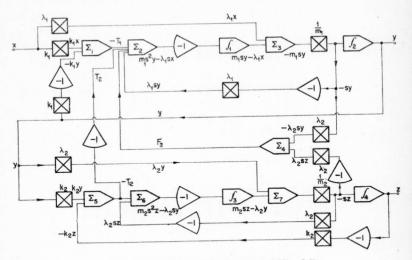

Fig. 3.8. Simulator for System of Fig. 3.7.

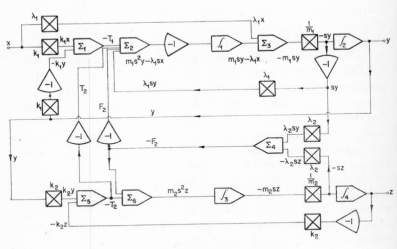

Fig. 3.9. Modified Form of Fig. 3.8.

3.4. ROAD VEHICLE SUSPENSION

The techniques described in the preceding sections, using summing amplifier, reversing amplifier and integrator, can be used to solve practical problems, and some examples will now be given. Although these examples are reasonably plausible it should perhaps be emphasized that the aim is to illustrate the application of analogue computing elements and methods rather than to show how to solve particular problems.

The first problem concerns the suspension system of a road vehicle [6], assumed to be running over a rough road. Figure 3.10

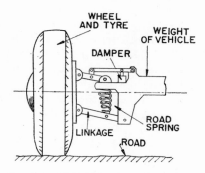

FIG. 3.10. Road Vehicle Suspension.

shows the parts of the suspension which will be considered here, *viz.* the tyre, the wheel, and the road spring and damper or shock absorber. Considered as a dynamic system, the input disturbances are the variations in the level of the road, measured from some mean position, and these disturbances are transmitted via the tyre to the "unsprung mass" of the axle, linkage, etc., and thence via the road spring and damper to the body of the vehicle. Assuming that the mass of the tyre can be lumped with the unsprung mass the system corresponds to that of Fig. 3.7, where k_1 represents the elasticity of the tyre, λ_1 represents the frictional losses in the tyre, m_1 is the unsprung mass, k_2 and λ_2 represent road spring and damper, and m_2 is an appropriate fraction of the mass of the vehicle. Thus the simulator of Fig. 3.9 can be used for this problem provided steady voltages proportional to m_1g and m_2g (where g is the acceleration due to gravity) are added to the inputs of amplifiers

2 and 6 respectively to represent the weights of the two masses. The output quantity y of this simulator gives the height of the centre of the wheel, measured from a horizontal datum line a distance r_0 above the reference line for x, where r_0 is the outer radius of the tyre in its unstressed condition. Thus whenever $y = x$ the tyre is only just in contact with the road, and exerting zero pressure. The output quantity z is the height of the corner of the vehicle, measured from a datum line displaced from the x datum by an amount defined by the unstressed condition of tyre and road spring.

If x were a step function, complete solutions of the problem could be obtained by ordinary analytical methods. However, a vehicle travelling along an ordinary road is not normally subjected to step functions of road level, but to continuous and somewhat random changes which vary in character and magnitude with the "goodness" or "badness" of the road, and in these circumstances the only "paper" method would be a step-by-step numerical solution. The simulator will give the required solution without change, provided a voltage varying with time in a manner representative of the road surface variations is available at the x terminal of Fig. 3.9. As before, the simulator gives a complete picture of the dynamic system, and the behaviour of all the elements of the system can be watched. Different sets of parameters, including variations of load of the vehicle, different proportions of sprung and unsprung mass, different settings of the suspension damper, etc., can be set into the simulator without difficulty. The simulator could be extended to study two wheels, or all four wheels simultaneously, by using two or four sets of amplifiers and integrators as shown in Fig. 3.9, with appropriate interconnections.

It is instructive to imagine that, with the value of x at zero, the effects of gravity can be "switched off". The gravity voltages are removed from the inputs of amplifiers 2 and 6, so that there is no input to the simulator, and all the amplifier and integrator outputs, including y and z, are assumed to be zero. Suppose now that gravity can be restored to the wheel and tyre only. This is simulated by switching the $m_1 g$ voltage to the input of amplifier 2, and the resulting output voltage, after two integrations, produces a change of y. Examination of the diagram shows that the value of y will be negative, which means that the wheel will move downwards, as would be expected. The appearance of a y voltage means that voltages representing T_1 will appear at the input of amplifier 1, and this will decrease the net output of amplifier 2. A stage will ultimately be reached where the T_1 voltage exactly neutralizes the $m_1 g$ voltage, so that the output of amplifier 2 will be zero, and the value of y will remain constant. This corresponds, of course, to the condition where the tyre has been compressed to an extent sufficient to support the weight of the unsprung mass. During the period while y is changing, frictional forces represented by the F_2 and $\lambda_1 s y$ inputs to amplifier 2 will appear. Also, the tension T_2 will change from its initial zero value for a time, and this, with F_2, will cause z to change. In the final state, however, z will assume the same values as y, and both will be constant; then T_2 and F_2 will both be zero. This corresponds with the dynamics, because the vehicle cannot, in the absence of gravity, exert any steady force, though it still has inertia and so can exert inertial forces. If there is no steady force on the spring it must be in its unextended condition, which means that wheel and vehicle must have moved through equal vertical distances.

A similar set of events can be described when the $m_2 g$ voltage is switched on to amplifier 6.

This discussion has assumed that the vehicle problem is linear, but in fact, of course, there will be non-linearities; in particular there will be a discontinuity when the tyre bounces out of contact with the road. This effect, and other non-linearities, could be built into the simulator by methods which will be described later (Section 4.3).

3.5. MOTION OF AN AEROPLANE

As a further example of the application of a simulator using only the basic amplifier and integrator elements, consider now the equations describing the longitudinal motion of an aeroplane. Assume that the aeroplane is initially flying along a straight line, not necessarily horizontal, at constant speed; but subsequently small movements of the elevator are made, which cause the aeroplane to diverge from the straight line, though it always remains in the vertical plane containing the line. Then the motion can be described by the following three equations [7, 8]:

$$\left.\begin{array}{r} m(\dot{u} + w_o q) = -mg \cos \theta_o . \theta + u X_u + w X_w \\ m(\dot{w} - u_o q) = -mg \sin \theta_o . \theta + u Z_u + w Z_w \\ B\dot{q} = w M_w + q M_q + \eta' M_\eta \end{array}\right\} \quad (3.3)$$

4*

in which

θ_o is the inclination to the horizontal of the initial flight direction.

θ is a small variation in this angle.

u_o is the initial velocity of the aircraft along the direction of its longitudinal (or "x") axis.

w_o is the initial velocity along the z-axis, which is perpendicular to the longitudinal axis and in the plane of symmetry of the aeroplane.

u and w are small variations in u_o and w_o.

q is the angular velocity about the y-axis, which is perpendicular to the plane of symmetry.

m is the mass of the aeroplane.

B is the moment of inertia about the y-axis.

g is the acceleration due to gravity.

η is the angle of deflection of the elevator.

X_u, X_w are aerodynamic derivatives representing respectively the forces along the x-axis per unit of u and w.

Z_u, Z_w are respectively the forces along the z-axis per unit of u and w.

M_w, M_q, M_η are respectively the moments about the y-axis per unit of w, q, and η.

Figure 3.11 shows some of these quantities.

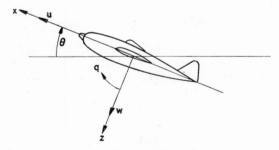

FIG. 3.11. Motion of an Aeroplane.

Besides the assumptions mentioned, others have been implied and made tacitly. The set of equations given is not intended to represent any particular aircraft, and for other purposes some other equations, including aerodynamic derivatives here neglected, may be more appropriate. The sign convention follows the standard practice for aerodynamic work.

Setting up the block diagram for the simulator is a straightforward procedure. First, assume that there are three summing amplifiers, one associated with each of the equations (3.3) giving output voltages respectively representing the highest-order derivative in each equation multiplied by its appropriate mass or inertia. These terms are $m\dot{u}$, $m\dot{w}$, and $B\dot{q}$, but it is slightly more conve-

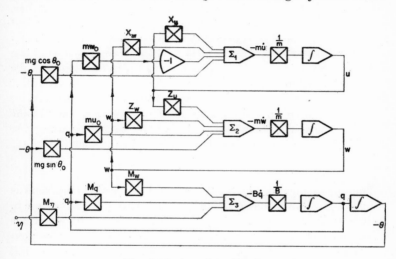

Fig. 3.12. Aeroplane Simulator.

nient to take the negatives of these terms, and this will be done here. The first summing amplifier (Fig. 3.12) is followed by a multiplier to multiply by $1/m$, and the voltage representing $-\dot{u}$ is fed into an integrator of unity time constant to give an output representing u. As before, the required multiplying action would be obtained in practice by adjustment of the integrator time constant. The same arrangement is used with the second summing amplifier, giving an output voltage representing w. For the third amplifier the multiplying factor is $1/B$, and the output of the integrator represents q. From the definition of q and θ it follows that $q = \mathrm{d}\theta/\mathrm{d}t$, so if the voltage representing q is fed into another integrator the output voltage will represent $-\theta$.

All the variables are now available for making up the input voltages for the summing amplifiers by passing the u, w, q, and $-\theta$ voltages through suitable multipliers. Again, the multipliers would not exist explicitly but would be introduced, in effect, by adjustment of amplifier gains.

It is important to notice that in setting up the diagram of Fig. 3.12 it has been assumed that all derivatives X_u, etc., are positive numbers. In fact, all the derivatives shown except X_w are usually negative numbers, so that the block which calls, for example, for multiplication by X_u implies multiplication by a negative number. Reversal of sign cannot be achieved merely by changing the gain of an amplifier or the time constant of an integrator, so that reversing amplifiers will be required. The most obvious arrangement would be to insert a reversing amplifier at each point where the diagram calls for multiplication by a derivative which has a negative value. However, some economy can be achieved by rearrangement. As an intermediate step to redrawing the diagram to take account of the negative signs it is helpful to rewrite the equations using the moduli of the derivatives, e.g. for the first of equations (3.3)

$$m(\dot{u} + w_o q) = -mg \cos \theta_o . \theta - u|X_u| + w|X_w|$$

The arrangement of Fig. 3.12, modified by reversing amplifiers as required, gives a reliable model of the behaviour of the aeroplane in its longitudinal mode, in so far as this is represented by equations (3.3), and as before, all the variables in the equations appear explicitly as voltages. Changes of parameters can easily be made, and the effects of different values of derivatives, or of mass, or inertia, on the response of the aeroplane to deflections of the elevator, can be studied.

Among the assumptions implied in the equations (3.3) is that of complete linearity; for example, the constancy of the derivative X_u implies that the force uX_u varies linearly with u. In fact, the variation is not usually linear and means for introducing nonlinear effects will be described later.

The arrangement of Fig. 3.12 can be used as a basis for the study of some problems in the automatic control of aeroplanes. For example, suppose that in a blind-landing system the preferred line of flight is a straight line inclined at an angle θ_o to the horizontal, θ_o being in this case small and negative. Then this line may be regarded as the line of flight used in describing equations (3.3), and an aircraft flying with constant speed along this line satisfies the initial conditions associated with these equations. Suppose that if the aeroplane diverges from the line, but remains in the same vertical plane, the radio equipment in the aeroplane gives out a voltage which is, say, of positive or negative sign depending on whether the aeroplane is above or below the line, and which has a magnitude proportional to the displacement. This voltage is used to move the elevators in such a way that the displacement tends to diminish. There are various ways in which this can be done; the voltage may be used to give some indication to the pilot, who then moves his control column in the appropriate manner; or in a completely automatic system the voltage may be fed to an autopilot which in turn operates the elevator. For the present purpose the pilot, whether human or automatic, will be ignored, and the elevator deflection η will be taken to be proportional to the voltage, giving

$$\eta = kh$$

where h is the displacement of the aeroplane from the line, and k is a constant.

Now from equations (3.3) it can be shown that the acceleration of the aeroplane along the z-axis is equal to

$$\ddot{z} = \dot{w} - u_o q$$

Assuming that θ remains small and that the x-axis of the aeroplane remains approximately parallel to the direction of flight,

$$\ddot{h} = \ddot{z} = \dot{w} - u_o q \quad \text{very nearly.}$$

Hence $\qquad \eta = k \int\!\int (\dot{w} - u_o q) \, \mathrm{d}t . \, \mathrm{d}t$

Now voltages representing both $-\dot{w}$ and q are available in the simulator of Fig. 3.12, so to extend this simulator to study the automatic blind-landing system it is only necessary to take the sum of $-\dot{w}$ and q in a summing amplifier, integrate twice, and feed the output, which now represents h, into the η terminal of Fig. 3.12. The complete arrangement is shown in Fig. 3.13. In this diagram account has been taken of the signs of the aerodynamic derivatives, in accordance with an earlier paragraph, and the derivative multipliers are now labelled $|X_u|$ ($=$ modulus of X_u), etc. By re-arranging the connections the negative signs can be accommodated with three additional sign-reversing amplifiers.

The simulator or Fig. 3.13 now represents, in the language of servo-mechanisms, a "regulator", which is intended to cause the aeroplane to fly along a fixed straight line, and there is no input terminal for a signal from an external source as there was in Fig. 3.12. In making a study of a system of this kind the interest lies

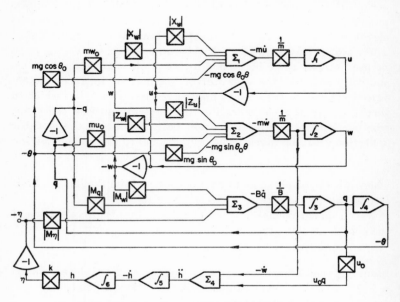

FIG. 3.13. Simulator for an Aeroplane with Auto-control.

in observing first of all whether the system is stable. With the arrangement shown the system would almost certainly be unstable, but in practice a more complex relation between h and η would be used to ensure stability. With a stable system interest lies in observing whether the aeroplane flies as close as desired to the fixed line, in the presence of whatever disturbing forces might occur. The most obvious kind of disturbance is a wind gust, and the effect of this can be studied, provided the variation of wind speed due to the gust can be adequately described in terms of the quantities available in the simulator. To take a very simple case, suppose that the gust changes the wind speed for a short period from zero to some fixed value and then back to zero, the change occurring in the x direction only, so that the only immediate effect is to change the value of u.

This can be simulated by replacing the sign-reversing amplifier operating on the u voltage by a summing amplifier and arranging this to add to the output of integrator 1 a voltage representing the gust velocity. The voltage is controlled by a switch, and if the switch is closed for a period equal to the duration of the gust the appropriate change will be made in the value of u, and the disturbance will be injected into the system. It is assumed throughout this discussion that the wind gust is of short duration; interest is confined to the disturbance of the lateral motion, and the effect on the ground speed, for example, is ignored.

The assumption that the gust has an effect in the x direction only is somewhat unreal, since it implies that the gust direction is inclined to the horizontal. A more realistic gust would change the wind velocity along a direction parallel to the ground, and to take account of this in the simulator involves resolution of the wind velocity into two components in the x and z directions. Provided the two components are known the disturbance in u can be injected as before, and the disturbance in the z direction can be injected by a corresponding modification to the w voltage. However, the resolution, if accurately performed, requires multiplication by $\cos(\theta_o - \theta)$ and $\sin(\theta_o - \theta)$, and these quantities change continuously, with the pitching motion of the aeroplane. This type of resolution cannot be achieved with the simple computing elements so far described, although means are available and will be described later.

If it is sufficiently accurate to take a mean value for $(\theta_o - \theta)$, i.e. θ_o, then the effect of the horizontal gust can be simulated. The voltage to be added to the output of integrator 1 is now proportional to the gust velocity multiplied by $\cos\theta_o$, and a voltage proportional to the gust multiplied by $\sin\theta_o$, is to be added to the output voltage of integrator 2. Figure 3.14 shows the relevant parts of Fig. 3.13, with the additions necessary to introduce the gust, whose velocity is taken to be u_g. Some small changes in the arrangement of the sign-reversing amplifiers are necessary to preserve correct signs for the w and $-w$ voltages.

The simulation of the blind-landing problem can be made a little more complete by a representation of the motion of the aeroplane along the inclined line. For the undisturbed motion the immediate practical value of this is trivial but as is often the case in building up simulators it is worth considering as a basis which can be modified to represent more complex conditions. The required

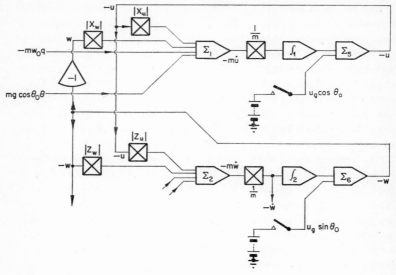

FIG. 3.14.

equipment is shown in Fig. 3.15, and it is mainly an integrator and summing amplifier to solve the equation

$$r = r_o - u_o t = r_o - \int_0^t u_o \, \mathrm{d}t$$

where r is the range of the aeroplane along the inclined line, measured from the point where this line meets the ground, and r_o is the initial value of r, at $t = 0$.

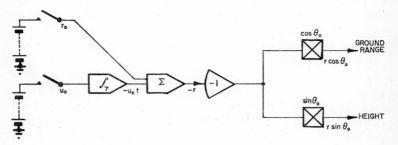

FIG. 3.15.

The output of the summing amplifier represents $-r$, and after sign reversal it is split into two channels, one of which is multiplied by $\cos \theta_o$ to give the ground range of the aeroplane while the other is multiplied by $\sin \theta_o$ to give the height. Since $\cos \theta_o$ and $\sin \theta_o$ are both less than unity the multipliers for these two quantities may be ordinary potentiometers.

If it is required to take into account in Fig. 3.15 the effect of a gust, then the most obvious method is to add a voltage representing $u_g \cos \theta_o$ to the input of integrator 7. This will then give a correct value for the slant range r (except for the error involved in assuming that the x-axis of the aeroplane remains parallel to the inclined line), and for some purposes that value of ground range given by ($r \cos \theta_o$) will still be sufficiently accurate if θ_o is a fairly small angle. The height as given by $r \sin \theta_o$ will, however, be in error by an amount $h \cos \theta_o$, where h is the distance of the aeroplane from the inclined line, measured perpendicular to the line. The correct height could be obtained by taking a voltage from Fig. 3.13 representing h, multiplying by $\cos \theta_o$ by means of a potentiometer, and combining with the voltage representing $r \sin \theta_o$ in Fig. 3.15.

Alternatively, the arrangement of Fig. 3.15 may be replaced by two similar arrangements, one to compute the ground range and the other to compute the height. The voltage source representing u_o is replaced by two sources, one representing $u_o \cos \theta_o$ and the other $u_o \sin \theta_o$, and the final multiplications by $\cos \theta_o$ and $\sin \theta_o$ are not required.

With these last modifications the simulator has now grown to a moderate size, using about twenty amplifiers and integrators. In practice, if it were required to extend the simulation still further this would probably be a suitable point at which to review the whole of the real problem, and the simulation of the problem. Such a review would have two main objectives. The building up of a complex simulator by a series of additions to a simple basic simulator is a convenient and straightforward procedure, and it has the further advantage that the size of the simulator can grow and the accuracy of representation of the real problem can be improved as the operator's knowledge and appreciation of the problem grow. However, it may well happen that this piecemeal development may not give the best arrangement for a simulator of a given degree of complexity. There is some suggestion of such a situation developing in the blind-landing simulator just discussed, in which any further extension might require that the two sets of axes involved—one set fixed to the aeroplane and the other set fixed to the ground—should be represented fully, instead of only partially as in Figs. 3.13 and 3.15. If this were so it would be desirable to rearrange the simulator on this basis rather than think only of extensions to an existing arrangement.

A second reason for a review is to avoid undue accumulation of errors. In any kind of computation in which the complexity of the problem being solved tends to increase from some relatively simple starting point it is important to ensure that any approximations made in the earlier stages remain valid. This is particularly the case in building up a simulator in the manner described above, since the comparative ease with which extensions can be made make it easy to overlook any approximations built into the simulator at some earlier stage. By contrast, the additional labour consequent on raising the order of differential equation to be solved on paper is often so great that a very careful examination would be made to ensure that the improvement in the accuracy of representation of the problem would be sufficient to justify the extra labour.

As an example of the way in which errors can be introduced by extending the simulator, consider the extension of Fig. 3.15 to give height and ground range in the presence of a gust. At first sight, since the only immediate effect of the gust is to change velocities and since furthermore the only velocity appearing in Fig. 3.15 is u_o, it might be thought that the only requirement would be to modify u_o in an appropriate manner. However, as seen above, although this gives a reasonable value for the ground range, provided θ_o is small, it may give only a poor approximation for height unless account is also taken of the displacement of the aeroplane from the inclined line.

CHAPTER 4

SIMULATORS FOR NON-LINEAR PROBLEMS

THE examples of applications of simulators given so far have all been made up from the three basic elements, *viz.* summing and reversing amplifiers and integrators, and they have all applied to problems which can be represented by linear differential equations with constant coefficients. These examples have been of value in demonstrating some features of simulators of this type, but since all the equations could, at least in principle, be solved by ordinary analytical methods, the advantages would probably not be great enough to justify general adoption of simulator methods for the solution of such problems. In certain cases it might be worth while to use a simulator if it were available, or even to build one specially, to solve problems having an arbitrary input, such as the road vehicle suspension problem, or problems involving equations of high order, such as the blind-landing problem, for which a large number of solutions were needed.

However, the usefulness of a simulator, compared with paper methods, is greatly enhanced when problems are to be solved which cannot be described in terms of linear differential equations with constant coefficients. For this purpose additional computing elements are required, and some of these will now be mentioned. Fuller description of the operation of these computing elements will be given later (Chapter 7); for the present purpose a brief outline of their capabilities will suffice.

The multiplier is a device which has two input terminals into which are fed two independent voltages. The output voltage is proportional to the product of the two input voltages, whether they are constant or variable with time. This kind of multiplier will be called a "two-variable" multiplier, when necessary, to distinguish it from the "multipliers" which have already been used for multiplying by constants.

By feeding the same input into both input terminals of a two-variable multiplier the square of a quantity can be obtained. There is a related device which will give the square root of an input quantity, and another which will divide one input quantity by a second input quantity, giving an output voltage proportional to the quotient.

The sine computer gives an output voltage proportional to $\sin \theta$ when fed with an input voltage proportional to θ. The cosine computer correspondingly gives an output proportional to $\cos \theta$. Related to these computers are the sine and cosine potentiometers, which give outputs proportional respectively to $\sin \theta$ and $\cos \theta$ when the angular position of a shaft is set to represent θ.

The arc tan computer gives an output voltage proportional to the angle whose tangent is the ratio of two input voltages, i.e. if the two input voltages are V_x and V_y, the output voltage is proportional to arc tan (V_y/V_x).

The function generator, or curve follower is fed with a voltage proportional to x and gives as an output a voltage proportional to some function $f(x)$. The particular function required must, of course, be set into the generator before use, but with appropriate changes and adjustments most types of generator can be used for a variety of different functions. Usually only single-valued functions can be handled, but with this restriction almost any continuous function can be reproduced, including trigonometric functions, parabolas for squaring variables, and also curves based on experimental results.

The limiter is a device which gives an output voltage equal to the input voltage when the input is below some predetermined level, but remains fixed at this level whenever the input exceeds this level, i.e. if V_1, V_O, V_L, are respectively the input, output and limiting voltages,

$$V_O = V_1, \quad V_1 < V_L$$
$$V_O = V_L, \quad V_1 \geqq V_L$$

The "trigger" is an electronic device which has two quiescent states, and transition from one state to the other occurs very rapidly if an input voltage passes through some critical value. Transition from one state to the other causes a redistribution of currents in the system, so that, for example, a relay can be caused to operate at the instant of transition.

4.1. A BALLISTICS PROBLEM

Some examples will now be given of simulators which need to use one or more of these elements to solve non-linear or "variable-coefficient" problems.

Take first a simple problem in ballistics, in which a gun, elevated at an angle θ to the horizontal, fires a missile with muzzle velocity V_M. The mathematical treatment of the problem *in vacuo* is simple. The vertical component of the initial velocity is $V_{VO} = V_M \sin\theta$, and the vertical component of the instantaneous velocity at any time t after the firing of the gun is equal to

$$V_V = V_{VO} - gt$$

where g is the acceleration due to gravity.

The instantaneous height h is given by

$$h = \int_0^t V_V \,.\, dt = \int_0^t (V_{VO} - gt)\, dt$$

or,

$$h = V_{VO}t - \tfrac{1}{2}gt^2$$

The initial value of the horizontal component of velocity is $V_{HO} = V_M \cos\theta$, and the instantaneous value V_H at any time after firing is equal to this initial value, since there is no horizontal force to provide deceleration. The horizontal range at time t is therefore

$$r = \int_0^t (V_{HO})\, dt = V_{HO}t$$

A simulator for the solution of this simple ballistics problem is, of course, unnecessary, but as a basis for extension to more difficult cases a suitable arrangement is shown in Fig. 4.1. The two parameters which might require to be changed are the muzzle velocity V_M, which is represented by an adjustable battery voltage, and the angle of elevation θ. In Fig. 4.1 the multiplication by $\sin\theta$ and $\cos\theta$ could be achieved, as before, by means of two ordinary potentiometers; but a more convenient arrangement is to use a sine potentiometer and a cosine potentiometer, and to mount these on one shaft so that a single adjustment for θ sets $\sin\theta$ and $\cos\theta$ simultaneously.

To find the range at which the missile strikes the ground, which is assumed to be horizontal, it is necessary to find the value of r at the instant when h passes through zero. There are two general methods by which this may be done. First, the two voltages representing h and r are recorded simultaneously by means of a moving-pen recorder or an oscillograph or by a cathode-ray oscilloscope fitted with a camera, with arrangements to provide on the records suitable scales of amplitudes and time. The "flight" of the missile is allowed to continue until it is certain that h has passed through zero. Then on examination of the records it will be possible to observe the value of r when h passes through zero. The second method depends on the use of the trigger device to operate

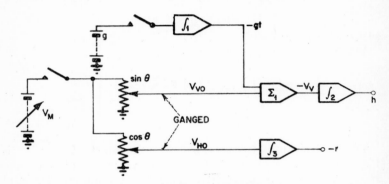

FIG. 4.1. Simulator for Ballistics Problem.

a relay when the input voltage passes through some critical value. For the present purpose the input voltage is the h voltage, and the critical value is zero. The relay is used to reduce to zero the input voltage to integrator 3 in Fig. 4.1, so that the output voltage remains at the value corresponding to $h = 0$. Although the trigger and relay operate very rapidly, the operating time may still be long enough to cause an appreciable error. This can be reduced by arranging the "critical value" of input voltage to be such that operation of the trigger and relay begins just before h reaches zero and the relay contacts close as h passes through zero. The exact value of "anticipation" can be determined either by measurement of the trigger delay, or by simulating a ballistic problem whose answer is accurately known.

The most serious disadvantage of this treatment of the ballistics problem is that it ignores air resistance, and the simulator can be extended to take account of this. For a given missile the resistance of the air depends on the velocity of the missile. The relationship is not simple, but over a certain range of conditions the force of resistance F may be taken as proportional to the square of the velocity, i.e.

$$F = R V^2$$

where R is a constant and V is the instantaneous velocity of the missile. In the presence of air resistance the previous assumption of constant horizontal component of velocity will not hold, and it will now be a variable, V_H.

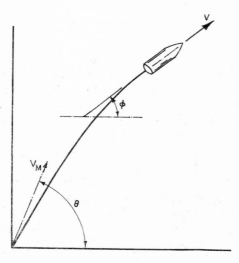

Fig. 4.2.

The resistance F can be resolved into vertical and horizontal components, and the vertical component of acceleration of the missile, taking the air resistance into account is

$$- (g + F \sin \varphi)$$

where φ is the instantaneous direction of flight of the missile relative to the horizontal (Fig. 4.2). The horizontal component of acceleration is

$$- F \cos \varphi$$

Also

$$V^2 = V_V^2 + V_H^2$$

$$\tan \varphi = \frac{V_V}{V_H}$$

At any time t after the firing of the gun the horizontal component of velocity of the missile is

$$V_H = V_{HO} - \int_0^t F \cos \varphi \, \mathrm{d}t$$

and the vertical component is

$$V_V = V_{VO} - \int_0^t (g + F \sin \varphi) \, \mathrm{d}t$$

The simulator is shown in Fig. 4.3. Assuming at first that voltages representing $F \sin \varphi$ and $F \cos \varphi$ are available, the arrangement of Fig. 4.1 is modified by adding $F \sin \varphi$ to the input voltage of integrator 1 to give the new vertical acceleration, and an additional amplifier (2) and integrator (4) are needed to take account of the horizontal component of resistance $F \cos \varphi$. The output voltages of amplifiers 1 and 2 now give the new values of V_V and V_H, and integrators 2 and 3 give the height h and ground range r as before. The next step is to compute V^2, and this is achieved by squaring V_V and V_H and adding. To square V_V the voltage representing V_V is fed into both input terminals of a two-variable multiplier, giving an output V_V^2. Another multiplier gives V_H^2, and the addition to give V^2 takes place in amplifier 3. Multiplication by R, which would in practice be achieved by adjustment of the gain of amplifier 3 coupled with a suitable choice of scale factors, gives $R V^2 = F$. Further taps from the outputs of amplifiers 1 and 2 are fed into an arc tan computer giving an output $\varphi = \text{arc tan} \, (V_V/V_H)$. This voltage is fed into sine and cosine computers giving $\sin \varphi$ and $\cos \varphi$, and two more two-variable multipliers give $F \sin \varphi$ and $F \cos \varphi$.

The arrangement of Fig. 4.3 can be further extended to deal with more complex versions of the ballistics problem. If the resistance function is of some other form than that assumed, appropriate changes can be made. If the function contains odd powers of V then a square-root computer is needed. If the function is such that it cannot be represented as the sum of powers of V, then a curve

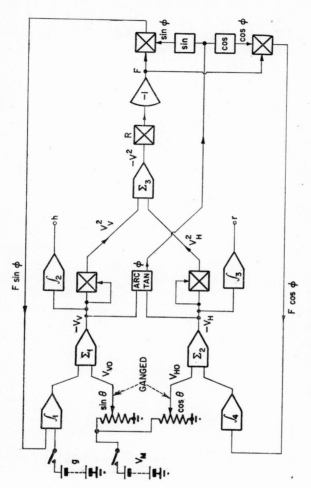

FIG. 4.3. Simulator for Ballistics Problem with Air Resistance.

follower is required, to give an output proportional to F when fed with a voltage proportional to V^2 or to V. The effect of change of air density with height can be included by replacing the resistance equation $F = R V^2$ by a more complicated equation giving F as a function of V and h. If the function is fairly simple the simulation can probably be achieved by using additional summing amplifiers and multipliers, but a curve-follower may be necessary for complicated functions.

The effect of a horizontal wind blowing directly up-range or down-range, i.e. in the plane containing the vector V, can easily be taken into account by adding or subtracting a voltage proportional to the wind velocity, V_W, to the voltage representing V_H which is fed into multiplier 2 in Fig. 4.3. The effect of this is to replace the resistance equation

$$F = R V^2 = R(V_V^2 + V_H^2)$$

by another equation

$$F = R\{V_V^2 + (V_H \pm V_W)^2\}$$

With this arrangement the wind velocity need not be constant; the effects of varying velocity can be reproduced by varying the "wind voltage" in an appropriate manner. If the wind direction is not in the plane of V the problem becomes three-dimensional instead of two-dimensional and the simulation becomes more complex. However, no new principles are involved, and the simulator block diagram can be drawn without difficulty if the appropriate set of simultaneous equations is first written down. At the expense of further complications, but again without introducing any new principle, the gyroscopic effects of a spinning shell, and the effects of curvature and rotation of the earth could be taken into account.

4.2. MOTION OF AN ELECTRON

As an example of a dynamic system in a different field of science, consider the motion of an electrically-charged particle in electric and magnetic fields. Suppose that gravity may be neglected, and that the particle moves in an otherwise completely empty space at speeds small enough for relativistic effects to be ignored. Assume at first that the fields are uniform, with the magnetic field H parallel to the z-axis in a Cartesian coordinate system, and the electric field F in a direction defined by the angles θ and φ in Fig. 4.4. If the

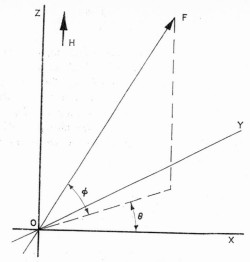

Fig. 4.4. Electric and Magnetic Fields.

mass of the particle is m, its charge q, and its velocity v, then its acceleration f is given by the vector equation [9]:

$$\frac{m}{q} f = F + v \times H$$

For simulator solution this is split into three separate equations:

$$\frac{m}{q} \ddot{x} = F_x + H_z \dot{y} - H_y \dot{z}$$

$$\frac{m}{q} \ddot{y} = F_y + H_x \dot{z} - H_z \dot{x}$$

$$\frac{m}{q} \ddot{z} = F_z + H_y \dot{x} - H_x \dot{y}$$

where F_x, etc., are the components of F in the directions of the axes. Figure 4.4 shows that

$$F_x = F \cos \varphi \cos \theta$$
$$F_y = F \cos \varphi \sin \theta$$
$$F_z = F \sin \varphi$$

The choice for the direction of H gives

$$H_x = H_y = 0$$

The simulator consists of three main sections, one associated with each coordinate, and one section is illustrated in Fig. 4.5. This section computes $\ddot{y}$ and $\dot{y}$ from F_y and $H_z \dot{x}$. The $\dot{x}$ term is provided by another section of the simulator, not shown, and the $\dot{y}$ voltage given by the section shown is used in a similar way by the other two sections. The complete simulator needs two sine potentiometers and two cosine potentiometers, and if these are mounted in two

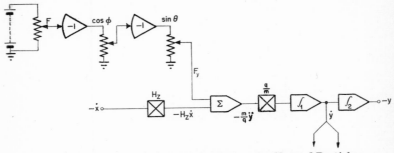

FIG. 4.5. Section of Simulator for Motion of a Charged Particle.

"ganged" pairs one shaft rotation represents θ and the other φ. The reversing amplifiers preceding the $\cos\varphi$ and $\sin\theta$ potentiometers are inserted to remove "loading" effects, and are not primarily for sign changing.

The simulator, even as it stands, is not restricted to steady fields; variations of the strength of H or F can be accommodated by the obvious adjustments if the changes are slow. If the changes are rapid, then voltages varying in a proportional manner are required, and these are used to replace the battery shown for F and to provide the second input for a two-variable multiplier to give $H_z \dot{x}$. Slow variations of the direction of F can be accommodated by adjustment of the θ and φ shafts, but for more rapid changes proportionally-varying voltages are needed, and the sine and cosine potentiometers are replaced by sine and cosine computers of the type already mentioned. For changes of direction of H it is necessary to introduce the H_x and H_y terms and to provide a set of sine and cosine computers and follow the same procedure as for F.

Non-uniform fields can also be represented. Suppose, for example, that the field H is parallel to OZ, but varies in strength according to some known function of the distance from OZ, i.e.

$$H_z = H_0 f(r), \quad \text{where} \quad r = \sqrt{(x^2 + y^2)}$$

Then r can be computed by means of two squaring multipliers, a summing amplifier, and a square-root device; or possibly by an arc tan computer to give $\alpha = \text{arc tan } (y/x)$ and a sine computer and divider to give $r = y/\sin \alpha$ if α remains within a limited range well away from zero. The voltage representing r is fed to a function generator to give $f(r)$ which in turn gives H_z.

4.3. ROAD VEHICLE SUSPENSION WITH "BOUNCE"

An interesting application of the trigger circuit is in the extension of the simulator of Fig. 3.9 (Section 3.4) to include the effects of the tyre bouncing out of contact with the road. During the bounce the

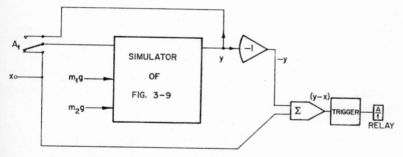

FIG. 4.6. Simulator for a Road Vehicle Suspension with Bounce.

pressure between tyre and road is zero, and the behaviour of the suspension system will be entirely unchanged if the section of the road traversed during the bounce is replaced by a different section, so shaped that the tyre remains just in contact with the road, but exerting zero pressure, during the whole bounce. At the end of the bounce the tyre will resume contact with the true road surface. The section of road to be used in place of the real road during bounce must have a shape such that it is always distant r_o below the centre of the wheel, where r_o is as before the outer radius of the tyre in the unstressed condition. To produce the desired effect in the simulator

x is subtracted from y as shown in Fig. 4.6 and the difference voltage is fed into a trigger circuit set to operate when the input voltage passes through zero. If now y increases relative to x so that $(y - x)$ passes through zero the trigger will operate and this will occur when the tyre leaves the road. The trigger operates a relay which switches the x input terminal from the normal source of x voltage, representing the real road surface, and connects it to the output of an amplifier giving a voltage representing y. Thus the "road" remains temporarily at distance r_o from below the wheel centre. When $(y - x)$ falls below zero the trigger releases the relay and the x input terminal is reconnected to the normal source of road surface voltage.

If the simulator were such that an explicit voltage appeared representing the pressure between the tyre and the road it would be sufficient to use the trigger circuit and relay to earth the point in the simulator where this voltage appeared, in accordance with the obvious fact that the pressure is zero when the tyre is out of contact with the road. In the simulator shown in Fig. 3.9 there is no such voltage, so the device of the fictitious road during bounce is used. A voltage representing the pressure between tyre and road could be produced if differentiators were allowed, or if the frictional losses in the tyre were so small that the friction coefficient λ_1 could be neglected. In the latter case it would only be necessary to earth the output terminal of amplifier 1 by means of the trigger-operated relay.

4.4. A NAVAL GUNNERY PROBLEM

As a final example of the application of simulators consider the rudimentary naval "battle" represented in Fig. 4.7. Two ships S and T are sailing with speeds V_S and V_T in directions defined by the angles ψ_S and ψ_T, and the line joining them is of length R and has a direction defined by the angle β. Let the initial coordinates of S and T be $(0, 0)$ and (x_{T_0}, y_{T_0}) respectively. Then the position of S at time t is given by

$$x_S = \int_0^t V_S \cos\psi_S \, dt$$

$$y_S = \int_0^t V_S \sin\psi_S \, dt$$

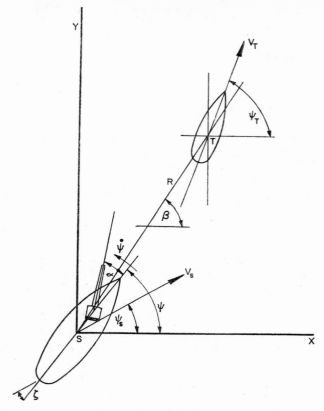

FIG. 4.7. Naval "Battle".

and these expressions hold whether V_S and ψ_S are constant or variable.

The position of T at the same instant is given by

$$x_T = x_{T_0} + \int_0^t V_T \cos\psi_T \, dt$$

$$y_T = y_{T_0} + \int_0^t V_T \sin\psi_T \, dt$$

A simple simulator for computing the two positions can be arranged following the procedures already described. The range R

can be computed by simulating the equation

$$R = \sqrt{[(y_T - y_S)^2 + (x_T - x_S)^2]}$$

and β can be found from

$$\beta = \arctan\left(\frac{y_T - y_S}{x_T - x_S}\right)$$

Suppose now that S is pursuing T, and intends to fire a shell. If S is to sail in the direction of T, S must be turned so that $\psi_S = \beta$, i.e. so that $\beta - \psi_S = 0$. However, when the ship is turning, the angle ψ_S which defines the direction in which the centre of gravity of the ship is moving is not equal to the angle ψ which defines the direction of the fore-and-aft line of the ship. There is no direct indication of the value of ψ_S, but the angle $\beta - \psi$ can be found by observing the direction of the target ship T relative to the fore-and-aft line of S, and for the present purpose it will be assumed that the angular deflection of the rudder ζ is made proportional to the angle $(\beta - \psi)$. This will tend to make $(\beta - \psi)$ equal to zero, and this condition means that the fore-and-aft line of S is pointing at T, which is a reasonable direction for the pursuit of T. In practice there would usually be a helmsman forming a link between the observation of the angle $(\beta - \psi)$ and the movement of the rudder, but the reaction time of the man is short compared with the time scale of events in this battle and it will be ignored. The man could be represented, if desired, by inserting a simple lag of about 0·3 second time constant in or after the summing amplifier which adds β and $-\psi$. Alternatively a more complicated network might be used; or if the man's behaviour was considered sufficiently important a real man could be included. In the latter case the man would need a visual indication of the angle $(\beta - \psi)$, and he would be provided with a "wheel" which would drive a potentiometer to give the ζ voltage to be fed back into the simulator.

In the steady state $\dot\psi_S$ and $\dot\psi$ will be equal, but it will be assumed that there is a time lag T_1 between a movement of the rudder of ship S and the corresponding rate of yaw $\dot\psi$, and another time lag T_2 between the development of this rate of yaw and the corresponding rate of turn $\dot\psi_S$ of the ship's track. Then

$$\left.\begin{aligned}
\zeta &= k_1(\beta - \psi)\\
\dot\psi + T_1\ddot\psi &= k_2\zeta\\
\dot\psi_S + T_2\ddot\psi_S &= \dot\psi
\end{aligned}\right\} \qquad (4.1)$$

Now suppose that the ship S fires a shell at T. At the instant of firing the direction of the gun barrel is at an angle α relative to the fore-and-aft line of the ship, so that the direction of the barrel relative to OX is $\psi + \alpha$. If, at the instant of firing, the ship is yawing at an angular rate $\dot{\psi}$, the end of the gun barrel will have a velocity relative to the C.G. of the ship, and in a direction at right angles to the direction of the barrel. The magnitude of this velocity will be equal to $B'\dot{\psi}$, where B' is the effective length of the barrel, i.e. the "horizontal component" of the length, which is $B\cos\theta$, where B is the true length and θ the angle of elevation. It is assumed here that the gun is attached rigidly to the ship at a point vertically above the centre of gravity, that the ship remains on an even keel, and the yaw takes place about a vertical axis through the centre of gravity. These are all somewhat unrealistic assumptions, but they are convenient for the present purpose, and they could be replaced by sounder assumptions later on. Some effects due to the ship's own speed, etc., have been ignored, but these too could be included if desired.

If the muzzle velocity of the shell is V_M, then on emerging from the muzzle when the ship is yawing, the total velocity of the shell will be the resultant of V_M and $B'\dot{\psi}$, and although the magnitude of the resultant will be substantially equal to V_M, since the other term is small, the direction of the shell will be turned through a small angle arc $\tan(B'\dot{\psi}/V_M) \doteqdot B'\dot{\psi}/V_M = (B\cos\theta)(\dot{\psi}/V_M)$. Hence the direction of the shell relative to OX is

$$\eta = \psi + \alpha + (B\cos\theta) \times (\dot{\psi}/V_M).$$

To study the flight of the shell, a simulator for the two-ship problem, as outlined above, must be combined with the "ballistic" simulator of Fig. 4.3. The block diagram is shown in Fig. 4.8; it follows the same principles as those described earlier, and will not be treated in detail. The upper section represents the motion of the target ship T, with potentiometers for setting the speed, V_T, the initial position (x_{T_0}, y_{T_0}), and the direction of the ship's track ψ_T. V_T and ψ_T can be changed during the problem, if desired. The reversing amplifier following the V_T potentiometer is not inserted for sign-changing, but to remove the "loading" effects which the sine and cosine potentiometers would otherwise impose on the V_T potentiometer.

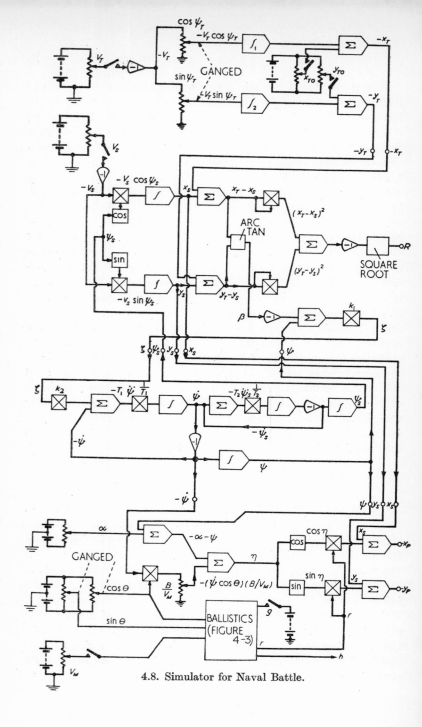

4.8. Simulator for Naval Battle.

The next section represents the motion of the ship S, and bears some resemblance to the first section, except that instead of a ganged pair of sine and cosine potentiometers for setting in ψ_T by hand, sine and cosine computers are used to produce voltages representing $\sin \psi_S$ and $\cos \psi_S$. This is necessary because ψ_S is not available as an independent variable but is computed from the rudder deflection by the third section of the simulator, which solves equations (4.1). The remaining section of the simulator computes the angle η, at which the shell flies, and uses this to compute the position of the shell. The block labelled "ballistics" represents the simulator of Fig. 4.3, and the output r is multiplied by $\cos \eta$ and $\sin \eta$ to give the coordinates of the position of the shell relative to the ship S. Addition of the coordinates of S, which are (x_S, y_S), gives the position (x_P, y_P) of the shell referred to OX and OY, and assuming that either a recorder or a trigger is used to determine when h is zero, the position of the "splash" of the shell relative to T can be found. If a recorder is used, then the position of T must be recorded, and if a trigger is used two sets of relay contacts are needed, one set to "freeze" the position of T by reducing to zero the input voltages to integrators 1 and 2, and the other to "freeze" the value of r by reducing to zero the input voltage of the integrator in the "ballistics" block which gives an output voltage representing r. This integrator corresponds to integrator 3 in Fig. 4.3.

The ships can be set "sailing" by closing the switches controlling V_T, V_S, x_{T_0}, y_{T_0}, and the shell is "fired" by closing the switches controlling V_M and g. In practice other switches or relay contacts would be used to hold the input voltages to integrators and other elements at zero until the computations actually begin. This point will be discussed more fully in Section 8.2.

Although the simulator now contains more than 60 computing elements, further extension is possible. A more realistic means for setting the bearing and elevation of the gun is obviously desirable, and the ballistic computation could be extended to include the effects of wind, variation of air density with height, or different resistance functions. The ship motion could be modified to include the effects of rolling and pitching of the ship, although the problem would then become three-dimensional, and the complexity of the simulator would increase considerably. Information would be required about the rolling, pitching and yawing motions induced by the waves. A more realistic relation could also be introduced between the bearing of the target ship and the rudder angle ζ; for example, a "lead" angle could be added so that S would tend to sail towards some future position of T rather than the "present" position.

However, sufficient indication has been given of the ways in which the various computing elements may be combined to solve real problems, and the possibilities of extending the ship simulator will not be pursued further.

CHAPTER 5

D.C. AMPLIFIERS

THE most important item in simulators of the type described earlier is the high-gain direct-coupled amplifier. This device has already been briefly mentioned, and a fuller account of the principles of operation and of some problems of design will now be given.

A great many practical circuits have now been devised for d.c. amplifiers, and since the time of publication of the first edition of this work a very wide range of factory-produced amplifiers [10], and complete computers [11], have become available so that it is rarely necessary for the user to design his own amplifier. The following discussion in this chapter and the next is therefore intended to indicate sufficient of the important features of d.c. amplifier design to guide the selection of the most suitable unit for a given installation. The discussion will deal first with amplifiers using thermionic valves, but reference to transistor amplifiers will be made later (Section 5.4).

Ideally, the d.c. amplifier should give an output voltage which is an exact magnified image of the input voltage, and in order that a high degree of feedback can be applied by simple means the amplifier should give a reversal of sign between input and output.

Thus if the input voltage is v, then the output voltage should be $-Mv$, where M is a positive constant, and the constant ratio of output to input voltage should be maintained if v varies with time. Practical amplifiers fail to give this ideal performance for a number of reasons, chief among which are the effects of non-linearities and of unwanted voltages combining with the desired voltages. The non-linearity appears as curvature of the graph relating input and output voltages, i.e. M does not remain constant when v varies. This curvature tends to increase rapidly as the output voltage approaches the "overload" value, but can usually be reduced to a tolerable level by the use of negative feedback and by restricting the excursion of the output voltage to a range well within the "overload" values.

The effect of unwanted voltages is to give an output voltage

$$V = -Mv + V'$$

where V' is a voltage which bears no relation, or at least no simple relation, to the input voltage. V' arises mainly from two causes, *viz.* "drift" and the effect of the grid current of the first valve.

The ideal requirement that $V = -Mv$ includes the requirement that $V = 0$ when $v = 0$, and d.c. amplifiers are fitted with some device such as an adjustable bias control by which this condition

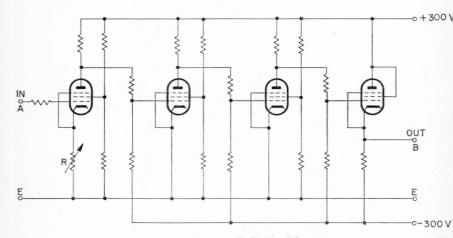

FIG. 5.1. D.C. Amplifier.

can be set up before computation starts. Such a control is shown at R in Fig. 5.1; but although this control may be carefully set to give "zero out for zero in" initially, the effects of drift and grid current during the computation may cause an error.

5.1. DRIFT IN THE SUMMING AMPLIFIER AND INTEGRATOR

To explain these effects reference will be made to Fig. 5.1, which although incomplete, illustrates some features common to many d.c. amplifiers. The coupling between each anode and the following grid is by means of a resistor chain, of which the lower terminal is connected to the negative h.t. supply "rail". The values of the resistors are adjusted so that in the absence of an input voltage each grid is at a small negative potential relative to the cathode, equal to the bias required for normal working. For the last stage, which is a cathode follower, the cathode terminal should be at earth potential when there is no input voltage to the amplifier. For the first stage the grid is at earth potential when there is no input voltage, so bias is provided by a cathode resistor.

Before the amplifier is used in a computing circuit the input voltage is reduced to zero by short-circuiting the input terminals, and R is adjusted so that the output voltage is zero. If the setting

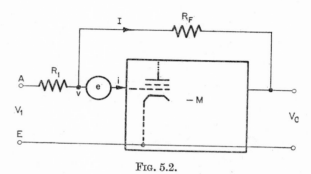

Fig. 5.2.

of R is then left unaltered it will be found after a time that the output voltage will slowly change from zero, even though the input voltage is still zero, and it is this slow departure from the condition of "zero out for zero in" which is called "drift". There are several contributory causes, including ageing and changes of temperature in valves and components, and changes in the high-tension and heater supply voltages. These effects can be minimized by the use of high quality components, suitable choice of valves and operating conditions, careful circuit design, and stabilization of supply voltages, and for some purposes satisfactory performance can be achieved by these means; but for highest accuracy additional devices for reducing drift have been devised, and some of these will be described in Sections 5.3 and 5.8.

The effect of drift in any one stage is equivalent to the introduction of a small voltage, and the magnitude of the drift voltage appearing at the output terminal will depend on both the magnitude of this fictitious small voltage and the amplifier gain between the point where the voltage appears and the output terminal. This means that drift is most serious in the first stage and less important in succeeding stages. It is convenient to refer the drift, wherever it may arise, to the grid of the first valve and to represent the magnitude of the drift by the value of the single voltage, applied at the first grid, which would give the observed output voltage if drift were absent.

This device is used in Fig. 5.2, where e is the drift voltage, referred to the first grid, i the grid current, R_F is a feedback resistor, and R_1 is an input resistor.

For this arrangement,

$$V_O = -M(v + e)$$

$$I R_F = v - V_O$$

$$v = V_1 - iR_1 - I R_1$$

$$= V_1 - iR_1 - \frac{vR_1}{R_F} + \frac{V_O R_1}{R_F}$$

$$= \frac{R_F}{R_1 + R_F} \left\{ V_1 - iR_1 + V_O \frac{R_1}{R_F} \right\}$$

Hence

$$-\frac{V_O}{M} = \frac{R_F}{R_1 + R_F} (V_1 - iR_1) + V_O \left\{ \frac{R_1}{R_1 + R_F} \right\} + e$$

and if M is very large,

$$V_O \doteqdot -\frac{R_F}{R_1} V_1 + iR_F - e \left\{ \frac{R_1 + R_F}{R_1} \right\}$$

$$= -G V_1 - e(1 + G) + iR_F \tag{5.1}$$

where $G = R_F/R_1$ is the effective gain of the amplifier with feedback. In the absence of feedback, and assuming for the present that grid current is zero,

$$V_O = -M V_1 - Me,$$

so that the addition of feedback has reduced the drift component of V_O in the ratio $M : (1 + G)$ and the component of V_O due to V_1 in the ratio $M : G$. The fractional error in V_O due to e is e/V_1 when feedback is not used, since

$$V_O = -M V_1 \left(1 + \frac{e}{V_1} \right),$$

and the corresponding fractional error with feedback may be shown, by rearranging equation (5.1), to be

$$\left(1 + \frac{1}{G}\right)\frac{e}{V_1}$$

so that the addition of feedback has increased the fractional or percentage error, although the increase will probably not be large, since G is not usually a small fraction. It is generally the percentage error which is important, rather than the absolute error, so that although negative feedback is of great value in improving the performance of the amplifier in other ways, it does not have any large effect on the inaccuracy due to drift.

Besides drift, there is in equation (5.1) a spurious component of output voltage due to grid current in the first valve of the amplifier. In Fig. 5.2 it may be imagined that there is within the valve a generator having one terminal connected to cathode and one to grid, so that grid current flows whenever a continuous external circuit is provided between grid and cathode. If the input terminals AE are short-circuited a curent will flow in R_1, and since the output impedance of the amplifier, measured between the output terminals, is not infinite, a current will also flow in R_F. Thus the grid will not be at the same potential as if there were no grid current. When the resistor R of Fig. 5.1 is adjusted during the zero-setting operation immediately before the amplifier is used, this potential due to grid current will automatically be taken into account, so that at first sight there should be no error from this cause. However, the magnitude of the grid current, and hence of the spurious potential will change as the valve warms up, and this will give a spurious output voltage. The potential due to grid current will also change if R_1 or R_F is changed, but in an amplifier with manual zero-setting this change will be compensated when the zero-set adjustment is next made, provided the total effective resistance between grid and earth during zero-setting is of the same value as when the computing connections are made. In practice, of course, there is no obvious method of determining whether a given spurious output voltage is due to grid current or to drift, but the distinction is important for some purposes, especially in the consideration of some drift-compensation devices.

Amplifier drift and grid current also affect the performance of the amplifier when it is used as an integrator, and because of the inte-

6*

grating action a steady spurious voltage or current at the first grid will give at the output not a steady voltage, but a voltage which increases linearly with time. Thus, in Fig. 5.3,

$$V_O = -M(v + e)$$
$$v = V_1 - IR_1 - iR_1$$
$$I = -(V_O - v)sC$$

Hence,

$$v = V_1 + (V_O - v)sT - iR_1 \quad \text{where} \quad T = R_1 C$$
$$= \frac{V_1 + V_O sT - iR_1}{1 + sT}$$

and

$$V_O = -M \left\{ \frac{V_1 + V_O sT - iR_1}{1 + sT} + e \right\}$$

or, if M is very large,

$$V_O \doteqdot - \left(\frac{V_1 - iR_1}{sT} \right) - e \left(\frac{1 + sT}{sT} \right)$$
$$= -\frac{V_1}{sT} + \frac{iR_1}{sT} - e \left(1 + \frac{1}{sT} \right)$$

In this equation the first term on the right represents the required integral of the input. The second and third terms represent spurious outputs due to grid current and drift. If i and e are con-

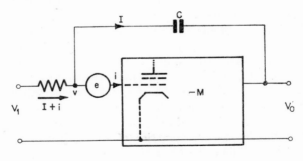

Fig. 5.3.

stant these two outputs will increase continuously, and unlike the corresponding errors which occur in a summing amplifier the spurious output due to grid current is not compensated in the zero-setting operation. For zero-setting in an integrator the usual procedure is to replace the capacitor temporarily by a resistor, the capacitor being short-circuited meanwhile to remove any residual change. If a drift voltage e is present at this stage the adjustment of the zero-setter will in effect introduce an equal and opposite potential. When the temporary feedback resistor is replaced by the uncharged capacitor, the drift voltage at the first grid will be unaltered, but the grid current, which was previously divided between the input resistor and the feedback resistor, now flows only in the input resistor, so that the spurious grid voltage due to grid current is now different, and the output voltage immediately begins to grow in response to this small input. It is possible to compensate for this effect; for example instead of completely disconnecting the temporary feedback resistor the end connected to the output terminal could be connected to earth instead so that the resistance between grid and earth remained unaltered. In practice, however, the performance of such compensation schemes is often disappointing, because the behaviour of grid current is less simple than has been assumed here. In particular, the internal impedance and e.m.f. of the valve, regarded as a generator of grid current, vary rapidly and non-linearly with changes of grid-cathode potential and cathode temperature.

The usual practical remedy for troubles due to grid current is simply to choose a valve whose grid current is sufficiently small. Fortunately, valves are available which suit most requirements, even though for the highest accuracy it may be necessary to use a valve of the "electrometer" type and accept the consequent reduction in gain due to the lower mutual conductance of such valves.

5.2. THE THREE-STAGE AMPLIFIER

To achieve the necessary reversal of sign between input and output most amplifiers use an odd number of stages, and since a single stage gives insufficient gain for many purposes the most popular arrangements use three stages. The circuit diagram of an amplifier of this type which has been used in analogue computers of moderate accuracy is shown in Fig. 5.4. Compared with the skeleton circuit of Fig. 5.1 the chief differences are the relative complexity of the interstage networks, and the use of pairs of valves in push–pull. The resistance chains for $V_1 - V_4$ are basically the same as in Fig. 5.1,

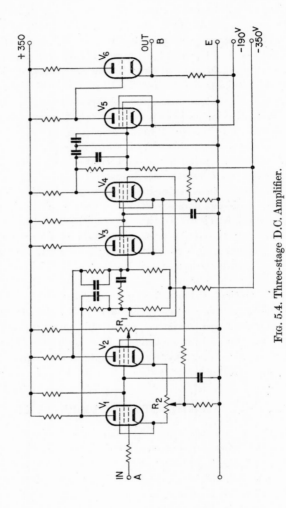

FIG. 5.4. Three-stage D.C. Amplifier.

but certain additional resistors have been introduced to give some compensation against the effects of varying h.t. supply voltages. The use of pairs of valves is also a compensation device [12]. V_1 and V_2 form a cathode-coupled pair, sometimes called a "long-tailed" pair, and if a positive voltage is applied to the input terminal the anode current of V_1 increases and that of V_2 decreases. If the heater voltage rises, the anode currents of both valves rise, and the anode potentials fall, so that ideally, with perfectly-matched valves, the difference between the anode voltages does not change. In practice, using a matched pair of "aged" valves, a useful measure of compensation is achieved. The anode voltages from V_1 and V_2 are passed on to V_3 and V_4, which form another long-tailed pair. If equal voltages of the same sign are applied to the grids of V_3 and V_4 these two valves behave as though they were connected in parallel, and the large common cathode resistance gives a large measure of negative feedback so that only a small change of anode current occurs. If, however, equal voltages of opposite sign are applied, the anode current of one valve increases and the anode current of the other valve decreases by an equal amount. There is thus no appreciable change of potential across the cathode resistor, and hence no feedback effect, and the magnitude of the anode current changes is about the same as in a normal amplifier stage. Thus the $V_3 - V_4$ stage amplifies normally any difference of potential between the two grids, resulting from a legitimate input signal to V_1 and V_2, but is almost unaffected by potential changes of the same sign which would be caused by change of supply voltage in the $V_1 - V_2$ stage. V_3 is used only as a compensating valve, and V_5 forms a single-valve stage fed from the anode of V_4. The resistance chains are so arranged that the anode of V_5 is at a slightly negative potential relative to earth, sufficient to provide the bias for V_6 which is a cathode follower with its cathode at earth potential. The resistor in the anode circuit of V_6 performs no circuit function, but is inserted to prevent excessive anode dissipation.

The capacitors are added to ensure that the amplifier is stable when feedback is applied. The gain of an amplifier of this type is about 50,000, or 90 decibels, and let us say it is desirable to maintain the gain at a roughly constant value at frequencies from zero up to 100 c/s. Above this frequency the gain falls off, but the manner in which it falls off is determined by the need to maintain stability when feedback is applied. Thus suppose the amplifier has equal input and feedback resistors, giving an overall gain of unity. Then the loop gain is 25,000, or 84 decibels, which is half the no-feedback gain since the resistors form, in effect, a two-to-one potential divider in the feedback loop. For satisfactory stability the phase margin [13–17] should be not less than about 30°, and this means that the gain cannot be allowed to fall more rapidly than 10 decibels per octave; that is to say that the gain at a given frequency f, expressed as a voltage ratio, must be not less than one third of the gain at a frequency $f/2$. This condition should be satisfied at all frequencies up to a point at which the loop gain has fallen to 0·5, expressed as a voltage ratio, (or − 6 db) so that the curve

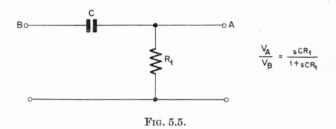

$$\frac{V_A}{V_B} = \frac{sCR_1}{1+sCR_1}$$

FIG. 5.5.

representing the fall in gain must be controlled while the gain falls by 90 db, i.e. over a range of nine octaves if the constant slope of 10 db per octave is maintained. Nine octaves above 100 c/s is approximately 50 kc/s, so that the loop gain characteristic must be controlled in shape from zero frequency up to at least 50 kc/s. In practice it is not easy to maintain the slope of the characteristic very near the desired 10 db/octave over the whole range, and regions of lower slope may appear, resulting in a higher frequency for the zero-gain point and a wider frequency range over which the shape must be controlled. If the feedback and input resistors are not equal the loop gain will be somewhat different, and will approach 90 db if R_F is small compared with R_1. Thus it is desirable to control the characteristic shape over a further octave if stability under all likely conditions is required. In some circumstances it may be permissible for the gain to fall more rapidly than 10 db/octave over part of the frequency band.

When the amplifier is used as an integrator, as in Fig. 1.4a, then the feedback components will make some contribution to the loop characteristic, and assuming that the voltage V_1 is supplied from a source which has a very low impedance, the effect will be equivalent to introducing the simple network of Fig. 5.5. At frequencies which are comparable with or less than the reciprocal of the time constant CR_1 this circuit will produce some attenuation and phase shift; but the values of CR_1 commonly used are such that at frequencies

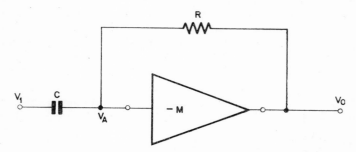

FIG. 5.6. Differentiator.

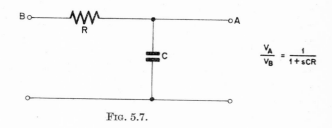

$$\frac{V_A}{V_B} = \frac{1}{1+sCR}$$

FIG. 5.7.

above, say, 100 c/s the reactance of C is very small compared with R_1 so that in the higher frequency region, where the loop characteristic must be controlled, the integrator components make no contribution to either phase shift or attenuation, and the requirements are the same as when the amplifier is used with a feedback resistor which is small compared with the input resistor.

If, however, the amplifier is used in a differentiator circuit (Fig. 5.6), the effective network introduced is that shown in Fig. 5.7 which has a transfer function

$$\frac{V_A}{V_B} = \frac{1}{1+sRC}$$

At frequencies above 100 c/s and normal values of RC, $sRC \gg 1$, so that

$$\frac{V_A}{V_B} \fallingdotseq \frac{1}{sRC}$$

This represents a rate of fall of gain of 6 db per octave (or two to one in voltage ratio for two to one in frequency) and a phase lag of 90°, so that the amplifier proper must have a rate of fall of gain of about 4 db per octave with a phase lag of 60° if the 30° phase margin is to be maintained. There is no fundamental difficulty in achieving this, but it is different from the characteristic required for a summing amplifier or integrator. Thus, while a high-gain d.c. amplifier can be designed which will operate either as a summing amplifier or an integrator, depending only on whether a resistor or capacitor is used as the feedback impedance, it is more difficult to design the same amplifier so that it will also operate as a differentiator. This is one of the reasons why differentiators are not used extensively in electronic computing machines. Another reason will be given in Section 6.7.

Referring again to the circuit of Fig. 5.4 two variable resistors are shown. R_1 is the "zero-set" control, whereby the potential of the output terminal is set to zero when the input terminal A is earthed. To take some account of grid current in V_1 this temporary earth connection may be made via a resistor of the same value as will appear between the grid and earth when the normal computing circuit is connected. The resistor R_2 is a preset control provided to improve the compensating action of V_1 and V_2.

In favourable circumstances, using well-stabilized supplies, with supply mains free from sudden changes of voltage, and with well-aged components running at steady temperature, an amplifier of this type, set for unity gain, may show a drift of 10 mV or less over a period of up to an hour. In other circumstances the drift may be several times larger. The first stage uses a low-grid-current valve, so that grid current effects are not troublesome. The overload output voltage is about ± 70 volts, although for the highest accuracy it is usual to restrict the output to about half this value. The output impedance of the amplifier, connected for an overall gain of ten times, is less than 0·1 ohm, and since the input resistance of a summing amplifier or integrator is not usually less than about 100,000 ohms, the input resistors of a number of amplifiers can be connected in parallel to the output terminal of another amplifier without errors due to loading effects, i.e. without appreciably altering the output terminal voltage.

Amplifiers of the type shown in Fig. 5.4 are thus suitable for use in computing machines of moderate accuracy, especially if the number of amplifiers is small, so that frequent adjustment of the zero-set control is practicable. They can also be used in larger numbers if aid is provided to reduce the delay and labour of zero setting, as in the early GEPUS machine [18].

Other versions of the three-stage amplifier have been designed, including some with push–pull output stages. This arrangement has the advantage that both "signs" of the output voltage are available and there is no need to use amplifiers for sign reversing. The resultant economy, however, is often smaller than might be expected, because in many cases, if the block diagram is carefully arranged, the number of reversing amplifiers needed is only a small fraction of the total number of amplifiers. Furthermore, the push–pull arrangement requires the provision of at least one extra valve and the provision and adjustment of an additional feedback component for each amplifier, and it is often considered that the small decrease in the number of amplifiers needed with the push–pull circuit is insufficient to justify the extra components. Nevertheless commercial installations are currently available which employ this principle.

5.3. THE DRIFT-CORRECTED AMPLIFIER

The drift-corrected amplifier is a development of the "three-stage" amplifier in which additional equipment is provided to reduce the drift which is the most objectionable feature of ordinary d.c. amplifiers.

The basic principles of the drift-corrected amplifier may be explained with reference to Fig. 5.8. This represents a high-gain d.c. amplifier, with input and feedback resistors, and in addition there is a second d.c. amplifier of gain A which takes as its input voltage the voltage v at the junction of the resistors, and feeds its output voltage into the amplifier M where it is combined with the normal input voltage. Suppose initially that V_1 is zero. Then, neglecting grid current for the moment,

$$V_O = - M (e + v + Av) \tag{5.2}$$

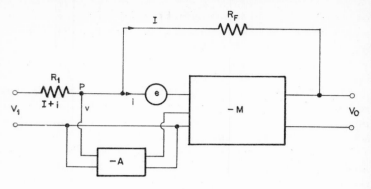

FIG. 5.8.

where e is a drift voltage, and

$$v = \frac{R_1}{R_1 + R_F} V_O$$

It is assumed here that the voltage Av is fed into the M amplifier in such a way that the system is stable when A is positive, i.e. when the auxiliary amplifier gives a 180° phase shift.

Eliminating v from these equations,

$$V_O = -Me - M(A + 1)V_O\left(\frac{R_1}{R_1 + R_F}\right)$$

i.e.

$$V_O\left\{1 + M(A + 1)\left(\frac{R_1}{R_1 + R_F}\right)\right\} = -Me$$

Or, making the usual assumption that M is very large,

$$V_O \doteqdot -\left(\frac{1}{A + 1}\right)\left(\frac{R_1 + R_F}{R_1}\right)e$$

$$= -\left(\frac{1}{A + 1}\right)(1 + G)e$$

where, as before, $G = R_F/R_1$.

Comparing this with equation (5.1) when V_1 and i are both zero shows that the input voltage produced by e has been reduced in the ratio $(A + 1):1$, so that if A is appreciably greater than unity a valuable reduction of the effects of drift is possible.

If V_1 is not zero,

$$V_O = -M(e + v + Av)$$

$$v = \frac{R_1}{R_1 + R_F}(V_O - V_1) + V_1$$

$$= \frac{R_F V_1 + R_1 V_O}{R_1 + R_F}$$

Hence

$$V_O = -Me - M(A + 1)\frac{R_F V_1 + R_1 V_O}{R_1 + R_F}$$

i.e.

$$V_O\left\{1 + M(A + 1)\frac{R_1}{R_1 + R_F}\right\}$$

$$= -Me - M(A + 1)\frac{R_F}{R_1 + R_F}V_1 \qquad (5.3)$$

Or, if M is very large,

$$V_O = -\frac{1}{A + 1}(1 + G)e - GV_1$$

where $G = R_F/R_1$, so that the output due to the input V_1 is apparently unaffected by the auxiliary amplifier. However, examination of the foregoing equations shows that the effective gain of the amplifier, for the voltage V_1, has been increased from M to $M(A + 1)$, so that the errors due to neglecting terms which do not contain M is reduced in the ratio $(A + 1) : 1$, and the benefits of feedback, such as improved linearity, etc., are increased.

If grid current flows from the first valve of the amplifier M, the auxiliary amplifier will not compensate for the consequent spurious output voltage. For assume in Fig. 5.8 that e and V_1 are zero, and that a grid current i flows as shown. Then

$$V_O = -M(v + Av)$$

$$I = -\frac{V_O - v}{R_F}$$

$$I + i = -\frac{v}{R_1}$$

whence

$$v = -\left(\frac{R_1 R_F}{R_1 + R_F}\right)i + \left(\frac{R_1}{R_1 + R_F}\right)V_O$$

and

$$V_O = -M(A+1)\left\{ V_O\left(\frac{R_1}{R_1 + R_F}\right) - i\left(\frac{R_F R_1}{R_1 + R_F}\right)\right\}$$

so that if M is very large,

$$V_O = iR_F \tag{5.4}$$

This output voltage is independent of the value of A and is unaltered if the auxiliary amplifier is absent, provided M is large. This general result can be deduced directly from Fig. 5.8 if it is assumed that the values of R_1 and R_F are of the same order. Since M is very large v must always be very small, and whenever v is not exactly zero V_O will be very much greater in magnitude and of opposite sign. Thus when V_1 is zero and grid current flows the current will divide between R_1 and R_F, but because of the appearance of a large V_O when v is not zero the current through R_1 will be only a very small fraction of i and the current through R_F will be very nearly equal to i. As M approaches infinity the value of v must shrink towards zero if the amplifier does not overload, so the current through R_1 also tends to zero and all of i flows through R_F, giving $V_O = iR_F$.

When the amplifier is used as an integrator, the auxiliary amplifier gives similar benefits so far as reducing the effect of drift and increasing the loop gain are concerned, but again there is no reduction of the error due to grid current. When the input voltage V_1 is zero a current very nearly equal to the grid current must flow through the integrator capacitor, corresponding to the flow of almost all the grid current through the feedback resistor in Fig. 5.8. By substituting $1/sC$ for R_F in the equations leading to equation (5.4) it may be shown that the output voltage due to grid current is given by

$$V_O = i/sC.$$

For a steady value of i this means that V_O must change continuously. However, as mentioned earlier, valves are available which have grid currents so small that the grid current error can be made acceptably small.

The use of the auxiliary amplifier reduces amplifier drift for both summing amplifier and integrator connections, and also enhances the linearizing and other benefical effects of negative feedback by increasing the effective amplifier gain from M to $M(A+1)$.

However, the foregoing demonstration of these effects of the auxiliary amplifier has been based on the assumption that this amplifier was itself free from drift. Inspection of Fig. 5.8 shows that if a drift voltage e' appears at the input terminal of amplifier A, then the term Av in equation (5.2) is replaced by $A(v + e')$ and the output voltage is then

$$V_O = -\frac{1}{A + 1}(1 + G)(e + e'A)$$

Assuming that $A \gg 1$, this means that an additional voltage $e'A/(1 + A) \fallingdotseq e'$ appears with the output voltage, indicating that amplifier A has no useful effects in reducing this drift voltage. If the benefits from the auxiliary amplifier are to be realized, therefore, it is essential that the amplifier A be drift-free.

The usual method of removing, or at least greatly reducing the effects of drift in the auxiliary amplifier is to use the input signal to modulate a carrier signal which is amplified, and then demodulated or rectified before being applied to amplifier M. The usual modulator and demodulator circuits, using thermionic or solid-state, rectifiers are not very suitable in this application because the residual potentials due to contact potentials and to unbalance between pairs or sets of valves or rectifiers tend to mask the small input potentials and to give spurious output voltages which bear little or no relation to the voltages it is required to amplify. Considerable success has, however, been achieved with a mechanical modulating device in the form of high-speed relay forcibly vibrated by an alternating current of a suitable frequency. One contact of the relay is earthed and the other is connected to the input terminal of amplifier A, a resistor being connected between this terminal and point P (Fig. 5.8) to prevent short-circuiting of the input signal to amplifier M. Thus when the relay is energised with alternating current there appears at the input terminal of A a square-wave voltage which alternates between zero and the voltage at point P. The alternating component of this square-wave provides a measure of the voltage at P, so the direct component can be discarded and amplifier A need only be capable of amplifying alternating potentials. The amplified voltage must be rectified and smoothed before being applied to the main amplifier, and the rectification is again usually performed mechanically, although the objections to thermionic or other rectifiers are now less strong since any residual potentials will effectively combine with the drift of amplifier M and will consequently be reduced by the action of amplifier A. The rectification can be performed by simply short-circuiting the

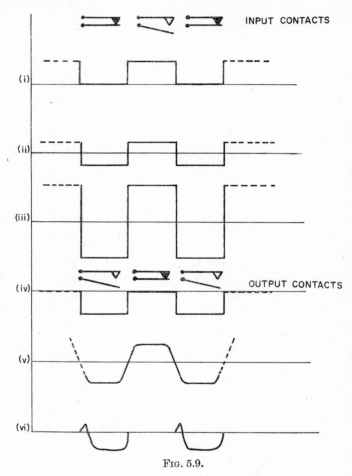

Fig. 5.9.

output terminals of the amplifier for alternate half-cycles, provided the contacts can be closed at the beginning of a half-cycle and opened at the end. This requirement can be met by using a second pair of contacts on the relay used for "chopping" the input signal. Assuming that the relay has two pairs of contacts, one pair of which opens when the other pair closes, the waveforms at various points in the circuit are illustrated by Fig. 5.9. Wave (i) is the chopped input wave appearing at the input terminal of amplifier A. Wave (ii) is the alternating component of (i), and (iii) is the amplifier output, drawn to a reduced scale. The action of the output contacts is to give wave (iv), which has a direct component proportional in magnitude to the original input voltage, but of opposite sign. This is consistent with the previous assumption that the auxiliary amplifier gives a reversal of phase.

The waveform (iii) assumes that the amplification is free from distortion, but in practice there will be some change of the wave-shape and possibly also a phase shift. The wave (v) shows the output wave of the amplifier when there is some attenuation of the higher-frequency components of the input wave and a phase lag. Both these faults are shown in greater magnitude than would be expected in practice, but even so the mean value of the rectified wave (vi) is still proportional to the amplitude of the input wave. The mean value is, however, somewhat less than that given by wave (iv), i.e. the effective gain of the amplifier is reduced. This is not of great importance provided the distortion of waveform and the phase lag remain reasonably constant.

Although in Fig. 5.9 the input and output contacts are shown as separate pairs, one contact of each pair is connected to earth, and it is possible to replace the two pairs by a single change-over, as shown in Fig. 5.10. This is the arrangement usually adopted in practice, since it eases the design of the relay.

The filter which is used to smooth the rectified output of the amplifier should be capable of reducing the residual ripple to about the same value as the drift voltages expected at the input of amplifier M, otherwise there will be objectionable ripple at the output of M. The high attenuation required can be achieved by using a filter with a number of sections, and having a cut-off frequency say within an octave or two of the chopping frequency, but this leads to stability difficulties. For if equation (5.3) is re-written with $e = 0$, the overall gain is given by

$$\frac{V_O}{V_1} = G \left\{ \frac{1}{1 + (1 + G)/M(A + 1)} \right\} \qquad (5.5)$$

which is very near the nominal value G; but from the stability point of view the remarks made earlier (Section 5.2) regarding the need

7 EAC

to control the decrease of gain of the amplifier M now apply to the total effective gain $M(A + 1)$, where A is a vector quantity representing both the amplitude and phase response of the auxiliary amplifier, including the filter. If the filter is of the resistance-capacitance type, each section will give a phase shift which approaches 90° as the frequency rises towards cut-off and remains close to 90° at all higher frequencies, so that even two sections give a phase-shift approaching 180°. Thus if the arrangement is to be

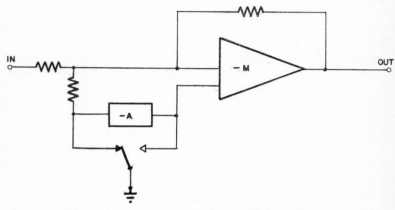

Fig. 5.10. Drift-correction using "Chopper" Relay,

absolutely stable (i.e. not conditionally stable in the Nyquist sense [13–17]) the filter should have no more than two sections, and in order to achieve adequate suppression of the alternating component using only two sections the cut-off frequency must be made much lower than the chopping frequency. At frequencies well above the "cut-off" (taken to be equal to $1/2\pi RC$), two sections of RC filter give an attenuation which increases at 12 db/octave (four-to-one fall in voltage ratio for two-to-one increase in frequency), so that for example an attenuation of 72 db, or a voltage ratio of 1 : 4000, is obtained at a frequency equal to 2^6 or 64 times the cut-off frequency. Owing to the need for controlling the shape of the feedback loop characteristic it may not be practicable to use two sections of equal time constant, and so the filtering action is somewhat less efficient than these figures indicate. An inductance-capacitance filter could, of course, be used, but a single section of low-pass filter also gives a slope of 12 db per octave and a phase shift of $-180°$ at frequencies above cut-off. Furthermore, there is less possibility of controlling the characteristic, and inductances are less convenient than resistors, so the RC type of filter is usually chosen. In practical designs the gain of amplifier A is often around 500 times, and the chopping frequency is not usually higher than about 200 cycles per second because of the difficulty of securing reliable operation of the chopper relay at higher frequencies. Thus, assuming that an attenuation of a few thousand times is required the cut-off frequency of the filter cannot be higher than about 2 c/s, so that the combination of amplifier, relay contacts, and filter form, in effect, a d.c. amplifier having a bandwidth from zero up to about 2 c/s.

The object of using the auxiliary amplifier A in conjunction with the main amplifier M is to give an amplifier of low drift. But since the scheme is only successful if A itself has a low drift the proposed solution seems at first sight to beg the question, and it is natural to enquire why amplifier A, with its choppers and filter cannot be used alone as the main amplifier, since it behaves as a d.c. amplifier of low drift. The main objection to this lies in the small bandwidth imposed by the filter. Problems in dynamics of the kind described earlier commonly include motions which have components of frequencies up to perhaps 10 or 20 c/s, and amplifiers used in computers to handle such frequencies must have bandwidths greater than this if reasonable accuracy is to be achieved [19,20]. A further objection is that the gain of the amplifier is too low for use as a main computing amplifier. There is, of course, no difficulty in increasing the gain above the value of 500 quoted earlier, but any increase in gain requires a corresponding increase in the attenuation provided by the filter, and assuming that the chopping frequency cannot be increased, the cut-off frequency of the filter must be still further reduced.

The narrow bandwidth also means, of course, that the benefits due to using the auxiliary amplifier are realized only over this narrow band. So far as drift correction is concerned, however, this restriction is unimportant since the drifts occurring in amplifier M are slow, and have no appreciable component beyond the filter cut-off frequency. The secondary benefits such as improvement of linearity are lost above the cut-off frequency, but this again is not serious, because with the degree of feedback normally used the

7*

performance of the amplifier M is usually adequate in all respects except drift.

As the gain of A falls off the combined gain $M(A + 1)$ also falls, but equation (5.5) shows that when A falls below unity the effective gain tends towards M, and does not fall below M no matter how small A may become. This is an important consequence of the particular method of connecting the amplifiers together. If an ordinary tandem connection were made, as in Fig. 5.11, the effec-

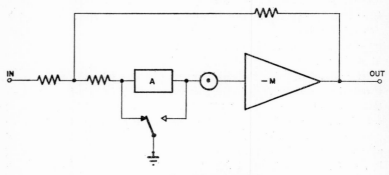

FIG. 5.11. Amplifiers in Tandem.

tive reduction of drift voltage e appearing at the input to M would be achieved as before, but the combined gain would be AM, and the bandwidth of the combination would be that of A. In particular, at frequencies where the gain of A was less than unity the combined gain would be less than M.

The earliest proposals for a drift-corrected amplifier of the type described above were published in the U.S.A. in 1948 [21, 22], although a different method had been described by Prinz [23] in 1947. Several other workers have contributed subsequently [24, 25]. Following the proposals made by Goldberg [24] a drift-corrected amplifier was developed by Lange, Burt and Holbourn, and was further developed by Elliott Bros. (London) Ltd. in a form suitable for use in the large TRIDAC [18] computing machine. This basic amplifier, and one which was developed at about the same time for the Short Bros. and Harland General Purpose Computer [26], have proved to be excellent designs for their time. Both machines have by now a long history of successful computations to their credit.

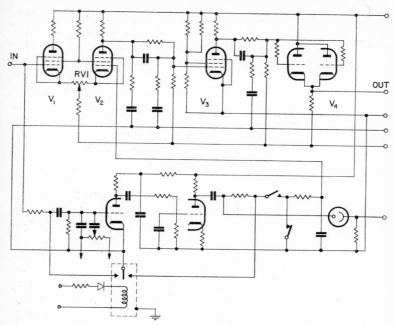

Fɪɢ. 5.12. Typical Drift-corrected D.C. Amplifier.

Considering more recent designs by comparison, there has been little change in the basic conception, the modern amplifier scoring over its predecessor by virtue of using more refined components. Of these, undoubtedly the most important contribution comes from very much improved chopper relays, whose reliability, consistency of operation, and low noise properties have reached a high state of excellence. Secondary improvements have been achieved by using better thermionic valves, and considerably higher quality resistors and capacitors. Printed circuit techniques, currently in use, greatly help to control the parasitic elements, giving rise to much greater consistency in performance between amplifiers of the same theoretical design, making quantity production relatively simple.

Figure 5.12 shows a typical modern d.c. amplifier, designed for a medium-sized computer facility at the College of Aeronautics, Cranfield. As in earlier amplifier designs, the main amplifier is fundamentally a three-stage unit, using a pair of 6BS7 valves as a long-tailed pair input stage. These valves have a good grid-current figure of about 6×10^{-11} ampere, and the grid of V_2 is used to accommodate the drift-correction signal from the auxiliary amplifier. The cathode circuit of the first stage includes the "balance" potentiometer, $RV1$, which enables the amplifier to be initially zeroed. The interstage coupling networks between the input stage and V_3, and between V_3 and V_4, provide the necessary d.c. signal path, and at the same time, control the high-frequency response to provide a stable characteristic for all feedback arrangements normally encountered in computing configurations. This amplifier, like the earlier Short Bros. amplifier, is especially designed to work with relatively large capacity loads simultaneously applied to its input and output terminals. The Cranfield amplifier is stable with 5000 pF at both the input and output terminals. This facility is imperative when the amplifier is to be used in an installation where centralized patching (Section 9.7), and automatic coefficient potentiometer setting (Section 9.6), are features, since long signal leads, giving rise to considerable capacitance loading, are inevitable. The output stage, V_4, of the main amplifier is a cathode follower, using both halves of the ECC81 double triode in parallel to obtain the required output, which is normally ± 60 volts driving a 10 kΩ resistive load. It is of interest to note that in most modern machines there has been a trend to provide a ± 100 volt output swing, probably merely for the sake of the round figure of one hundred. For driving the same load as the above amplifier does, but to ± 100 volts, nearly four times the power would be required. For a large installation this is a serious penalty in primary power supplies and temperature rise to pay for a slight easement of the arithmetic in the scaling of the analogue variables. Of course, a factor against the reduction in the voltage output is the threshold noise level. However, the Cranfield amplifier, with care in the physical lay out, the provision of adequate screening, earthing, and guard-ring techniques, gives a noise level below 20 μvolts peak-to-peak, referred to the input grid. This gives an adequate dynamic range for the amplifier.

The auxiliary, or drift-correcting amplifier, is a two-stage unit using one half of an ECC83 double triode for each stage, and a synchronous chopper relay, working at 100 c/s, driven from a rectified heater supply. The gain of this unit is 1000, which, with the main amplifier's gain of 15,000, gives a drift performance of better than 5 μvolts/hr, referred to the input grid.

Fig. 5.13. D.C. Amplifier.

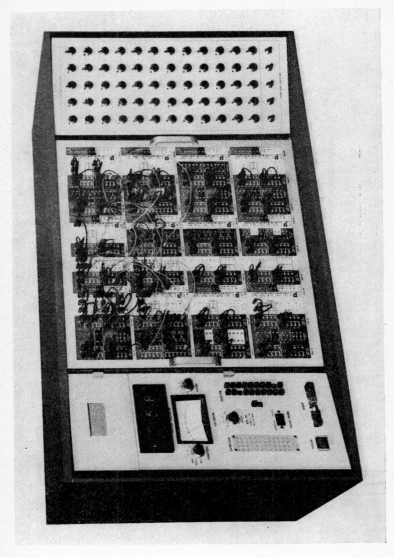

Fig. 5.14. Transistor Analogue Computer—TR 48 (Electronic Associates Inc.).

The h.t. supplies are $+300$ volts and -300 volts only, taking 25 mA and 11 mA from each supply respectively, and 1·2 amp at 6·3 volts 50 c/s, for the filaments and relay combined.

The frequency response characteristics are:

Open circuit: Gain is 3 db down from d.c. gain at 180 c/s.

Closed loop: Gain is 3 db down from d.c. gain at 250 kc/s with 1 : 1, or unity gain feedback, or

Gain is 3 db down from d.c. gain at 50 kc/s with 10 : 1 external gain.

The phase shift at 100 c/s and unity gain configuration is 0·007° lagging.

The Cranfield amplifier is rather better than earlier designs, although it should only be regarded as a good average of contemporary designs. A production unit is illustrated in Fig. 5.13.

5.4. TRANSISTOR AMPLIFIERS

While the preceeding discussion provides an introduction to the design techniques of d.c. amplifiers based wholly on thermionic devices, the development of the transistor operational amplifier cannot be ignored. It is fairly true to say, however, that the transistor d.c. amplifier has not yet become an unqualified success, and only one or two designs have appeared in the last year or so which are comparable with the thermionic type. Nevertheless, there are many commercial machines [10, 11, 27] employing transistor components, performing valuable simulator studies of moderate accuracy. Transistor techniques offer many rewards when their shortcomings can be properly overcome at reasonable cost. The primary advantages to be expected are low power consumption and high-density packaging, leading to small, compact, and rugged computers (see Fig. 5.14).

The fundamental difference between transistor and thermionic valves is that the former are current-controlled devices while the latter are essentially voltage-controlled. The way operational amplifier techniques have grown has led to the acceptance of voltage-controlled operation, and to have the necessary constant-voltage sources means that the power sources for signals, as well as supplies, have to be of low output impedance. There is no physical reason why the dual current-controlled system should not be used, where the variables in the computer are represented by current magnitudes instead of voltage magnitudes. However, this would imply that constant-current sources should be freely available. Such high-impedance sources are not so easily obtained in practice, and the use of current-simulated variables has not found favour so far. Thus the design trend is to make voltage-operated transistor d.c. amplifiers, despite the inherently low input impedance associated with optimum transistor working.

5.5. INPUT IMPEDANCE CONSIDERATIONS

A very high input impedance is easy to achieve with a thermionic amplifier, and any serious discussion as to whether the input impedance should be high or low has hardly arisen. In the transistor case, however, the choice of input impedance is not so clear. The significant factors in the choice are neatly summarized in an analysis due to Beneteau *et al.* [28] who considered the amplifier network as shown in Fig. 5.15.

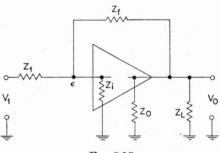

FIG. 5.15.

From this figure it was derived that the operational voltage transfer function is

$$\frac{V_O}{V_1} = - \frac{Z_f}{Z_1} \left\{ \frac{1}{1 - (Z_f Z_i + Z_1 Z_i + Z_1 Z_f)/M_v Z_1 Z_i} \right\}$$

making the reasonable assumption that $Z_f \gg Z_o Z_L/(Z_o + Z_L)$ and where M_v is the amplifier voltage gain; this can be written as

$$\frac{V_O}{V_1} = - \frac{Z_f}{Z_1} \left\{ \frac{1}{1 - 1/M_v A} \right\} \tag{5.6}$$

For $M_v A \gg 1$

$$\frac{V_O}{V_1} \simeq - \frac{Z_f}{Z_1}$$

which is the desired operational transfer function.

From the same figure, the amplifier current gain M_i is necessarily related to M_v by the equation

$$M_i = \frac{Z_1(Z_o + Z_L)M_v}{Z_o Z_L} \qquad (5.7)$$

For operational amplifiers, a good power gain is essential in order to obtain the desirable low output impedance characteristic. For this reason the common-emitter configuration is used since it can be shown to give the best power gain and it also has the property that when the load resistance equals the output resistance the stage current and voltage gains are equal in magnitude. In contrast, the common-base configuration develops less than unity current gain and stages cannot be directly coupled without some impedance transformation. The common-collector connection can only provide unity voltage gain, because of the inherent proportional relationship between input and load impedances [30]. For d.c. amplifiers, it is also known that the voltage-gain times input-impedance product is also sensibly constant, i.e. $M_v Z_i$ is nearly constant. Therefore to obtain an accurate and efficient design, the factor A in equation (5.6) must be maximized. This really is another way of saying that the input impedance Z_i must be made as small as possible in the amplifier design.

This is shown by letting $Z_i \ll Z_1$ and Z_f

whence $\qquad Z_1 Z_i/(Z_f Z_1 + Z_i Z_1 + Z_i Z_f) \simeq Z_i/Z_f$

Also from (5.7)

$$M_v = \frac{M_i Z_o Z_L/(Z_o + Z_L)}{Z_1} = M_i Z_o'/Z_1$$

so that from equation (5.6)

$$\frac{V_O}{V_1} = - \frac{Z_f}{Z_1} \left\{ \frac{1}{1 - 1/M_v A} \right\} = - \frac{Z_f}{Z_1} \left\{ \frac{1}{1 - \dfrac{1}{M_i A \, Z_o'/Z_i}} \right\}$$

$$= - \frac{Z_f}{Z_1} \left\{ \frac{1}{1 - 1/M_i B} \right\}$$

and if the product of $M_i B$ is large, again the desired operational transfer function $V_O/V_1 \simeq -Z_f/Z_1$ results.

Thus, providing the values of the products $M_v A$ and $M_i B$ are the same, the amplifiers will appear to be the same. However, it is also known that the closed-loop stability is affected differently for the low and high input impedance cases by changes in Z_f, with the high input impedance providing greater stability [29].

5.6. COUPLING BETWEEN TRANSISTOR STAGES

The detailed design of transistor d.c. amplifiers [30] is a specialized topic, particularly since new varieties of solid-state devices continually appear in great abundance and with great variation in cost. For example, recently developed 50 volt transistors can pro-

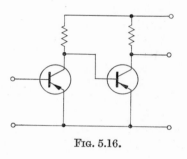

FIG. 5.16.

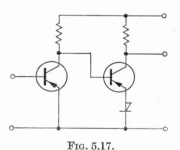

FIG. 5.17.

vide output voltage swings of the same order of magnitude as is obtained from thermionic valves. Until the component situation stabilizes it would be unwise to predict that a particular trend is

emerging, except perhaps to draw attention to an increasing acceptance of the use of hybrid systems, using both solid-state and
thermionic devices in optimal arrangements.

Direct coupling of transistor stages presents rather similar
problems to those found in d.c. thermionic amplifiers. Firstly there
is the need to maintain proper bias levels in relation to the signal.
Secondly, the generation of spurious drift signals must be minimized.

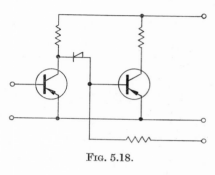

Fig. 5.18.

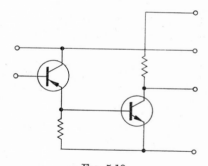

Fig. 5.19.

Figure 5.16 shows the most elementary form of coupling where
two common-emitter stages are simply connected. Such an arrangement gives a rather non-linear amplifier because the second stage
biasing is not adequate. An improvement sometimes employed
is the insertion of a zener diode in the emitter circuit which controls
the second stage bias (Fig. 5.17). If a collector-to-base voltage drop
is required, the breakdown diode can again be used as shown in
Fig. 5.18, although an alternative scheme is to use complementary

transistors, i.e. a PNP type followed by a second-stage NPN type. This method enables the signal output to be symmetrical about zero volts, and the circuit for this is shown in Fig. 5.19. Other interstage coupling arrangements are possible and are described in specialized literature [31].

However, the major problem of solid-state d.c. amplifier design is the reduction of drift, which is considered next.

5.7. DRIFT IN TRANSISTOR AMPLIFIERS

A thermionic device, by its very nature, operates at an elevated temperature, so that the variations in ambient temperature are relatively insignificant as far as temperature-sensitive parameters of the device are concerned. Solid-state components are essentially "room-temperature" devices, with little thermal capacity, and with parameters which are inherently temperature sensitive. The drift current can be expressed as [30]:

$$I_{\text{drift}} = I_{co} + \frac{\Delta V_{be}}{R_s} + \frac{I_b \Delta \alpha'}{\alpha'}$$

where I_{co} = leakage current flowing between base and collector due to the presence of thermally generated electron-hole pairs.

$\dfrac{\Delta V_{be}}{R_s}$ = base-emitter voltage change required to maintain a constant collector current as temperature is varied (approx. 2 mV/°C).

$\dfrac{I_b \Delta \alpha'}{\alpha'}$ = component due to change in α' which is proportional to initial base current.

The leakage current I_{co} for a common germanium transistor is about 3 μA at 25°C, but is typically much smaller for a silicon transistor, at about 10 mμA at the same temperature. Currents for both types increase roughly by a factor of two for each 8°C rise in temperature.

The effect of variations in V_{be} can be greatly reduced by the use of special compensation networks employing other temperature-sensitive elements including thermistors, junction diodes, and also other transistors [32]. However, it is often adequate to arrange the input circuit in the form of a symmetrical emitter-coupled system as shown in Fig. 5.20, provided both transistors are thermally closely coupled to the same heat sink to maintain them at a common temperature. An important drift-control method is to place all

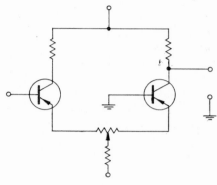

Fig. 5.20.

sensitive components in one or more temperature-controlled ovens. This is an entirely practical technique because of the inherently small size obtained with transistor design.

5.8. CHOPPER TECHNIQUES

Despite all the circuit refinements outlined above, the best drift voltage remains at no better than 5–10 μvolts per °C, which is still excessive for high performance computer application, and as in the thermionic amplifier case, the necessity arises for modulation techniques. As before, the Goldberg method using a mechanical chopper relay is a possibility, although the circuit does not correct for the error due to base current flowing in the input and feedback impedances. This trouble can be eliminated by inserting a good quality capacitor in the input lead to the first stage. This provides a good solution, although, if the amplifier is inadvertently saturated, the system blocks due to the charge which is developed across this capacitor. A discharge switch can be provided to reset the amplifier after such an overload.

An alternative system suggested by Okada [23] avoids the need for the capacitor by providing a chopper amplifier network which is identical to the main amplifier network at very low frequencies, even to having similar input and feedback impedances. These two networks are arranged so that the leakage current flows in the chopper amplifier auxiliary input and feedback impedances, which automatically provides the proper compensating signal to be applied to the main amplifier. The penalty for this more effective correction is the need to duplicate input and feedback impedances which, of course, can lead to a greater complexity in the amplifier switching arrangements.

It is pertinent when using transistor amplifiers to consider employing solid-state choppers. Like the basic amplifier itself, the design of chopper networks has not yet settled down to a well-established pattern. Probably all the standard switching modulator techniques have been tried, using both diodes and transistors. The problem of effectively replacing a mechanical switch with an electronic counterpart is of course an immensely important one. In this highly sensitive application as a low-level, drift-free modulator, the chance of more than moderate success is unlikely, as semiconductor components are plagued by extreme sensitivity to temperature variations, and are not truly irreversible devices. Furthermore, in chopper operation, a spike usually appears in the output waveform which is proportional to the product of the emitter-to-base capacitance, and the source resistance. The spike represents an unwanted breakthrough and can severely limit the overall effectiveness of such solid-state chopper networks.

CHAPTER 6

COMPUTING WITH PRACTICAL AMPLIFIERS

SOME indications have already been given, in Section 1.4, of ways in which high-gain d.c. amplifiers can be used for sign-reversing, summing, and integrating, but it was assumed there that the amplifiers had ideal characteristics. Some consideration will shortly be given to the effects of practical shortcomings, but before this it will be useful to examine other circuits which can be used for summing and integrating with high-gain d.c. amplifiers. Examination of these alternatives will show why the circuits already mentioned are preferred and will also help in understanding the operation of these circuits.

6.1. SUMMATION BY NETWORKS

A voltage proportional to the sum of two more or voltages can be produced by means of the circuit shown in Fig. 6.1. If the current flowing through terminal A is zero,

$$\frac{V_1 - V_A}{R_1} + \frac{V_2 - V_A}{R_2} + \frac{V_3 - V_A}{R_3} - \frac{V_A}{R_A} = 0$$

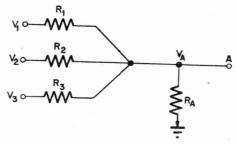

FIG. 6.1. Summation Network.

101

or,

$$\frac{V_1}{R_1} + \frac{V_2}{R_2} + \frac{V_3}{R_3} = V_A\left(\frac{1}{R_A} + \frac{1}{R_1} + \frac{1}{R_2} + \frac{1}{R_3}\right)$$

If R_A is very small compared with R_1, R_2, and R_3,

$$\frac{V_1}{R_1} + \frac{V_2}{R_2} + \frac{V_3}{R_3} = \frac{V_A}{R_A} \tag{6.1}$$

very nearly,

and $$V_A = a_1 V_1 + a_2 V_2 + a_3 V_3$$

where $$a_1 = R_A/R_1, \quad a_2 = R_A/R_2, \quad a_3 = R_A/R_3.$$

Thus the circuit operates as a summing circuit provided R_A is sufficiently small; but although V_A then bears the proper proportional relation to V_1, V_2, and V_3, its absolute value is small. To remedy this, a high-gain amplifier may be connected as shown in Fig. 6.2. Then

$$V_O = -M(a_1 V_1 + a_2 V_2 + a_3 V_3) \tag{6.2}$$

If the output and input voltages are to be of the same order of magnitude then Ma_1, etc, must be of the order of unity. The error due to the approximation in equation (6.1) can be made as small as desired by using a sufficiently high value of M and a correspondingly small value of R_A. This arrangement is sound in principle, and would work well if a suitable amplifier could be provided. However, the output voltage V_O is now directly proportional to M, so that only very small variations in the value of M can be permitted if reasonable accuracy of computation is to be achieved. The two requirements of high value of M and high constancy of this value

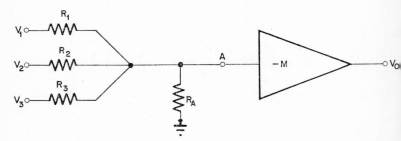

Fig. 6.2.

are not easy to satisfy simultaneously in a practical amplifier, and it is natural to enquire whether negative feedback can be used to improve to constancy of gain. The simplest feedback arrangement is that shown in Fig. 6.3, and although this does not help to stabilize the value of M directly it is beneficial in a somewhat un-

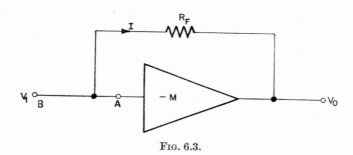

FIG. 6.3.

expected manner. Assuming that V_1 is supplied from a zero-impedance source the voltage at the input terminal A is equal to V_1, the output voltage is $V_O = -MV_1$, and the overall gain has not been altered by the addition of the resistor R_F. However, since there is now a potential difference across R_F there must be flowing in it a current

$$I = \frac{(V_1 - V_O)}{R_F} = \frac{V_1(1 + M)}{R_F}$$

The current at A is still zero, so the current must flow via the input terminal B. Thus, when a voltage V_1 is applied, a current I flows, so the circuit must now present a resistive input impedance of value

$$Z = \frac{V_1}{I} = \frac{R_F}{1 + M} \tag{6.3}$$

Now it was pointed out above that MR_A/R_1 in Fig. 6.2 should be of the order unity, i.e. R_A should be of the same order as R_1/M. Assuming that R_F in Fig. 6.3 is of the same order of magnitude as R_1 in Fig. 6.2, then by equation (6.3) Z is of the same order as R_1/M, i.e. of the same order as R_A. Hence, it would be possible to remove R_A in Fig. 6.2 and provide the necessary low resistance by adding a feedback resistor to the amplifier, as in Fig. 1.3a.

8 EAC

Now from equation (6.2),

$$V_O = - M\left(\frac{V_1 R_A}{R_1} + \frac{V_2 R_A}{R_2} + \frac{V_3 R_A}{R_3}\right)$$

$$= - M R_A\left(\frac{V_1}{R_1} + \frac{V_2}{R_2} + \frac{V_3}{R_3}\right) \qquad (6.4)$$

Thus some variation of the value of M would be permissible if R_A could be varied in a corresponding manner so as to keep the product $M R_A$ constant. If R_A were an actual resistor any such variation would be impractical, but if R_A is replaced by the input impedance Z of the amplifier of Fig. 6.3 a close approximation to the desired variation is achieved. Equation (6.4) shows that if the value of M increases, R_A is required to decrease, and equation (6.3) shows that Z changes with M in the required direction. More precisely, if $R_A = Z$, equation (6.3) gives

$$M R_A = Z M = \frac{M R_F}{1 + M}$$

so that provided M is high,

$$\frac{M}{1 + M} = 1, \quad \text{very nearly,}$$

and
$$M R_A = R_F = \text{constant,}$$

so that V_O in equation (6.4) is very nearly independent of M, provided M always has a high value.

6.2. INTEGRATION BY NETWORKS

A corresponding analysis can be given for the integrator. For the circuit of Fig. 6.4,

$$V_C = \frac{1}{C}\int I \cdot \mathrm{d}t$$

$$I = \frac{(V_1 - V_C)}{R}$$

so that
$$V_C = \frac{1}{T}\int V_1 \cdot \mathrm{d}t - \frac{1}{T}\int V_C \cdot \mathrm{d}t \qquad (6.5)$$

where
$$T = RC.$$

Thus V_C is proportional to the time integral of V_1, as required, provided the time integral of V_C is negligibly small compared with the time integral of V_1; i.e. provided V_C is negligible compared with V_1. If T is made very large, and if a high gain amplifier is connected after the circuit of Fig. 6.4 to give an output voltage V_O of the same

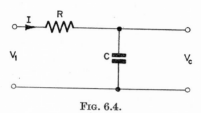

FIG. 6.4.

order as V_1, the requirement $V_C \ll V_1$ will be met, since V_C will be of the order of V_1/M. However, the amplifier will again need to have a high and constant value of M, so as before, a feedback arrangement is considered. In Fig. 6.5, the input current is equal to the current flowing in the capacitance, which is

$$I = \frac{C\, \mathrm{d}(V_1 - V_O)}{\mathrm{d}t} = C(1 + M)\frac{\mathrm{d}V_1}{\mathrm{d}t}$$

since
$$V_O = -M V_1 .$$

Now if a voltage equal to V_1 were applied to a capacitance C', the current flowing would be

$$I' = C'\frac{\mathrm{d}V_1}{\mathrm{d}t}$$

Hence the arrangement of Fig. 6.5 has a capacitive input impedance of the same value as a single capacitance of value $C' = (1 + M)\, C$.

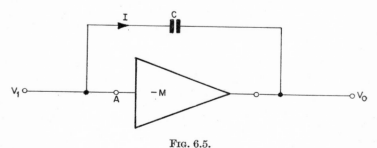

FIG. 6.5.

8*

Any change in the value of M, besides changing the degree of amplification of the voltages arriving at terminal A of the amplifier, also produces a change in the value of the input capacitance which almost exactly compensates.

The replacement of the capacitor C of Fig. 6.4 by the arrangement of Fig. 6.5 produces the arrangement of Fig. 1.4a, the so-called "Miller" integrator. The mechanism by which the input capacitance of the amplifier in Fig. 6.5 appears to have a value $(M + 1)$ times the capacitance between the output and input terminals is exactly similar to the undesirable effect which increases the input capacitance of an amplifying valve by an amount equal to the grid-anode capacitance multiplied by the stage gain [17]. This effect was described by Miller [34] and has since been described by his name. The similarity of the effect occurring in Fig. 6.5 has led to the arrangement being called the Miller integrator, although it is very doubtful whether Miller foresaw any such useful application, and the credit is probably due to Blumlein [35, 36].

It is important to appreciate that the time constant of integration of Fig. 1.4a is $T = RC$, and is substantially independent of the value of M provided M is very large. The expression "time constant" used in this way has not the same significance as when used in connection with the circuit of Fig. 6.4. A "time constant of integration" is merely a parameter which appears in equations such as (6.5) and has no useful relation with the time for the output voltage to reach a fraction $(1 - 1/e)$ of its final value.

6.3. IMPERFECT REVERSING AND SUMMING AMPLIFIERS

Turning now to the effects of the imperfections of practical amplifiers, consider first the sign-reversing amplifier, which may be regarded as a special case of the summing amplifier. The ideal high-gain amplifier for this application would have infinite gain, zero output impedance and infinite input impedance, and exact proportionality between the infinitesimal input voltage and the output voltage for all values of these voltages. The most serious shortcoming of the practical amplifier is drift, which has already been discussed. The next imperfection is that the gain is infinite, and it is important to determine how great the gain must be in order to justify the approximations depending on the gain being very large. The relation between input voltage and output voltage for the arrangement of Fig. 1.2 is given by equation (1.2):

$$\frac{V_O}{V_1} = - \frac{R_F M}{R_F + R_1(1 + M)} = - \frac{R_F}{R_1 + \dfrac{1}{M}(R_1 + R_F)}$$

If M is infinite, then V_O/V_1 has the value $-R_F/R_1 = -G$, say, which is the nominal gain of the amplifier with feedback. If M is large but not infinite the gain with feedback is equal to

$$-G' = - \frac{R_F}{R_1 + \dfrac{1}{M}(R_1 + R_F)} \tag{6.6}$$

$$= - \frac{R_F}{R_1\left\{1 + \dfrac{1}{M}(1 + G)\right\}}$$

whence
$$G' = G\left(1 - \frac{1 + G}{M}\right) \text{very nearly.}$$

Thus, if G' is not to differ from G by more than, say 0·1 per cent, then the minimum value for M is

$$M = 1000(1 + G).$$

In normal computations it is unusual to use values of G greater than about 10, since larger values give rise to voltage swings which tend to overload output stages or else need unduly small input voltages. A value of M of at least 10,000 is therefore desirable. If errors greater than 0·1 per cent can be accepted, a smaller value of M will suffice, but in practice it is often found that no great economy can be achieved as a result of reducing the degree of precision demanded unless errors of the order of a few per cent are permissible. The reason for this is that in order for the amplifier to be stable when feedback is applied it must provide a reversal of phase between input and output voltages, at least in the working range of frequencies from zero upwards. This requirement can be met by using an odd number of amplifying stages, and the usual choice is between a single-stage amplifier, giving a value of M ot 150 or less, and a three-stage amplifier which can be designed without great difficulty to give a gain of about 50,000.

With $M = -50$ the error between actual and nominal gain G' and G is about 4 per cent even if G is unity, and the error is over 7 per cent if $M = 150$ and $G = 10$. These errors can be reduced if, instead of taking $G = R_F/R_1$, the amplifier gain is measured and the values of input and feedback resistors are adjusted to give the desired gain, or if the appropriate values of the resistors are calculated from equation (6.6). In small computing machines this procedure is sometimes acceptable if there are no other objections to the low gain. For larger machines, however, this method of setting the gain is inconvenient, and as will be seen later, it is still more inconvenient in the summing amplifier. A high value of M is usually desirable for other reasons, and it may be assumed that in the larger computing machines the value of M will be of the order of 20,000 or greater, so that errors due to inequality of G' and G will be a fraction of 0·1 per cent.

If the amplifier is being used as a summing amplifier to add, say, three voltages V_1, V_2, V_3 applied through input resistors R_1, R_2, R_3 with a feedback resistor R_F, the output voltage V_O is given by equation (1.4):

$$\frac{V_1}{R_1} + \frac{V_2}{R_2} + \frac{V_3}{R_3} = -V_O \left\{ \frac{1}{R_F} + \frac{1}{M} \left(\frac{1}{R_1} + \frac{1}{R_2} + \frac{1}{R_3} + \frac{1}{R_F} \right) \right\}$$

If $R_F/R_1 = G_1$, $R_F/R_2 = G_2$, $R_F/R_3 = G_3$,

$$V_O = - \frac{G_1 V_1 + G_2 V_2 + G_3 V_3}{1 + \frac{1}{M}(G_1 + G_2 + G_3 + 1)} \tag{6.7}$$

Hence, the effective gain between V_1 and V_O is equal to

$$-G_1' = - \frac{G_1}{1 + \frac{1}{M}(G_1 + G_2 + G_3 + 1)}$$

and there are corresponding expressions applying to V_2 and V_3. Thus, in the unlikely event of G_1, G_2, G_3 all having values around 10, a value of M about 30,000 would give errors of 0·1 per cent, so that again in most large computing machines errors of this type are likely to be less than 0·1 per cent.

The above considerations of the desirable value of M apply most obviously when M is a positive number, but in practice the amplifier will give phase shifts at the higher frequencies, so that M should properly be regarded as a "vector", i.e. as a quantity having both magnitude and an associated phase angle. Any phase shift in M will, in general, give a phase-shift between input and output voltages, but it can easily be shown that if the phase-shift in M is as much as 90°, provided the magnitude of M is still a few thousand, the phase shift between input and output voltages with normal gains will be less than 0·1°. Furthermore, an amplifier such as that shown in Fig. 5.12 will give phase-shifts of only about 40° at 100 c/s, and correspondingly less at lower frequencies, so that errors due to phase-shift in the amplifier are unlikely to be significant.

In discussing the value of M it has been implied that it was desirable to make the effective gains equal to the ratio of two resistors, e.g. $G_1' = G_1 = R_F/R_1$. As in the case of the reversing amplifier, however, it is possible to achieve a desired ratio between output and input voltages even when M is not large by suitable choice of resistance values.

Equation (6.7) may be rewritten:

$$V_O = -G_1' V_1 - G_2' V_2 - G_3' V_3,$$

where

$$G_1' = \cfrac{\cfrac{R_F}{R_1}}{1 + \cfrac{1}{M}\left(\cfrac{R_F}{R_1} + \cfrac{R_F}{R_2} + \cfrac{R_F}{R_3} + 1\right)} \qquad (6.8)$$

and there are corresponding equations for G_2' and G_3'. Thus when M is not large the gain between V_1, say, and V_O depends not only on R_F and R_1 but also on R_2, R_3, and M. When values of M, G_1', G_2', and G_3' are known and R_F has been chosen the values of R_1, R_2, and R_3 can be found by simultaneous solution of equation (6.8) and the corresponding equations for G_2' and G_3'. This is a tedious calculation, and furthermore if any one of the quantities G_1', G_2' or G_3' is changed then new values for all three input resistors must be calculated, and this is unacceptable for a flexible computer.

6.4. OUTPUT LIMITATIONS

Another respect in which the practical amplifier fails to satisfy the requirements laid down for the ideal amplifier is that the available output voltage is limited. As the input voltage rises steadily from zero the output voltage rises also, and initially the two voltages are proportional, but as the rise continues the output increases less rapidly than it would in a perfectly linear amplifier. Thus the gain of the amplifier, defined for this purpose as the ratio of the rate of increase of the input voltage to the rate of increase of the output voltage, decreases as the output voltage increases. The decrease of gain is inappreciable over what is usually called the "working range" of the amplifier, and examination of equation (6.6), for example, shows that if M has a value of, say, 30,000 a decrease of 20 per cent or even 50 per cent on this value will prob-

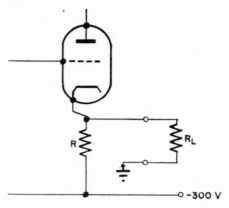

FIG. 6.6. Cathode Follower with Load.

ably not be serious. However, as the output voltage reaches the "overload point" the gain begins to fall very rapidly, and even the high degree of feedback normally employed in summing or sign-reversing amplifiers is insufficient to prevent large errors appearing. Thus, in using amplifiers for these purposes it is necessary to ensure that the output voltage does not reach the overload level.

Besides this limitation on output voltage there is another aspect of the limitation of output from the amplifier. Figure 6.6 represents a cathode-follower output stage in which the output voltage to the load R_L is zero when there is no input to the amplifier and the cathode current in this condition is, say, I_o, so that $RI_o = 300$. Suppose that the cathode current in the valve can increase to $(I_o + \Delta I)$ and fall to $(I_o - \Delta I)$ without serious non-linearity. At the higher value there will be a current I_L, say, in R_L, and the current in R will be increased from I_o to $(I_o + I_R)$. If the voltage across the load is V_L, the currents will be related by the equations

$$V_L = I_L R_L$$
$$V_L + 300 = (I_R + I_o)\, R$$

or $$V_L = I_R R \quad \text{since } R I_o = 300.$$

Hence $$I_L R_L = I_R R.$$

Also, $$\Delta I = I_L + I_R,$$

from which, by elimination of I_R,

$$I_L = \frac{R}{R + R_L}\, \Delta I.$$

This shows that the maximum current which may be drawn by the load is a fraction $R/(R + R_L)$ of the permissible swing of the cathode current from the mean value. Suppose $I_o = 20$ mA, $\Delta I = 7.5$ mA, and $R_L = 10,000$ ohms; then $R = 15,000$ ohms, $I_L = 4.5$ mA, and $V_L = 45$ volts. Thus, if a low-current output stage is used to feed a low-resistance load, care should be taken that excessive currents are not drawn.

6.5. INPUT AND OUTPUT IMPEDANCES

The requirement that the ideal amplifier should have infinite input impedance and zero output impedance arises from the desirability of being able to feed the output voltage from one amplifier to the input terminals of a number of other amplifiers in parallel without disturbing the value of the output voltage. If the output impedance of an amplifier is Z_O and the open-circuit voltage is V, and if the input impedance of each of the following amplifiers is Z_i, the voltage appearing at the output terminal of the first amplifier when it is feeding n amplifiers in parallel is

$$\frac{V\dfrac{Z_i}{n}}{Z_O + \dfrac{Z_i}{n}}$$

Assuming that Z_O is small compared with Z_i there will be a fractional error of approximately $n Z_O/Z_i$, and if this is to be, say, one part in a thousand, Z_O must be less than $Z_i/1000n$. Now the input impedance of a high-gain amplifier with a feedback resistor but no input resistor is shown by equation (6.3) to be equal to $R_F/(1 + M)$, and if $R_F = 2$ megohms and $M = 30,000$, the input impedance is roughly 70 ohms. Assuming that the minimum value of input resistor is about 100,000 ohms the input impedance of a summing or sign-reversing amplifier is therefore equal to the resistance itself, to within less than 0·1 per cent.

The normal range of input resistor values is from about 100,000 ohms to a few megohms, so that if ten amplifiers are to be fed in parallel the minimum value of Z_i/n is about 10,000 ohms, and the value of Z_O for a "loading" error of less than 0·1 per cent must be less than 10 ohms. The output impedance of a high-gain d.c. amplifier without feedback is the output impedance of the last stage, which is commonly a cathode follower, with an impedance of 500 ohms or less. If the value of M is, say, 30,000, and the value of G is 10, the negative feedback, while reducing the gain by 3000 times, will also reduce the output impedance in a similar ratio, so that the output impedance of the amplifier with feedback is not greater than about 0·2 ohm. Hence for the range of values considered, no appreciable error will result from feeding a number of amplifiers in parallel from one other amplifier.

If the high-gain amplifier has no cathode-follower output stage the output impedance of a normal amplifier stage, without feedback, might be between 10,000 and 50,000 ohms, so that with a feedback reduction of 3000 times the impedance would be between about 3 ohms and 20 ohms, which might be acceptable for some purposes.

For single-stage amplifiers, with $M = 50$, say, the output impedance would probably lie between 10,000 and 50,000 ohms, but the gain with feedback would probably be kept to some lower value than 10 in order to maintain a useful degree of feedback. Similarly, the range of input and feedback resistor values would be kept smaller. For an overall gain of five times the output impedance would be 1000 to 5000 ohms, and the input impedance of the amplifier with no input resistor would be 20,000 ohms for a one-megohm feedback resistance. Such impedances can only be ignored for calculations where errors of up to 10 per cent, say, can be ignored. Compensation is possible in certain respects; for example the input resistor to an amplifier may be reduced by an amount equal to the output impedance of the preceding amplifier; but such arrangements are inflexible and of limited practical use. Apart from the inconvenience of using resistor values which bear no simple relations to the gains desired, the compensation depends on the value of M remaining constant. The single-stage amplifier with a cathode-follower output stage added has an output impedance of a few ohms with normal values of G, and this is usually acceptable.

In the discussions on amplifiers with feedback it has been assumed that the input and feedback resistors always have exactly the correct values. In practice, of course, the values will not be absolutely accurate even initially, and the errors will most likely change with time. If errors due to inaccurate resistance values are to be less than 0·1 per cent it might seem that at first sight that the values themselves must be within this limit, but it is useful to remember that the basic requirement is that the ratios of the resistor values should be correct, the absolute values being less important. Thus it would be permissible to use a set of resistors which were all, say, exactly 10 per cent above their nominal values. For errors in resistance values to be less than 0·1 per cent the resistors should be wirewound, as ordinary carbon resistors cannot be relied on to maintain their values to such close limits, even though the initial values might be correct. In cases where larger errors can be tolerated it may be possible to use high-stability carbon resistors, but it will be advisable to check their values from time to time.

6.6. IMPERFECT INTEGRATORS

When the amplifier is used as an integrator, with a capacitor as the feedback element, the value of M again has an important influence on the accuracy, though the errors arise in different ways. Assuming that the capacitor is discharged at $t = 0$, it follows from equation (1.6) that, if $T = R_1 C$,

$$V_O = -\frac{M V_1}{1 + s(T + MT)} \qquad (6.9)$$

which approaches the desired value $-V_1/sT$ as M approaches infinity. The equation may be rewritten in the form

$$V_O = -V_1 \left(\frac{M}{M+1}\right)\left(\frac{1}{sT}\right)\frac{s(M+1)T}{1 + s(M+1)T} \qquad (6.10)$$

which shows that the error due to using a finite value of M appears
in two parts. There is a simple "scaling" error represented by
$M/(M + 1)$; and the pure integration which would be provided by
an ideal integrator is, in effect, "contaminated" by the addition of
a simple R.C. differentiation circuit (Fig. 6.7) of time constant
$(M + 1) T$. The scaling factor is usually negligible, but can be
allowed for if desired, so that effectively the error in integration is
solely due to the differentiation effect. If, in the integrator, $T = 1$
and $M = 50,000$, then the time constant of the differentiation is
$(M + 1)$ seconds, which would require values in Fig. 6.7, of say,

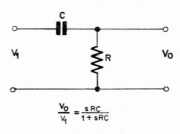

$$\frac{V_O}{V_1} = \frac{s\,RC}{1 + sRC}$$

FIG. 6.7.

$50,000\,\mu\text{F}$ and $1\cdot0$ megohm. It is sometimes useful to assess the
error in a practical integrator by considering the effect of such a
differentiating circuit on the proposed input voltage.

Alternatively, the errors may be estimated by finding the output
which the practical integrator will give when the input voltage is
of some simple form. Suppose, for example, that V_1 is a step function. The equation (6.9) shows that the integrator behaves like a
simple R.C. "smoothing" circuit (Fig. 5.7) of time constant
$(T + MT)$, followed by an amplifier of gain $- M$, so the response
to the step is [37]

$$V_O = - V_1 M [1 - \exp\{-t/(T + MT)\}].$$

This result can also be obtained using equation (6.10), and it is
instructive to derive the solution of this equation in two steps.
First, the input step function is operated on by the differentiator
term $\dfrac{(M + 1)\,sT}{1 + (M + 1)sT}$, which gives a function very similar to the
original step except that instead of remaining at a constant value
after the initial rise the voltage very slowly decays, with time

constant $(M + 1) T$, in proportion to $\exp \{- t/(M + 1) T\}$. There is also a very small change of amplitude corresponding to the term $M/(M + 1)$. The second step is the exact integration of this decaying wave, according to the term $1/s T$, which gives

$$V_O = - V_1 \left(\frac{M}{M + 1} \right) \frac{1}{T} \int_0^t \exp \{- t/(M + 1) T\} \, \mathrm{d}t$$

$$= - V_1 M [1 - \exp \{- t/(M + 1) T\}]$$

since $V_O = 0$ when $t = 0$.

Expanding the exponential, and neglecting terms after the third,

$$V_O = - V_1 M \left\{ 1 - \left(1 - \frac{t}{T + MT} + \frac{t^2}{2(T + MT)^2} \right) \right\}$$

$$= - V_1 M \left\{ \frac{t}{T + MT} - \frac{t^2}{2(T + MT)^2} \right\} \tag{6.11}$$

The effect of the t^2 term is to cause the output voltage to rise somewhat more slowly than it would in an ideal integrator. This corresponds to the slow decay of the differentiated step given by the term $\dfrac{(M + 1) sT}{1 + (M + 1) sT}$ in equation (6.10).

If the error in equation (6.11) is to be less than 0·1 per cent, the term in t^2 must be less than the term in t in the ratio 10^3 or greater, i.e.

$$\frac{t^2}{2(T + MT)^2} \cdot \frac{T + MT}{t} < 10^{-3}$$

or

$$M > \frac{500t}{T}.$$

Values of M between 30,000 and 10,000 have been mentioned earlier, and if a value of 50,000 is chosen this leads to the restriction $t < 100 T$ if the 0·1 per cent error limit of error is not to be exceeded. It is not easy to generalize on the importance of this restriction, because although it is quite possible that the total time for some computations will exceed 100 times the shortest integrator time constant in the system, it is unlikely that there will be a steady input to the integrator for the whole of this time. If there is a steady input, then neglecting for the moment the error due to the finite value of M,

$$V_O = -\frac{1}{T} \int_0^{} V_1 \, \mathrm{d}t$$

$$= -\frac{V_1 t}{T} \quad \text{if } V_1 \text{ is a step function;}$$

and if $t = 100\,T$, $V_O = -100\,V_1$, so that the amplifier is likely to overload unless V_1 is less than about one volt.

In any simulator which includes integrator time constants which are short compared with the computing time for one solution, care must be taken to see that integration errors of this type are not overlooked. A convenient general rule can be derived from equation (6.11). Assuming that M is large,

$$V_O = -V_1 \left(\frac{t}{T} - \frac{t^2}{2\,M\,T^2} \right) \quad \text{very nearly}$$

$$= -V_1 \frac{t}{T} \, (1 + \varepsilon)$$

where $\varepsilon = -t/2\,M\,T$ is the fractional error. Now ε is small, so that

$$V_O = -V_1 \frac{t}{T} \quad \text{approximately}$$

$$= V_1 (2\,M\,\varepsilon)$$

and hence, $\varepsilon = \dfrac{V_O}{V_1} \dfrac{1}{2\,M}$ approximately.

Thus for a step function input, and for a given value of M, the ratios t/T or V_O/V_1 for a given fractional error can be determined.

Another simple input function which can be used to determine the effect of a finite M value is a square-wave. Suppose the input is zero at $t = 0$, but rises instantaneously to a value V_1 and remains there for an interval t_1, after which it reverses its sign instantaneously after each successive interval of length t_1. During the first interval the output voltage at time t will be

$$V_O = -V_1 \frac{t}{T} \left(1 - \frac{t}{2\,M\,T} \right),$$

from equation (6.11), assuming that M is very large; and at the end of the first interval the output voltage will be

$$V_{O1} = - V_1 \frac{t_1}{T} \left(1 - \frac{t_1}{2MT}\right)$$

so that the error voltage will be $V_1 t_1^2/2MT^2$. Now the reversal at the end of the first interval may be imagined to take place in two stages. First, the input is reduced to zero, and the output voltage remains constant at its value immediately prior to $t = t_1$, which is V_{O1}; the input is then immediately changed to $- V_1$. The total output during the second interval is therefore the sum of V_{O1}, which represents the charge on the capacitor at $t = t_1$, and the voltage due to the integration of $- V_1$ during the elapsed part of the second interval. At the end of the second interval the output voltage is therefore

$$V_{O2} = V_{O1} + V_1 \frac{t_1}{T} \left(1 - \frac{t_1}{2MT}\right)$$
$$= 0$$

where both the main terms and the error terms have cancelled. In succeeding pairs of intervals this process is repeated, so that the error never exceeds the value it reaches at the end of the first interval. Even this error is somewhat artificial, since its sign depends on the choice of the sign of V_1 for the first interval. If the first interval were half the length of the succeeding intervals the error would oscillate between two values of opposite sign and of magnitude equal to $V_1 t_1^2/8MT^2$, which is a quarter of the value of the error in V_{O1}.

Thus, the greatest error which can occur in the integration of a square-wave input is equal to the integration error which accumulates during half a period of the wave, and the rule derived for integration of step function can be applied. Taking $M = 50,000$ and permissible error as 0·1 per cent, this means that integration of square waves will be satisfactorily accurate provided the periodic time of the wave is not greater than about 200 times the integrator time constant.

If the input to the integrator is a sine wave of frequency $\omega/2\pi$,

$$V_O = - \frac{MV_1}{1 + j\omega(T + MT)}$$

where the s of equation (6.9) has been replaced by $j\omega$.

The modulus of the ratio $\dfrac{V_O}{V_1}$ is

$$\left| \frac{V_O}{V_1} \right| = \frac{1}{\sqrt{\left[\dfrac{1}{M^2} + \omega^2 T^2 \left(1 + \dfrac{1}{M^2} \right) \right]}} \qquad (6.12)$$

whereas in an ideal integrator with $M \to \infty$ the modulus would be $1/\omega T$. Rewriting equation (6.12),

$$\left| \frac{V_O}{V_1} \right| = \frac{1}{\omega T \sqrt{\left[\left(1 + \dfrac{1}{M^2} \right) \left\{ 1 + \dfrac{1}{\omega^2 T^2 (1 + M^2)} \right\} \right]}}$$

$$\fallingdotseq \frac{1}{\omega T} \left(1 - \frac{1}{2 M^2} \right) \left\{ 1 - \frac{1}{2 \omega^2 T^2 (1 + M^2)} \right\}$$

taking binominal expansions to two terms.

The error due to the $1/2 M^2$ term will nearly always be negligible, so that for 0·1 per cent error

$$2 \omega^2 T^2 (1 + M^2) = 1000, \quad \text{or,} \quad \text{if } M \text{ is } 50{,}000,$$

$$\omega T \fallingdotseq 4{\cdot}5 \times 10^{-4}, \quad \text{or} \quad \frac{1}{f} \fallingdotseq 1{\cdot}4 \times 10^4 \, T;$$

so that provided the period of the sine wave is less than about 10,000 times the integration time constant the error will be less than 0·1 per cent.

For a sine wave input there will be, besides the small error in amplitude, an error of phase between V_O and V_1, in addition to the normal 90° lag which would be given by an ideal integrator. The magnitude of the error is equal to

$$\operatorname{arc} \tan \{ 1/\omega (T + M T) \} \quad \text{radian}.$$

If $M = 50{,}000$ and the period of the wave is $1000\,T$, this gives about 0·2 degree, which is not usually important. This error decreases as the periodic time of the wave decreases relative to the time constant T.

In an integrator with sinusoidal input the ratio of output to input voltages is less sensitive to changes in the value of M than in the case of a summing or sign-reversing amplifier. This can be shown by differentiating equations (6.12) and (6.6) with respect to M and comparing the derivatives. This effect is a consequence of the phase shift in the feedback network, and was treated by H. S. Black in his classic paper on feedback amplifiers [14].

As in the case of amplifiers with resistive feedback the integrator can perform accurately only if the values of the feedback and input impedances are accurate, though it is the time constant given by the product of resistances and capacitance rather than their separate values which must be accurate. There is, however, an additional source of error in the integrator because the capacitor is

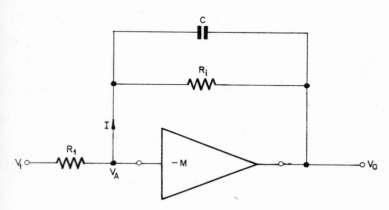

FIG. 6.8. Integrator with Leaky Capacitor.

not free of resistive effects, as an ideal capacitor would be. In particular the imperfect insulation of the dielectric gives the effect of resistance in parallel with the capacitance, as shown by R_i in Fig. 6.8. Taking R_i into account, the dependence of V_O on V_1 can be derived in the usual way

$$V_O = -M V_A$$

$$I = \frac{(V_A - V_O)}{R_i} + (V_A - V_O) s C$$

$$I = \frac{(V_1 - V_A)}{R_1},$$

and after eliminating I and V_A,

$$V_O \left(\frac{1}{M R_1} + \frac{s C}{M} + \frac{1}{R_i M} + s C + \frac{1}{R_i} \right) = -\frac{V_1}{R_1}$$

9 EAC

For the present purpose it is permissible to neglect sC/M in comparison with sC, and $1/R_iM$ in comparison with $1/R_i$, so that

$$V_O\left(\frac{1}{MR_1} + sC + \frac{1}{R_i}\right) = -\frac{V_1}{R_1}$$

or,

$$V_O = -\frac{V_1}{sT + \dfrac{1}{M} + \dfrac{R_1}{R_i}}$$

In an ideal integrator the denominator would contain sT only, and it appears from this equation that in addition to the error due to the non-infinite value of M, which has already been discussed, there is now an error due to the non-infinite value of R_i. The magnitude of this error can be illustrated by replacing the arrangement of Fig. 6.8 by an integrator using a perfect capacitor and an amplifier of gain M'. For this arrangement, from equation (6.9)

$$V_O = -\frac{V_1}{sT + \dfrac{1}{M'}}$$

and this will give the same performance as the arrangement of Fig. 6.8, if

$$\frac{1}{M'} = \frac{1}{M} + \frac{R_1}{R_i}$$

or

$$M' = M\frac{1}{1 + \dfrac{MR_1}{R_i}}$$

If $M = 50{,}000$ and $R_1 = 2 \times 10^6$ ohms, R_i must be at least 10^{12} ohms if M' is to be within 10 per cent of M, or 10^{11} ohms if $M' = M/2$. Such insulation resistances can be achieved in capacitors of $1\cdot 0\ \mu$F, which is the order of size commonly used in computing machines of the type discussed in earlier chapters, if polystyrene is used as the dielectric. The "insulance" of polystyrene, i.e. the product of insulation resistance and capacitance, is approximately 200,000 megohm–microfarad, which is some ten to twenty times better than mica, and the dielectric absorption effects are smaller in about the same ratio.

Resistive losses in the dielectric of the capacitor, corresponding to a non-zero power factor, may be represented by adding a resistor R_s in series with the capacitor of Fig. 1.4 a. Then

$$\frac{V_O}{V_1} = -\frac{R_s + \dfrac{1}{sC}}{R_1}$$

$$= -\frac{1}{sCR_1} - \frac{R_s}{R_1}$$

Thus in addition to the pure integral term the output also contains a term proportional to the input voltage. The power factor of polystyrene capacitors as used in analogue computers is about 0·005, which means that R_s is usually negligible. It is important to take account of the quality of the insulation of the mounting and connexion arrangements associated with the integrator capacitor circuit. Relay contact spacers and patchboard socket insulators are notably difficult design areas. Great care is needed to minimize leakage currents by the use of high quality components and materials, and by the application of guard-ring techniques.

The foregoing analysis of computer errors is not exhaustive, but it is sufficient to indicate the main causes and possible remedies.

For the specialist, reference to more detailed studies is possible [38, 39, 40].

6.7. THE DIFFERENTIATOR

Besides its use as summing amplifier, sign-reverser and integrator, the high-gain d.c. amplifier may also be used, with capacitor input and resistor feedback, as a differentiator (Fig. 5.6). In ideal circumstances the differentiator is as satisfactory as the integrator, but in practice differentiation is usually avoided whenever possible. There are three reasons for this. First, the differentiator arrangement is more difficult to stabilize, especially in a flexible machine where it may be required to use the same amplifier as a summing amplifier on one occasion, and as integrator or differentiator on other occasions. Second, the differentiating action tends to increase the "spikiness" of a varying input voltage, and hence tends to increase the chance of overload. Third, and probably most important, the differentiator tends to degrade the "signal-to-noise ratio" of the output voltage by amplifying the residual power-supply ripple and

9*

other higher-frequency disturbances which are always present to some extent. The question of stability has already been discussed (Section 5.2), and the other objections can be illustrated more fully by a simple analysis of the arrangement of Fig. 5.6. Following the usual procedure it is easily shown that

$$V_O = - V_1 \left(\frac{sT}{1 + \frac{1}{M} + \frac{sT}{M}} \right)$$

which may be rewritten

$$V_O = - \left(\frac{M}{M+1} \right) \left(\frac{V_1 sT}{1 + \frac{sT}{M+1}} \right) \qquad (6.13)$$

This equation shows that, compared with an ideal differentiator, the use of a finite value for M gives an error which appears in two parts. There is first a "scaling" error represented by $M/(M+1)$, and secondly, the pure differentiation is, in effect, "contaminated" by the addition of a simple R.C. smoothing circuit (Fig. 5.7) of time constant $T/(M+1)$. The error due to this contamination corresponds closely with the error due to using a finite value of M in an integrator.

If the input to an ideal differentiator is a step function of voltage the output is an impulse function, having an infinite amplitude and infinitesimal duration such that the "area" of the impulse, i.e. the product of amplitude and duration, is proportional to the amplitude of the input step. If a step function is applied to a practical differentiator the output rises to a value given by setting $s \to \infty$ in equation (6.13), which is

$$V_O = - M V_1,$$

assuming that the amplifier does not overload. In practice, of course, overloading would occur for almost all values of M and V_1 of practical interest, so that the differentiator is useless when its input contains step functions. Even when the input rises at a finite, rather than an infinite rate, overloading may occur. If the input voltage rises at a steady rate of k volts per second, then $V_1 s$ in equation (6.13) may be replaced by k, and the output voltage is, ignoring the $sT/(1 + M)$ term for the moment,

$$V_O = -\frac{M}{M+1}(kT) = -kT \quad \text{very nearly,}$$

from which some estimate of the permissible rate of change of the input voltage can be made when T is known.

If the input voltage to a differentiator is sinusoidal, of frequency $\omega/2\pi$, then equation (6.13) becomes

$$\frac{V_O}{V_1} = -\left(\frac{M}{M+1}\right)\left(\frac{j\omega T}{1 + \dfrac{j\omega T}{M+1}}\right) \tag{6.14}$$

so that, at frequencies such that $\omega T \ll M$, the differentiator behaves as an amplifier with a gain which increases linearly with frequency. Now suppose that a differentiator has a time constant of 1·0 second, and the input has a small 50 c/s content of magnitude v. Then the 50 c/s content of the output voltage will be very nearly equal to $\omega v = 314v$, which will be intolerable unless v is a small fraction of a volt. If chopper-stabilized amplifiers are being used the input signal may contain, say, 1 mV of ripple at 100 c/s which would give an output ripple of more than half a volt. At still higher frequencies the gain, according to equation (6.14) will continue to rise towards the asymptotic value M, but as the frequency rises above a few hundred cycles per second it is likely that the value of M will fall, so that the maximum value will be appreciably less than the low-frequency value of, say, 50,000. For an amplifier of the type shown in Fig. 5.12 the maximum gain of a differentiator with $T = 1$ would be several thousand times.

Thus, a single differentiator with a time constant of the order of 1·0 second is liable to give a serious increase in the noise content of the variable voltage, and the use of two or more such differentiators in any tandem connection is usually out of the question.

The liability of a differentiator to overload when the input voltage varies rapidly, and the error due to the $sT/(M + 1)$ term in the denominator of equation (6.13) are both aggravated if T is increased, so in cases where the use of a differentiator is unavoidable it is often advisable to use as small a time constant as possible. A smaller value of T reduces the amplification of residual ripple and noise, but the amplitude of the desired voltage is reduced in the same ratio, so that the signal-to-noise ratio is apparently not improved. However, this argument assumes that the ripple is fed into the differentiator with the legitimate input voltage, whereas there may be appreciable injection of ripple within the differentiator amplifier, say from the heater of the first valve, or from the chopper amplifier. In such cases it will be advantageous to use a small value of T and compensate for the reduction of output voltage by raising the level of the input voltage. A reduction of T with a compensating increase of gain *after* the differentiator would generally leave the signal-to-noise ratio unchanged.

CHAPTER 7

NON-LINEAR COMPUTING ELEMENTS

IT HAS already been shown that, except for the simplest simulators, computing elements capable of performing operations other than adding, integrating and differentiating are needed. The most important of these additional elements are multipliers, dividers, and generators of trigonometric and other analytic or arbitrary functions. Networks for the production of many discontinuous functions such as limiting and backlash devices, and trigger circuits, are also required. It is in the development of these elements that the analogue computer designer has needed to be at his most ingenious, and a large variety of methods have been proposed to perform these functions, some of them wholly electronic, and some electro-mechanical.

All these devices are classified as non-linear computing elements. Although in the simulators described elsewhere in this work it is generally necessary to use electronic devices because the time lags in mechanical devices are not acceptable it is often easier to achieve high precision by mechanical means, and electro-mechanical computing elements are sometimes used in positions where the rates of variation are sufficiently slow.

Multiplication is the most important of the non-linear operations, and many techniques, both electronic and electro-mechanical, have been proposed. Of the electronic methods, experience has indicated that two are outstandingly better than the rest. These are the "variable mark/space" multiplier, and the "quarter-squares" multiplier, both of which are described subsequently, in some detail, although some attention is paid to the less successful devices.

7.1. VARIABLE MARK/SPACE MULTIPLIER

Multipliers of this type make use of a square-wave in which the "mark/space" ratio is varied in accordance with one input voltage and the amplitude of the wave is made proportional to the other voltage. Such a wave is shown in Fig. 7.1, where the "mark" and "space" intervals are respectively M and S seconds long. If the input voltages are V_X and V_Y, the M/S ratio is adjusted so that

$$V_X = k_1 \frac{M - S}{M + S} \quad \text{or} \quad \frac{k_1 + V_X}{k_1 - V_X} = \frac{M}{S} \qquad (7.1)$$

where k_1 is a constant. The wave has positive and negative values equal to $+ V_Y$ and $- V_Y$, so that during one complete cycle the area under the curve is $M V_Y$ while the voltage is positive, and $S V_Y$ while it is negative. The difference in these two areas is pro-

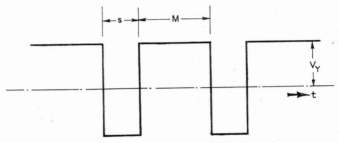

FIG. 7.1. Square-topped Wave with "Mark" longer than "Space".

portional to the mean value, or d.c. component of the wave, so that if the wave is passed through a filter to remove the alternating components the output will be

$$V_O = k_2(M V_Y - S V_Y)$$

where k_2 is a constant. Thus, from this equation and equation (7.1)

$$V_O = k_2 V_Y (M - S) = k_2 V_Y \frac{V_X(M + S)}{k_1} = V_X V_Y \frac{k_2}{k_1} (M + S).$$

$(M + S)$ is the periodic time for one cycle of the wave, and assuming this is constant, $k_2(M + S)/k_1$ is also constant, equal to K, say, so that

$$V_O = K V_X V_Y$$

An important feature of this principle is that it can accept both positive and negative inputs for both V_X and V_Y, and gives an output voltage of the correct sign. Thus, as V_X decreases from the value indicated in Fig. 7.1 the mean value of the wave will fall, until when $V_X = 0$ the mark and space are equal and the mean value is zero. If V_X becomes negative, $M < S$, so the mean value is negative. Provided a suitable modulator is used, the effect of reversing the sign of V_Y is to replace the wave of Fig. 7.1 by Fig. 7.2, which obviously has a mean value of the same magnitude but opposite sign.

A multiplier using the variable mark/space principle was designed by H. Sutcliffe about 1947. Another multiplier using the

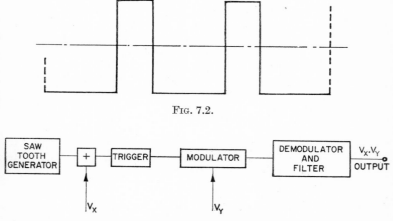

FIG. 7.2.

FIG. 7.3. Variable Mark/Space Multiplier.

same principle with a different circuit was developed by C. A. A. Wass and D. W. Allen [41] and later improved by M. Squires, and the operation of this device is illustrated in Fig. 7.3. A sawtooth generator produces a voltage with the wave-form shown in Fig. 7.4a. The exact shape of this wave is unimportant provided that the rise is linear and that the return is either very rapid or else linear. The wave is adjusted to be symmetrical about earth potential, so that the instants at which the voltage passes through zero are all equally spaced in time. The V_X voltage is then added to the saw-tooth wave, and the sum is fed into a trigger device which changes very rapidly from one state to another when the input voltage passes through zero. When the trigger is in one state it gives a large positive output voltage, and in the other state it gives a

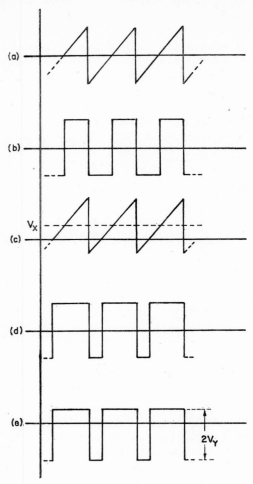

FIG. 7.4. Multiplier Waveforms.

large negative voltage. Assuming for the moment that V_X is zero, the trigger will spend equal intervals alternately in its two states, and will give an output wave of the form shown in Fig. 7.4b.

Suppose now that V_X is given a constant positive value. The combined voltage will now vary with time as shown in Fig. 7.4c, and the output from the trigger will be as in Fig. 7.4d, with a mark/

space ratio greater than unity. It is easily shown, in fact, that provided the sides of the saw-tooth wave are straight the mark/space ratio satisfies equation (7.1). The output from the trigger is passed to a modulator which has as a second input the voltage V_Y. The action of the modulator, which will be described more fully later, is to produce a wave of the same mark/space ratio as (d), but with a peak-to-peak amplitude equal to $2V_Y$, as in (e). This wave bears

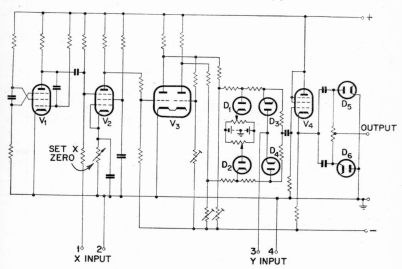

7.5. Variable Mark/Space Multiplier.

some resemblance to that of Fig. 7.1, but there is the important difference that whereas Fig. 7.1 shows a wave with equal positive and negative peak values and a positive mean value, the wave of Fig. 7.4e has unequal peak values and zero mean value. The output voltage from the modulator is assumed to pass through a capacitor, so it must always have a zero mean value, and the positive and negative peak values vary with V_X, as well as with V_Y, though the peak-to-peak value is independent of V_X. This output voltage is fed into a demodulator and filter, described more fully below, which gives an output proportional to $V_X V_Y$.

Figure 7.5 shows the circuit arrangement of an early form of the "variable mark/space" multiplier. V_1 is a transitron oscillator which generates the saw-tooth wave at 1000 c/s. V_2 serves as the

trigger of Fig. 7.3, although it is not strictly a trigger valve, but is
so arranged that the anode-current is large when the suppressor
grid is positive and very small when the suppressor is negative. V_3
is a double-triode phase-splitter which, with diodes D_1, D_2, D_3, D_4,
forms the V_Y-modulator. V_4 is a cathode-follower buffer stage, and
diodes D_5, D_6 are demodulators. The action of the modulator can
be followed with the help of the simplified circuit of Fig. 7.6. The
terminal A receives the output from one side of the phase-splitter,
which is a wave having a mark/space ratio corresponding to V_X
and a constant amplitude which is larger than the maximum value

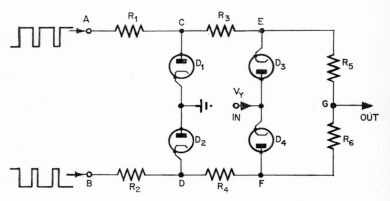

FIG. 7.6. Modulator for Multiplier.

of V_Y. Terminal B receives the corresponding wave of opposite
phase. When A is positive B is negative, so that diodes D_1 and D_2
conduct, and assuming that their impedances in the conducting
condition are zero the two points C and D are at earth potential. If
V_Y is positive D_3 conducts and D_4 does not, so that E is at potential
V_Y, and assuming the resistors have equal values, the output
terminal G has a potential $2V_Y/3$. When A becomes negative and
B positive the diodes D_1, D_2 no longer conduct, but D_3, D_4 conduct
so that all the points E, F, G are at potential V_Y. Thus the voltage
at G alternates, with the correct mark/space ratio, between the
values V_Y and $2V_Y/3$, which is equivalent to a square wave of peak-
to-peak amplitude $V_Y/3$ plus a steady voltage of value $\frac{1}{2}(V_Y + 2V_Y/3)$
$= 5V_Y/6$. If V_Y is negative the output is similar except that it
is reversed in sign.

This modulator has the advantages that the amplitude of the wave from the phase splitter is unimportant provided it is large enough, and it operates with a single V_Y input, whereas some modulators require a phase splitter to provide both V_Y and $-V_Y$. The chief disadvantages are that the output contains a d.c. component, and careful matching of diodes is necessary for best results, especially if V_Y is small. The battery and adjustable resistors between D_1 and D_2 in Fig. 7.5 are provided to improve the performance of the diodes.

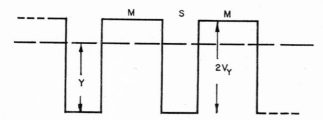

FIG. 7.7. Input Wave to Demodulator.

The demodulator is fed with a wave of the form shown in Fig. 7.7, which has the correct amplitude and mark/space ratio, but has zero mean value. Thus, if the peak-to-peak amplitude is $2V_Y$, and if the negative and positive peak amplitudes are respectively y and $(2V_Y - y)$, then

$$yS = M(2V_Y - y),$$

or

$$y = 2MV_Y/(M + S),$$

and

$$2V_Y - y = 2SV_Y/(M + S).$$

Now D_5, D_6 (Fig. 7.5) and the associated components comprise, effectively, two peak rectifiers, and if the time constants are long compared with the periodic time of the square wave the two capacitors will charge, respectively, to $+2MV_Y/(M + S)$ and $-2SV_Y/(M + S)$. The voltage at the centre tap of the resistor is the mean of these two values, which is $V_Y(M - S)/(M + S) = = V_XV_Y/k_1$ by equation (7.1). The residue of alternating voltage at the output terminal is negligible in many circumstances, but can be reduced by further filtering if desired.

With careful adjustment this multiplier will give results which are accurate to within about 2 per cent of the maximum output voltage. The errors are largest when the output voltage is near zero, because the diode impedances then have an importance influence. This multiplier has a rather poor frequency response, chiefly on account of the filter associated with the demodulator. This filter is rather crude, and the saw-tooth frequency is only 1000 c/s, so that appreciable phase-shifts occur if the input voltages have components at more than one or two cycles per second.

An improved version of the variable mark/space multiplier is shown in Fig. 7.8. The saw-tooth, with a frequency of 2500 c/s is generated by a separate generator which can be common to a number of multipliers. The combined saw-tooth and X voltage are not applied directly to the grid of V_2, which is the first valve of a Schmitt trigger circuit (Section 7.11), but through a circuit which includes the double diode V_1. The object of this circuit is to avoid drawing grid current in the grid circuit of V_2. While the combined voltage is negative the circuit has no effect, except that the negligibly small forward impedance of the right-hand diode is in series with the lead to the grid. Then at a point in the voltage rise more positive than the triggering point, but not sufficiently positive for the onset of grid current, the left-hand diode conducts and the right-hand diode cuts off. Thus the grid is not driven further positive, although the combined voltage continues to rise, and the left-hand diode ensures that the impedance presented to the combined voltage remains unchanged and avoids d.c. effects which might be caused by diode currents charging the input capacitor.

The double triode is a phase splitter which feeds the modulator $(V_5 V_6)$. This modulator is different from the one shown in Fig. 7.5, and has several advantages. It is less susceptible to differences in curvature of the diode characteristics, and more important, it gives an output voltage corresponding to Fig. 7.1, such that the mean value of the output wave is proportional to $V_X V_Y$, and no demodulating action is necessary. It requires, however, that the square-wave input shall have positive and negative peak values which are accurately limited to equal and constant values; and for any input voltage V_Y an equal and opposite voltage $-V_Y$ must be provided, from a low impedance source. The limiting action is provided by the diodes V_7 and V_8, and the $-V_Y$ signal is provided by the reversing amplifier V_9 and cathode follower V_{10}. The modulator is shown also

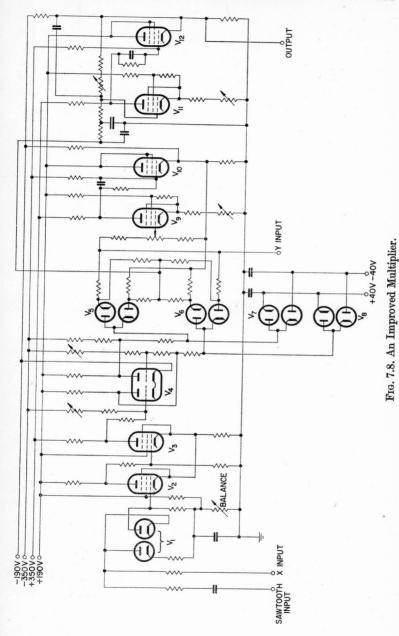

FIG. 7.8. An Improved Multiplier.

in Fig. 7.9. Assuming that the amplitude of the square wave is greater than V_Y or $-V_Y$, the diodes D_2 and D_4 conduct during the positive part of the wave, and D_1 and D_3 conduct during the negative part. When D_2 and D_4 conduct the two resistors R form a centre-tapped pair between equal positive and negative voltages and, assuming symmetry, there is no potential at the output due to $-V_Y$. However, since D_1 and D_3 are not conducting $+V_Y$ is

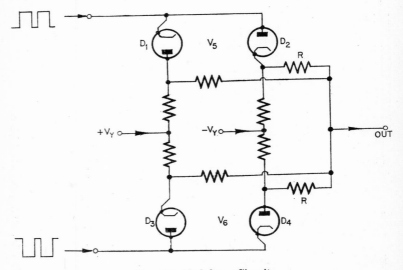

Fig. 7.9. Modulator Circuit.

connected to the output terminal by two series pairs of resistors in parallel (Fig. 7.10). Thus, the output voltage is a proportion of V_Y, say qV_Y, where q is a constant determined by the values of the resistors. During the negative part of the square wave, diodes D_1 and D_3 conduct, so that the output voltage is $-qV_Y$, where q has the same value as before, provided the resistor values are suitably chosen. The output voltage therefore has the correct waveform and has peak amplitudes $\pm qV_Y$, so that it is only necessary to remove the alternating component by means of a filter to give a voltage proportional to $V_X V_Y$. Two stages of filtering are provided by the components in the grid circuit of V_{11}, which is a d.c. amplifier. V_{12} is a cathode follower to give a low output impedance.

This multiplier gives answers which are accurate to better than 1 per cent of full scale, and this accuracy is maintained up to frequencies of 3 or 4 c/s for the V_X input and up to about 20 c/s for the V_Y input. The reason for the difference is that the only appreciable reactances which give errors when the V_Y voltage varies are the capacitors in the output filter, whereas for variations in the V_X voltage the capacitor used in the circuit for adding the saw-tooth

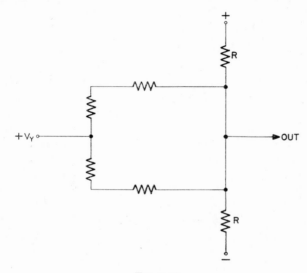

Fig. 7.10.

and V_X voltages gives attenuation greater than and additional to that given by the filter. Similarly, the phase-shift due to the filter alone is such that for variations of V_Y up to 10 c/s the output phase is in error by not more than 10°, whereas variation in V_X of 4c/s also gives a phase error of 10°. Further developments of the variable mark/space method, with considerable improvement in accuracy, have recently been reported [42, 43, 44].

7.2. OTHER ELECTRONIC MULTIPLIERS

Of the other principles which have been used for electronic analogue multiplication, the most important is the "quarter-squares" or "parabolic" multiplier, using a "biased-diode"

10 EAC

technique, which will be described in Sections 7.7, 7.8, 7.9, together with other computing elements utilizing biased diodes. However, there have been several other electronic methods which have had varying degrees of success, and which must be included in this review. The first of these is the "crossed field" multiplier [45].

This device makes use of a special cathode-ray tube which has, in place of the usual fluorescent screen, a pair of collector plates so arranged that the undeflected electron beam falls equally on both the plates; but a deflection of the beam in the vertically upward (Y) direction causes an increase of current to the upper collector, and vice versa. Deflection of the beam in the horizontal (X) direction does not change the current distribution. The tube has the usual two pairs of deflector plates, and in addition has a coil which produces a magnetic field in a direction parallel to the undeflected beam. One of the voltages to be multiplied is applied to the horizontal deflection (X) plates, and the other voltage is used to produce a proportional current in the coil. In the presence of the X-deflecting voltage the electron beam is no longer parallel to the magnetic field, so that there is an additional deflection, this time in the Y direction, due to the magnetic field. This deflection is proportional to the product of the strength of the magnetic field and the X deflection, i.e. to the product of the two input voltages. The currents from the collecting plates are passed to an amplifier which gives an output voltage of such polarity that, when applied to the Y plates of the tube, the beam deflection is reduced, and the gain of this amplifier is made so large that the beam returns almost to its undeflected position. Thus, the Y-deflection voltage is proportional to the Y deflection which would be produced by the two input voltages, i.e. it is proportional to the product of the two input voltages.

This multiplier was developed into a moderately satisfactory computing element, yielding results accurate to about 0·5 per cent of full scale at frequencies of several kc/s. Another modification of this principle is due to Grundlach and Schmidt [46, 47] at Darmstadt Technischer Hochschule and this uses a similar cathode-ray tube, but with an additional set of electrostatic plates which set up a hyperbolic field.

Both these electron tube methods have been successfully developed, but likewise, both require the special manufacture of cathode-ray devices of high precision. It has been found that, while the bandwidth of this type of multiplier is very wide, reaching several hundred kc/s, practical difficulties in setting them up to obtain the possible accuracy of about 0·5 per cent is extremely tedious. However, for repetitive simulators, as described in Section 10.2, they may still have some future.

A relatively recent device, employing a long-known physical effect, is the "Hall-effect" multiplier. A slab of semiconductor material, usually indium arsenide, is placed between a pair of coils

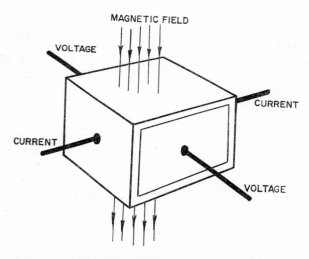

FIG. 7.11. Hall Effect System.

which provide a magnetic field. A pair of electrodes are connected to the semiconductor at right-angles to the axis of the coils, and another pair of electrodes are connected mutually at right-angles to other electrodes and the coil axis. When a current is applied to the coil, representing one input variable, and a current is applied to the semiconductor material through a pair of electrodes to represent the other variable, then the "Hall-effect" voltage so developed across the other pair of electrodes is the product of the input variables. Such multipliers proposed by Lofgren and by Chasmar and Cohen [48, 49] have achieved accuracies of about 0·5 per cent, and are now available commercially. Their bandwidth is rather limited to only about 100 c/s as a useful upper frequency.

10*

Several other multipliers have been proposed, including: double-modulation systems; a "probability" multiplier depending on the fact that the combined probability of two independent events is the product of their separate probabilities; and a "logarithmic" multiplier in which voltages are generated proportional to the logarithms of the input voltages. The last two methods have the interesting facility that more than two input voltages can be multiplied in one operation, but generally these principles have not been widely applied.

7.3. ELECTRO-MECHANICAL DEVICES

Besides the purely electronic methods a number of electro-mechanical multipliers have been designed, and Fig. 7.12 shows a popular arrangement. The amplifier, motor, and potentiometer P_1 fed with fixed voltages $\pm V_F$ constitute a straightforward position servo; whenever the input voltage V_X is different from $-V_O$, where V_O is the voltage on the slider of P_1, the net input to the amplifier is not zero, and the motor turns in a direction to reduce the amplifier input voltage to zero. Thus, if the amplifier has a sufficiently high gain the motor turns until $V_O = -V_X$, and if the potentiometer is linear, i.e. if the slider voltage is proportional to the angle of deflection θ, then $\theta = kV_X$, where k is a constant. The angle θ is measured from the centre point of the potentiometer, being taken as positive on one side and negative on the other side of this point. Now if the potentiometer P_2 is also linear and is fed with voltages $\pm V_Y$, where V_Y is the second input voltage, the voltage

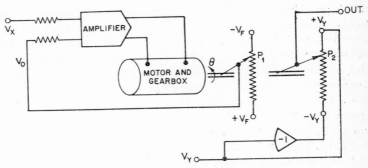

Fig. 7.12. Electro-mechanical Servo-multiplier.

at the potentiometer slider is proportional to $V_Y\theta$, i.e. to $V_Y k V_X$, or to $V_X V_Y$.

This multiplier has the advantage of simplicity and gives a correct output whatever the signs of V_X and V_Y, but it has a number of disadvantages which limit its application, although its limits are less serious now than a few years ago. By necessity a special servo-amplifier is needed to drive the motor, and even so, the frequency response of the system is severely restricted by the limited angular acceleration of the motor shaft combined with the potentiometer inertia and friction. However, small low-inertia motors are now readily available which, in combination with low-torque potentiometers, can provide a useful bandwidth of up to 10 c/s. The accuracy of multiplication is largely determined by the accuracy of the potentiometers, and particularly by the differences between them. Considerable departure from linearity can be tolerated provided the two potentiometers are identical, so that for any value of θ the proportion of V_F given by P_1 is the same as the proportion of V_Y given by P_2. In practice, however, the variations from linearity tend to be erratic. Nowadays, these errors can be made relatively small by using normal high-precision potentiometers which are available from several manufacturers, with a departure from linearity less than 0·1 per cent. The friction and inertia of modern computing potentiometers is almost negligibly small. If a multiplier of this type is used to feed directly into a resistive load the part of the potentiometer (P_2 in Fig. 7.12) between slider and earth is shunted by the load and there is consequently an error in the voltage applied to the load unless the load resistance is very high compared with the potentiometer. Thus, in the circuit of Fig. 7.13, from simple network considerations, the ratio of the output voltage to the input voltage, assuming zero source impedance, is given by

$$\frac{V_O}{V_1} = \frac{K}{K\varrho(1-K)+1}$$

where $\varrho = R/R_L$ and $0 \leq K \leq 1$.

For the case where the load resistance is infinite, i.e. $\varrho = 0$, $V_O/V_1 = K$. The error, ε, will be the difference between the unloaded, and the loaded case, so that

$$\varepsilon = K\left\{\frac{K\varrho(1-K)}{K\varrho(1-K)+1}\right\}$$

A common method of reducing this error is to insert a buffer amplifier, but a simple alternative is to connect a resistor, of value equal to the load resistance, between the slider of the feedback potentiometer (P_1, Fig. 7.12) and earth. It can easily be shown that this provides almost exact compensation. This assumes that the two potentiometers have equal resistances, but if the resistances should be unequal a similar measure of compensation can still be obtained by connecting to the feedback potentiometer a resistor whose value bears the same relation to this potentiometer as does

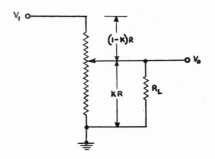

Fig. 7.13. Loaded Potentiometer.

the load resistance to the output potentiometer. In a similar manner, compensation for the shunting effect of the feedback resistor on the feedback potentiometer can be obtained by connecting a suitable resistor to the output potentiometer. Other methods of load compensation are pursued further in Section 7.5. Servo-multipliers of the type discussed have found very widespread application, particularly in training equipment such as flight and nuclear reactor simulators (Section 11.3), where speed of response is compatible.

An interesting, and sometimes very useful, modification of this simple servo-multiplier configuration, is obtained by replacing the feedback position potentiometer with an electrical tachometer which generates a voltage proportional to the servo shaft speed. If this voltage is fed back to the servo-amplifier the instantaneous position of the motor shaft will represent the time-integral of the input signal. In this way, the multiplier performs an integration as well as a multiplication. The technique has not found widespread application, although there are several installations, such as TRIDAC [18], where it is in successful operation. The main difficulty is the problem of obtaining accurate initial conditions.

7.4. DIVIDERS AND SQUARE-ROOT DEVICES

It is sometimes necessary to use dividers in analogue computing machines, though for reasons which will appear they are avoided whenever possible. An analogue divider is a device which, when fed with two voltages V_X and V_Y, gives as output a voltage V_Z such that $V_Z = KV_Y/V_X$. It is not possible to make a divider which will operate correctly when the V_X voltage passes through zero, since $V_X \to 0$ requires $V_Z \to \infty$ if V_Y is finite, and V_Z is limited by the overloading of the amplifiers used. Thus any computer which uses a divider should be so arranged as not to demand division by

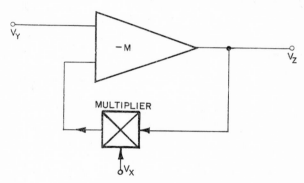

FIG. 7.14. Feedback-type Divider.

small numbers, and it is generally desirable to keep the range of divisors as small as possible.

There are several principles on which dividers have been based, including the "reciprocal" method, which uses a biased-diode arrangement described later, the "feedback" method, and the electro-mechanical method. The feedback method makes use of a multiplier and a high-gain summing amplifier, connected as shown in Fig. 7.14. The relation between the voltages is given by

$$V_Z = -M(V_Y + V_Z V_X)$$

or,

$$-MV_Y = MV_Z V_X + V_Z$$

and provided $MV_X \gg 1$,

$$V_Y = -V_Z V_X, \text{ very nearly,}$$

or $\qquad V_Z = -V_Y/V_X.$

This result represents an example of the well-known principle that the overall characteristic of a high-gain feedback amplifier is the inverse of the characteristic of the feedback network. At first sight it might be assumed, apart from the limitation imposed on V_X by overloading when V_X is small, and by the requirement

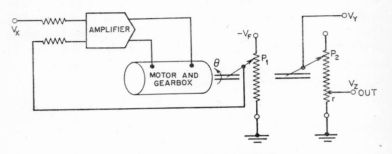

FIG. 7.15. Electro-mechanical Divider.

$MV_X \gg 1$, that positive and negative values of both V_X and V_Y could be handled, but this is not so. Assuming that the multiplier itself is able to deal with both signs of V_X and V_Y, if the system is stable for one sign of V_X it will generally be unstable for the other sign. Thus, if the amplifier has, as is usual, an overall phase shift of 180° at low frequencies, stability requires that there should be no phase reversal in the feedback path. In the present case this requires that the output voltage $V_X V_Z$ of the multiplier must be of the same sign as its input V_Z; i.e. V_X must be positive. If it is required to work with negative values of V_X an additional phase reversal must be inserted in the loop, but the divider will then be unstable for positive values of V_X. Besides these elementary considerations of phase reversals, the question of stability also involves consideration of the amplitude and phase characteristics of the multiplier at higher frequencies. The multiplier is, in effect, a variable gain device operating in the feedback loop, and the whole divider will be stable only if the Nyquist criterion [13–16] is satisfied for all likely values of V_X. Provided overloading is avoided there is no restriction on the value or sign of V_Y.

The electro-mechanical divider uses an amplifier, motor, and first potentiometer as in the type of multiplier shown in Fig. 7.12, but with a different arrangement for the second potentiometer. The arrangement is shown in Fig. 7.15 and since the divider is only effective for positive values of V_X it is only necessary to consider positive values of θ, so the first potentiometer is connected between $- V_F$ and earth. The second input voltage V_Y is connected to the slider of P_2, which has a total resistance R_o extending over an angular range θ_o, so that the resistance R between slider and earth is $\theta R_o/\theta_o$. The output is taken from a tap on the potentiometer at a resistance r from the earthy end, and the output voltage V_Z is therefore $rV_Y/R = rV_Y\theta_o/\theta R_o$. Now as explained in connection with the electro-mechanical multiplier $\theta = KV_X$, so that $V_Z = rV_Y\theta_o/R_oKV_X = k\,V_Y/V_X$, where k is a constant.

This divider has the advantage of simplicity, and the stability problem is no greater than for the multiplier, but there are some disadvantages. In particular, the limitation on the value of V_X is even more severe than that imposed by the amplifier overload. This is because the relation $V_Z = rV_Y/R$ is valid only for values of R greater than r; if R is less than r the relation gives V_Z greater than V_Y, which is absurd. Thus, V_X can only be allowed to vary between some maximum value, say V_M, which corresponds to $\theta = \theta_o$, and a lower limit $r\,V_M/R_o$, and although this lower limit can be reduced by reducing r this gives correspondingly lower output voltages. Furthermore, if r is made a small fraction of the whole winding it will include relatively few turns of wire, and the accuracy of the computation may be degraded if the jump from one turn to the next is greater than errors due to other causes. The output voltage can never be greater than V_Y, but there is no restriction on the value or sign of V_Y. The system as shown is stable for positive values of V_X if the amplifier gives an overall sign reversal. For negative values of V_X, the fixed voltage $- V_F$ must be replaced by $+ V_F$, or else the number of amplifying stages must be changed to give no phase reversal.

The frequency response of this kind of divider is limited by the available motor acceleration, as in the case of the electro-mechanical multiplier, so that the most favourable application is to the

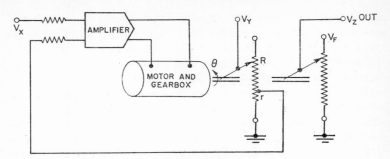

FIG. 7.16. Alternative Arrangement for Divider.

division of two voltages which vary only slowly, with a limited range of values of constant sign for the divisor voltage.

An alternative connection for a divider is shown in Fig. 7.16, the two potentiometers being interchanged compared with Fig. 7.15. The feedback voltage is seen to be $V_Y r/R$, which is equal to $V_Y r \theta_o/\theta R_o$, and when the motor comes to rest this is balanced by the input voltage V_X, so that

$$V_X = - V_Y r \theta_o/\theta R_o.$$

The output voltage V_Z is given by

$$V_Z = \theta V_F/\theta_o$$
$$= - V_F V_Y r/V_X R_o$$
$$= K V_Y/V_X.$$

This arrangement has no obvious advantage over that of Fig. 7.15 except that the sign of the output can easily be changed, and it has some disadvantages. As shown, the system is stable only when V_X and V_Y are of opposite sign, and if V_X and V_Y are of the same sign either a sign-reversing amplifier must be used, or a different number of stages must be employed in the amplifier. Instability will occur if the slider moves on to the "r" section of the first potentiometer; for suppose V_Y has a negative fixed value and V_X is positive and increases steadily. To provide a steadily-increasing feedback voltage to balance V_X the value of θ must be steadily reduced, but when the slider reaches the tapping point the feedback voltage is equal to V_Y, and can increase no further. If $|V_X|$ is larger than $|V_Y|$, the motor will continue to turn in the direction of decreasing θ until the limit of travel is reached.

Another type of electro-mechanical divider can be formed by using the second potentiometer of Fig. 7.15, without the V_Y input, as a variable input resistor for a high-gain amplifier with a fixed feedback resistor. The overall gain of this arrangement is then inversely proportional to V_X.

The disadvantage of some of these dividers, that they can handle divisors of only one sign, is generally unimportant, because it is over-ridden by their inability to operate with divisors near zero. It is unusual to find, in any practical problem, a divisor which can have both positive and negative values, but no values near zero.

If in the arrangement of Fig. 7.14 the terminal of the multiplier marked V_X is connected to the output terminal of the amplifier, so that $V_X = V_Z$, and if the gain of the amplifier is very large,

$$V_Z^2 = V_Y \quad \text{very early,}$$
or, $$V_Z = \sqrt{V_Y}$$

so that this combination of multiplier and amplifier can be used as a square-root device. Any of the multiplier types already described can be used in this way, and the biased-diode type of multiplier to be described in Section 7.8 can also be used. There is, however, a more direct way of computing square roots with biased-diodes which will be mentioned in this later section.

7.5. CURVE FOLLOWERS AND SINGLE-VARIABLE FUNCTION GENERATORS

A curve follower, or function generator, is a device which, when fed with an input voltage V_1 gives as output a voltage V_O such that $V_O = f(V_1)$, where f is some predetermined function, usually single-valued but not necessarily monotonic. The functions which are most commonly used in this way are sines and cosines, parabolas, and functions expressed as curves derived from experimental results.

Several curve followers have been developed using cathode-ray tubes and photocells, and Fig. 7.17 shows the principle of one of these invented independently and almost simultaneously in 1946 by D. J. Mynall [50] and D. M. Mackay, [51] and later developed by Squires and Pieper.

The function to be reproduced is first drawn as a graph on thin card, to a suitable scale. Then the part of the card above the curve is cut away, leaving a silhouette type of "mask", as shown in Fig. 7.17. Alternatively, the part of the card below the curve is painted black, and a photograph is taken on a glass plate, giving a mask which is clear glass above the curve and opaque below.

The mask is fixed close to the screen of the cathode-ray tube, with the axes of the graph parallel to the X and Y deflection directions of the tube, and a photocell is placed behind the mask as shown. Thus, when the spot of the cathode-ray tube screen is above

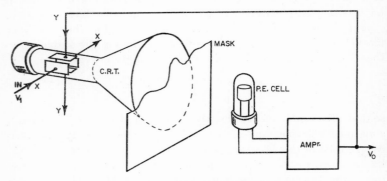

Fig. 7.17. Curve-follower Function Generator.

the edge of the mask its light falls on the photocell, but when the the spot is below the edge the light is cut off. The output from the cell is passed through an amplifier, and the amplified voltage is applied to the Y-deflection plates of the tube with such a sign that the spot is deflected downward. The spot cannot be deflected below the edge of the mask, because then there would be no light falling on the cell, and the deflection voltage would disappear, and with a suitable value of amplifier gain the spot comes to rest with half its area showing above the edge of the mask. This condition can be maintained almost independently of the height of the mask, or of any X-deflection which may be present. Suppose now that the graph from which the mask was made is $y = f(x)$, and suppose an input voltage V_1 is applied to the X plates of the tube. This will give a deflection in the X direction proportional to V_1, equal to $k_1 V_1$, say, but because of the action of the mask, cell, and amplifier, there will also be a deflection in the Y direction given by

$$y = f(k_1 V_1).$$

The voltage to give this deflection is the output voltage V_o of the amplifier, and $y = k_2 V_o$, where k_2 is a constant very nearly equal to k_1. Hence,

$$V_O = \frac{1}{k_2} f(k_1 V_1)$$

and with an appropriate choice of scaling factors the output voltage represents the desired function of the input voltage.

For various practical reasons, such as non-linear relation between deflection voltage and spot deflection, lack of uniformity of the screen, non-orthogonality of the two pairs of deflecting plates, etc., it is difficult to reduce the errors with this device to less than about 2 per cent, and furthermore, operation becomes uncertain if the slope of the graph is greater than about 80°. However, the time of response can be made very short, so that the device can be used in repetitive simulators, and the function being generated can easily be changed by inserting a different mask.

Another curve follower using a cathode-ray tube and photocell has been designed by R. H. Forrest and K. H. Treweek [52]. This has the facility for following a line on a transparent plate or film, and does not need the area below the line to be opaque. The arrangement is generally similar to that shown in Fig. 7.17, but a small alternating potential is applied to the Y plates, in addition to the normal deflecting voltage. This alternating potential elongates the spot vertically to a length slightly greater than the thickness of the line on the film. Thus, the output of the photocell is an alternating potential, and if the upper part of the spot shows above the line this potential is in phase with the potential applied to the Y plates, whereas if the lower part of the spot shows below the line the phases are opposite. The photocell output is passed to a phase-sensitive rectifier and then amplified, which gives deflecting voltages which can be used to bring the centre of the spot always very close to the centre of the line.

Besides its use as a function generator this device can also be used as a film "reader". Suppose a record has been made of variation of some quantity with time by photographing the spot of a c.r. oscilloscope on a steadily-moving photographic film, or by some similar method. Then, with no potential on the X plates the film can be moved steadily in the X direction between the c.r. tube and photocell of the Treweek device, and the output voltage of the amplifier will be proportional to the quantity originally recorded. This arrangement could be used, for example, for inserting "road bumps" into the simulator suggested for investigating the suspension of road vehicles (Section 4.3), or for injecting the effects of variable wind into simulators for ballistic and aeronautic problems.

In another device of this kind developed by Lange and Herring the function is again recorded as a black line on a transparent film, but there is no feedback from the photocell output to the deflecting plates. Instead, a saw-tooth voltage is applied continuously to the Y plates, so that the photocell gives a pulse every time the spot passes the line on the film. Another pulse is given when the spot passes a reference line on the edge of the film, and the time interval between the two pulses is proportional to the value of the function, provided the saw-tooth is linear. This arrangement has the advantage that there is no limit to the slopes of functions which can be followed, and in particular stepped waves create no difficulty.

A number of different electro-mechanical function-generators have been devised, usually making use of an amplifier, motor, and feedback potentiometer to give a shaft position proportional to an input voltage, as for the multiplier of Fig. 7.12. The linear potentiometer P_2 is replaced by one with a suitably "shaped" winding fed from a constant voltage, so that the voltage on the slider represents the desired function of the shaft position. This arrangement is very suitable for sine and cosine functions, using sine and cosine potentiometers. For other functions the use of metal film potentiometers may be advantageous because of the difficulty of producing special wire-wound potentiometers.

Sine–cosine potentiometers are of three main types; the "flat-card" type, the "shaped-card" type, and the "mechanical linkage" type. In the first type a thin resistance wire is wound uniformly on a flat parallel-sided card or strip, and the ends are connected to points at fixed equal positive and negative potentials. The slider is carried on a spindle whose axis is perpendicular to the plane of the card, and in line with the centre of the winding. The arrangement is illustrated schematically in Fig. 7.18, which shows that the number of turns between the centre O and the slider is proportional to $\cos \theta$. The voltage at the slider, however, is not exactly proportional to $\cos \theta$ because the slider does not remain on the centre line of the card; for example, when $\theta = 90°$ the potential at the end of the slider is not zero, but differs by the voltage drop along the part of a turn between the slider and O. This inherent error can be kept small by using many turns of fine wire, and also by making the width W of the card large compared with the length of the wiper arm. The use of a large number of turns also helps to reduce the size of the voltage jump as the wiper passes from one turn to the next, but there will inevitably be errors due to the finite number of turns, the most obvious of these, though not

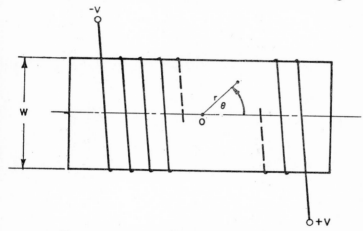

FIG. 7.18. Card-type Sine–Cosine Potentiometer.

necessarily the most serious, being in the region of $\theta = 0$ and $\theta = 180°$, where the motion of the slider is almost parallel to the wire, and the slider may stay in contact with one particular turn over appreciable angles. There is a tendency for this turn and a few adjacent turns to be displaced by the slider, and it is important that the winding should be carefully done and the turns cemented firmly to the card.

Apart from these considerations the accuracy of this device depends chiefly on the linearity of the winding, i.e. the constancy of the voltage drop per unit length of wire and of the number of turns of wire per unit length of card. Allowing for all causes the error will not be much below 1 per cent unless great care is taken, but the comparative simplicity of the device makes it attractive for applications where moderate accuracy suffices. In the form shown in Fig. 7.18 the device is a cosine potentiometer, giving a slider voltage proportional to $\cos\theta$, but the same device can be used as a sine potentiometer, giving an output proportional to $\sin\varphi$ if $\varphi = 90° - \theta$. ☞ Attempts were made to produce a sine–cosine potentiometer on the principle of Fig. 7.18 but with the wire winding replaced by a

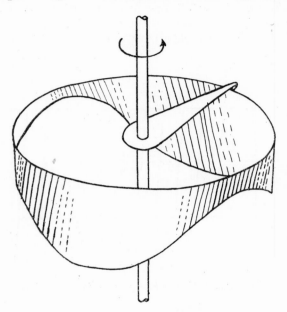

FIG. 7.19. Shaped-card Potentiometer.

uniform layer of carbon-based resistance material, conducting strips the full width of the card being fixed at opposite ends and connected to the fixed supply so as to give a uniform fall of potential from one end to the other. Although this arrangement was cheap it was difficult to make the carbon layer sufficiently uniform and resistant to wear. Metal- and the newer carbon-film techniques are nowadays successfully replacing the older carbon-layer methods.

In the "shaped-card" type of sine–cosine potentiometer (Fig. 7.19) the wire is wound on a strip of card which is bent into the shape of a cylindrical surface, and one edge of the card, on which the slider runs, is in a plane perpendicular to the axis of the cylinder, exactly as for an ordinary potentiometer. The other edge of the card, however, is shaped so that when the ends of the winding are connected to a source of constant potential the potential at the slider represents the sine or cosine of the shaft angle. Potentiometers of this type have been made in large sizes, capable of great accuracy and a high degree of resolution [53], but they have not so far found wide application in general-purpose analogue computers.

Of the various mechanical linkages that have been used in conjunction with linear potentiometers the most obvious is the simple

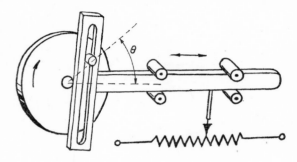

FIG. 7.20. Scotch Yoke Mechanism.

crank and connecting rod. This is simple, but does not give a good approximation to sinusoidal motion unless the connecting rod is very long.

Another mechanical sine-linkage is the "scotch yoke", shown in Fig. 7.20. The longer part of the T-shaped member runs in guides, while the cross member has a slot in which runs a crank pin, fitted to an arm or disc, whose angular position represents θ. Ideally, this arrangement can give exact sinusoidal motion, but in practice it is difficult to avoid backlash due to the imperfect fit of the pin in the slot.

Another linkage, which is capable of good accuracy, is the "swash-plate" device shown in Fig. 7.21. A flat circular plate is fixed to a shaft in such manner that the axis of the shaft passes through the centre of the plate, but the axis is inclined at an angle of, say, 45° to the surface of the plate. Round the edge of the plate runs a collar, retained by grooves or flanges so that the collar is free to turn relative to the plate, in the manner of a strap on an eccentric sheave. A lug is fixed to the collar and constrained by guides to

11 EAC

move parallel to the axis of the shaft, and the slider of the potentiometer is attached to the lug. The mechanical and electrical errors
in this arrangement can be kept to 0·1 per cent if the design and
manufacture are of the highest quality. By modifying the lug and
slide arrangement a number of sliders can be driven by a single
swash-plate mechanism, so that a number of different quantities
represented by V_1, V_2, etc., can be simultaneously multiplied by
$\cos \theta$ or $\sin \theta$ if $\pm V_1$, $\pm V_2$, etc., are applied to the separate wind-
ings of potentiometers driven by the swash plate. Furthermore, a

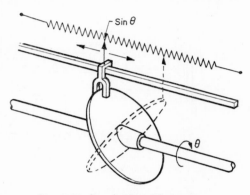

FIG. 7.21. Swash-plate Mechanism.

second lug and potentiometer slider can be attached to the collar,
displaced 90° from the first, so that multiplication by both $\cos \theta$
and $\sin \theta$ can be accomplished with one swash plate.

Sine and cosine potentiometers of the types described give an
output voltage proportional to $V \sin \theta$ or $V \cos \theta$, where V is the
voltage applied across the winding and θ is the angular position of
a shaft. When driven by a "position servo", as used in Fig. 7.12,
they can be used to produce the sine or cosine of an angle represented by the input voltage to the servo. They can also be used with a
knob and dial on the input shaft for manual setting of θ, and this
is useful when both $\sin \theta$ and $\cos \theta$ are needed (e.g. in Fig. 3.12)
since by ganging a sine potentiometer and a cosine potentiometer
the two functions can be set by a single control. Interesting and
sometimes useful results can be obtained by using a sine or cosine
potentiometer as the feedback potentiometer in the arrangement
of Fig. 7.12.

Besides the mechanisms described, devices depending on cams have also been used; but for sine and cosine variations they are usually less satisfactory than other methods. For non-sinusoidal variations, however, cams have been used to a limited extent, though they are difficult to make accurately, and the need for a fairly high

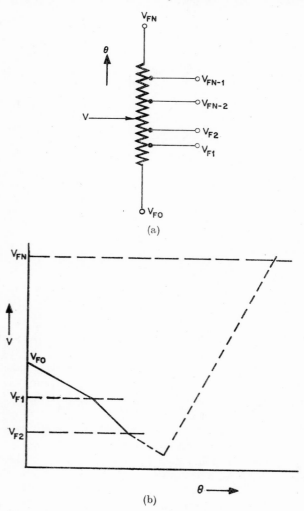

(a)

(b)

FIG. 7.22a, b. Approximate Function Generator.

11*

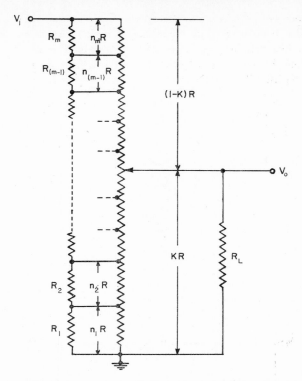

FIG. 7.23. Shunted Tapped Potentiometer Function Generator.

pressure to keep the follower in contact with the cam tends to increase the driving power required.

An important device for the approximate generation of arbitrary functions is shown in Fig. 7.22 a. This is a potentiometer with a number of taps which are connected to a set of fixed voltages V_{F0}, V_{F2}, ..., V_{FN}. Between any pair of taps the voltage varies linearly with the rotation θ of the servo driven shaft, so that the complete graph of slider voltage against θ is made up of a number of straight lines, as in Fig. 7.22 b. The intervals in θ are fixed by the positions of the taps, but the slopes of the straight-line segments are fixed by the differences $(V_{F1} - V_{F0})$, etc., and these can be varied at will, subject to the limitation of permissible dissipation in the winding.

Such potentiometers are easily obtained with a winding linearity of 0·1 per cent and with up to 33 tappings available. Tapped potentiometer networks have been studied mainly by Shen [54] and Garner [55], the latter having produced a generalized theory for the construction of resistive shunting networks to enable arbitrary functions to be set up. It can be shown that all such networks as that shown in Fig. 7.23 are equivalent to a generalized

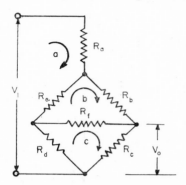

FIG. 7.24. Generalized Network.

bridge-network of the form shown in Fig. 7.24. Using the notation given in the diagram, the generalized relationship between the input voltage and the output voltage is given by

$$\frac{V_O}{V_1} = \frac{R_c \, (Z_1 R_d + R_e \, R_f)}{(Z_1 Z_2 Z_3 - Z_1 R_d^2 - Z_2 R_e^2 - Z_3 R_f^2 - 2 R_d R_e R_f)}$$

Where
$$Z_1 = (R_b + R_f + R_e)$$
$$Z_2 = (R_c + R_d + R_f)$$
$$Z_3 = (R_a + R_e + R_d)$$

and R_a to R_f have values according to the position of the section of the potentiometer in which the wiper is operating, as shown in Appendix II.

By arranging that the voltage obtained with the slider set at each tapping point lies on the desired arbitrary function, the above formulae enable the values of the necessary shunt resistors to be found with little trouble. An extension of this method is to optimize the linear approximation by taking into account the load being driven by the function generator.

A further useful application of this type of function generator is the inverse of the above operation. Up to now the discussion has been on how to produce a non-linear output from an otherwise linear potentiometer. Referring back to Section 7.3, it was noted that when a linear potentiometer was loaded, the input–output relationship was undesirably distorted. For a constant load it is possible [56] to determine a non-linear potentiometer law, such that

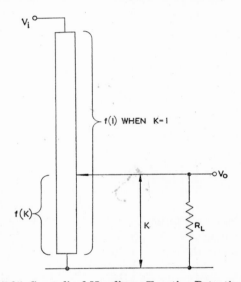

FIG. 7.25. Generalized Non-linear Function Potentiometer.

when the load is present, the resulting input–output relationship becomes linear. Using the nomenclature of Fig. 7.25, the non-linear law that the potentiometer must initially possess so that when loaded by a resistance R_L the overall result will be linear, is given by

$$f(K) = \frac{R_O}{2}\left[1 - \frac{R_L}{KR_O} + \sqrt{\left\{ \left(\frac{R_L}{KR_O} - 1 \right)^2 + 4\,\frac{R_L}{R_O} \right\}} \right]$$

Potentiometers made to this law and the customer's load specification are now manufactured as standard items by British manufacturers of servo-potentiometers. If it is desired to approximate this law by means of a tapped potentiometer, the

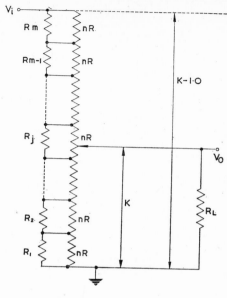

method is not difficult. The circuit to use is that shown in Fig. 7.26
where each potentiometer section between taps is of equal length.
Three quantities must be specified, namely the minimum input
resistance that the final device should present to the source, denoted
by R_i, the initial potentiometer resistance R, and the load resistance
R_L. The shunt resistors, R_1 to R_m can then be calculated from the
formula

$$R_j = \frac{nR(\alpha_j - \alpha_{j-1})}{(1 - \alpha_j + \alpha_{j-1})}$$

where

$$\alpha_j = \frac{\left[\left(\dfrac{V_O}{V_i}\right)_j \dfrac{R_i}{(R_L - R_i)} - 1\right] + \sqrt{\left\{\left[\left(\dfrac{V_O}{V_i}\right)_j \dfrac{R_i}{(R_L - R_i)} - 1\right]^2 + 4\left(\dfrac{V_O}{V_i}\right)_j^2 \dfrac{R_i}{(R_L - R_i)}\right\}}}{2\left(\dfrac{V_O}{V_i}\right)_j \dfrac{nR}{R_L}}$$

One additional technique concerning linearizing of loaded potentiometers, is the use of a ganged pair of potentiometers in the

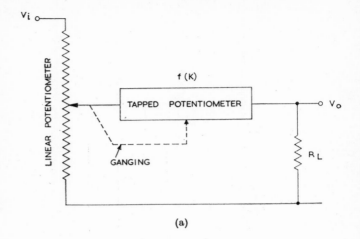

(a)

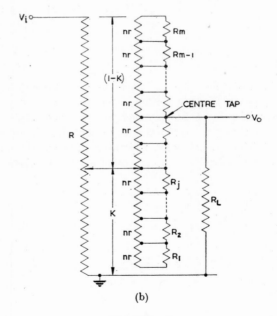

(b)

FIG. 7.27 a, b.

circuit arrangement shown in Fig. 7.27a. It can be shown [57] that providing the "shaped" potentiometer in the slider circuit has the law

$$f(K) = \frac{R}{4} - KR(1 - K)$$

then the overall input–output relationship is

$$\frac{V_O}{V_i} = K\left[\frac{R_L}{R_L + \dfrac{R}{4}}\right]$$

where the factor $R_L/(R_L + R/4)$ is a constant for any given load. Therefore, the device is linear for *any fixed* load, but has an insertion attenuation, depending upon the load. This unit can also be designed on tapped potentiometer principles, and the shunt resistors calculated using the relationship

$$R_j = \frac{R[1 - (2j - 1)\,n]}{(2j - 1)}$$

with the notation given in Fig. 7.27 b.

For any of the above circuits some rounding of the sharp discontinuities in the curve can be achieved by fitting two sliders to the potentiometer, displaced from each other by a suitable small angle, and taking the output from the centre tap of a resistor connected between them although this is rarely necessary.

7.6. NON-OHMIC RESISTOR FUNCTION GENERATORS

Cartmell and Taylor have shown that a cheap and effective method of obtaining a limited range of monotonic power laws is by the application of non-linear silicon-carbide resistors, sometimes known by the trade names "thyrite" and "metrosil". These devices obey the law

$$i = kv^x$$

where i is the conducted current, v is the voltage across the terminals, and k is a constant. The parameter x is also constant, of value greater than unity for a given thyrite sample. An effective squarer circuit has been constructed by J. E. Fisher using a

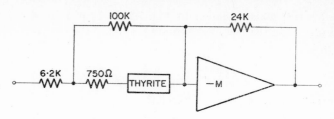

Fig. 7.28. Thyrite Function Generator.

type 100a Metrosil, which has an x-value of about 3, by the use of padding resistors in the amplifier configuration shown in Fig. 7.28. Such circuits, while cheap in equipment, require considerable experimentation in setting up.

7.7. BIASED-DIODE DEVICES

Many applications have been made of thermionic valves in which the shapes of characteristic curves, such as anode current/grid voltage curves have been used to produce desired non-linear effects, but it is difficult by such means to achieve accurate and stable results because of the effects of supply voltage changes and variations between different valves of the same type. The current tendency is to use arrangements in which the valve characteristics have at most only a minor effect, and this applies particularly to a class of non-linear devices which use biased-diodes and fixed resistors. A description of this sort of arrangement was given by Deeley and MacKay [58] in 1949, though the basic idea was known earlier [59]. The following account is based mainly on the work of Burt and Lange [60] who were among the original workers in the U.K.

The basic principles of the biased-diode device are illustrated in Fig. 7.29, in which V_1 is the input voltage, V_B is a bias voltage, and the output quantity is the current i flowing in R_3. In Fig. 7.29a, suppose that V_B is negative and V_1 increases steadily from zero, and assume that the diode impedance is either zero or infinite, according as the anode is positive or negative with respect to the cathode. At first the anode of the diode will be negative, so no current will flow in R_3, but when V_1 is sufficiently positive the diode will start to conduct, and thereafter the output current will

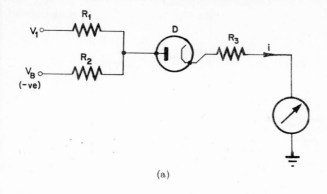

(a)

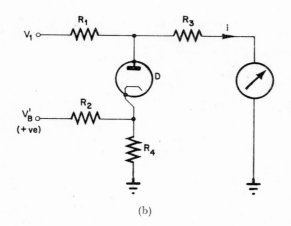

(b)

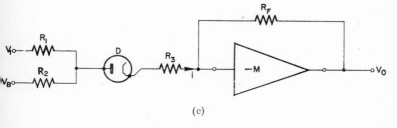

(c)

FIG. 7.29 a, b, c. Biased-diode Circuits.

increase in proportion with V_1. It is easily seen that current flows when

$$V_B + \frac{R_2}{R_1 + R_2} (V_1 - V_B) > 0$$

i.e. when

$$R_1 V_B + R_2 V_1 > 0.$$

The value of the current is

$$i = \frac{\dfrac{R_1 V_B + R_2 V_1}{R_1 + R_2}}{\dfrac{R_1 R_2}{R_1 + R_2} + R_3} = \frac{R_1 V_B + R_2 V_1}{R_1 R_2 + R_2 R_3 + R_3 R_1}$$

The curve relating i and V_1 is shown at (a) in Fig. 7.30.

In Fig. 7.29 b V_B' is positive, and again V_1 may be supposed to increase from zero, so that initially the diode does not conduct, and a current i flows, given by

$$i = \frac{V_1}{R_1 + R_3}$$

When V_1 reaches a value such that

$$V_1 \left(\frac{R_3}{R_1 + R_3} \right) - V_B \left(\frac{R_4}{R_2 + R_4} \right) > 0$$

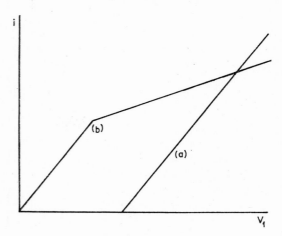

FIG. 7.30.

the diode begins to conduct, so that a redistribution of currents occurs, and the current in R_3 rises less rapidly.

When the diode conducts the current is:

$$i = \frac{R_4}{R_3 + R_4} \left| \frac{V_B + \left(\dfrac{R_2}{R_1 + R_2}\right)(V_1 - V_B)}{\dfrac{R_1 R_2}{R_1 + R_2} + \dfrac{R_3 R_4}{R_3 + R_4}} \right|$$

$$= \frac{R_4(V_B R_1 + V_1 R_2)}{R_1 R_2(R_3 + R_4) + R_3 R_4(R_1 + R_2)}$$

This gives a characteristic of the type shown at (b) in Fig. 7.30.

In practice the output is usually required as voltage rather than as a current, so the meter of Fig. 7.29 a is replaced by a high-gain amplifier with a feedback resistor, as shown in Fig. 7.29 c, and correspondingly for Fig. 7.29 b. It is easily shown that when the gain M is very large the output voltage is

$$V_O = -i R_F.$$

By reversing the signs of V_1 and V_B and reversing the diode connections, in either Fig. 7.29 a or 7.29 b, negative output current can be produced, and by combining several elementary circuits a characteristic can be produced which consists of a number of straight-line segments whose slopes and lengths can be adjusted so that they form a series of chords or tangents or secants to a given curve. One simple combination, shown in Fig. 7.31, includes a

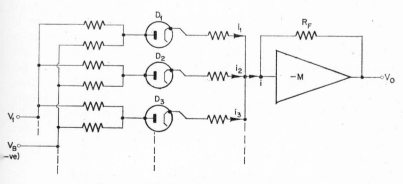

FIG. 7.31. Multiple Biased-diode Circuit.

number of circuits of the type shown in Fig. 7.29 a, and the resistance values are chosen to give a different voltage for each diode, so that as V_1 rises from zero the diodes start to conduct successively. Thus the total current rises more and more steeply as more and more diodes conduct, and the output voltage changes in a corresponding way. Curves for the first three diodes are shown in Fig. 7.32.

If more diodes are used, and the biasing voltages set closer together the straight segments of the combined characteristic become

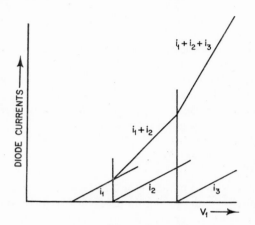

FIG. 7.32. Diode Currents in Fig. 7.31.

shorter, giving a closer approximation to a smooth curve. In principle the errors due to finite length of the straight segments can be reduced to any desired extent by using more diodes, but in practice the forward impedance of the diodes, variation of diode impedance with heater voltage, etc., set a limit. However, it is possible without great difficulty to achieve errors of about 1 per cent, and if great care is taken in selecting, ageing, and matching the diodes, and if wire-wound resistors are used, with carefully chosen bias values, errors as small as 0·05 per cent are possible. Solid state diodes may be used instead of thermionic diodes though precautions may then be needed to avoid the effects of variable ambient temperature.

Curves representing almost any single-valued function can be produced by this technique, and two of the most important are the

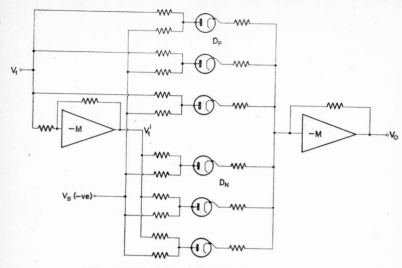

FIG. 7.33. Generator for Parabolic Function.

parabola and the sine. The curve of Fig. 7.32 indicates how the positive half of a parabola $y = k x^2$, or $V_O = -k V_1^2$, can be produced, with the circuit shown in Fig. 7.31, which is repeated in the upper half of Fig. 7.33. The negative half is produced by an identical circuit, but with a sign-reversing amplifier inserted between the input voltage V_1 and the resistance network, as shown in the lower half of Fig. 7.33. When V_1 is positive V_1' is negative so that the diodes D_N do not conduct, but the diodes D_P behave as those in Fig. 7.31. If the sign of V_1 is changed from positive to negative with no change in magnitude, V_1' will have the same sign and magnitude as V_1 before the change, so that diodes D_N will conduct, diodes D_P will be cut off, and the output voltage will be unchanged. In practice, of course, it would probably be necessary to use more than three diodes for each side, depending on the desired accuracy and the range of voltages to be covered.

7.8. THE QUARTER-SQUARES MULTIPLIER

An important application of the "squaring" circuit of Fig. 7.33 is in the biased-diode multiplier, which makes use of the relation

$$xy = \tfrac{1}{4}\{(x+y)^2 - (x-y)^2\} \qquad (7.2)$$

FIG. 7.34 a, b. Biased-diode with Two Input Voltages.

In this multiplier the squaring circuit is used to produce voltages proportional to $(V_1 + V_2)^2$ and $(V_1 - V_2)^2$, and for this purpose the basic circuit of Fig. 7.29 a is modified by the addition of another input resistor, R_1', as shown in Fig. 7.34 a. If $R_1' = R_1$, a simple application of Thevenin's theorem [128] shows that V_1, V_2, R_1, R_1', may be replaced by a voltage $\frac{1}{2}(V_1 + V_2)$, applied through a resistor $\frac{1}{2}R_1$ (Fig. 7.34 b). If more diodes and resistors are added, as indicated in Fig. 7.35, the output voltage V_O is proportional to $-(V_1 + V_2)^2$, so long as $(V_1 + V_2)$ is positive. To handle negative values of $(V_1 + V_2)$ an identical set of diodes and resistors is used, but with input voltages $-V_1$ and $-V_2$, produced by means of sign-reversing amplifiers. These two sets of diodes and resistors are indicated respectively by sections I and II of Fig. 7.36, where for clarity only one diode-resistor combination of each set is shown, and the sign-reversing amplifiers for $-V_1$ and $-V_2$ are omitted. If a third identical set of diodes and resistors were added, with input voltages V_1 and $-V_2$, this would add to the output voltage a

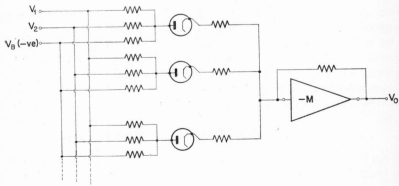

FIG. 7.35. Squared-sum Generator.

component proportional to $(V_1 - V_2)^2$, assuming $V_1 - V_2$ to be positive, but equation (7.2) shows that this component is to be subtracted from the $(V_1 + V_2)^2$ term, not added to it, and this could be achieved by inserting a sign-reversing amplifier between the common cathode resistor connection for this set of diodes and the input of the summing amplifier. There is, however, a simple method of reversing the sign of the $(V_1 - V_2)$ voltage, which involves only reversing the signs of all the input voltages, including

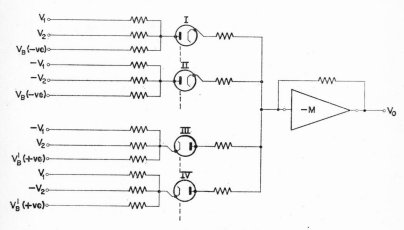

FIG. 7.36. Biased-diode Multiplier.

V_B, and reversing the connections of all the diodes. This gives the arrangement indicated by section III of Fig. 7.36. The diodes of this section can conduct only when $(-V_1 + V_2)$ is negative, or when $(V_1 - V_2)$ is positive, and the current flowing in the diode anode resistor is reversed in direction compared with sections I and II. For negative values of $(V_1 - V_2)$ a fourth set of diodes and resistors, with input voltages $+V_1$ and $-V_2$, are needed.

The complete arrangement, as indicated in Fig. 7.36, thus gives an output voltage

$$V_O = -k'\{(V_1 + V_2)^2 - (V_1 - V_2)^2\} = -k_1 V_1 V_2,$$

where $k_1 = 4k'$ is a scaling factor which depends on the choice of the values of the resistors including, of course, the feedback resistor of the feedback amplifier.

12 EAC

7.9. SINE AND OTHER FUNCTIONS

An arrangement of biased-diodes and resistors may be used to give an output proportional to $\sin \theta$, where $\theta = V_1/K$ and V_1 is an input voltage. Such an arrangement is shown in Fig. 7.37. Since $\sin \theta$ has a finite slope at the origin the first element in Fig. 7.37 is a

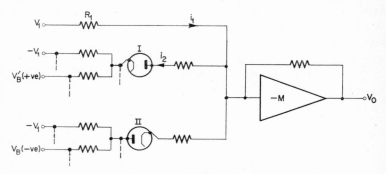

FIG. 7.37. Sine Generator.

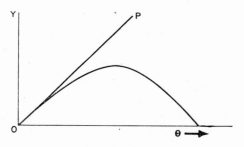

FIG. 7.38.

single resistor, R_1, which would by itself give the straight line OP in Fig. 7.38. A set of diodes and resistors indicated by I in Fig. 7.37, and fed with an input voltage $-V_1$ from a sign-reversing amplifier, gives a current i_2 of opposite direction to the current i_1 in R_1, so that the total current rises less rapidly as V_1 increases. As more diodes of the set become conducting, i_2 increases more rapidly, and when V_1 exceeds a value $K\pi/2$, i_2 is increasing more rapidly than i_1, so that the total current begins to fall. When $V_1 = K\pi$ the currents i_1 and i_2 are equal, so the sum, and hence V_O, are zero.

This arrangement will give $V_O = -k \sin(V_1/K)$ over the range $\theta = 0$ to $\theta = \pi$, and could be extended, if desired, for larger angles. However, when $V_1/K = \pi$ all the diodes in set I are conducting, and they would continue to conduct for higher values of V_1, so that the total current would be the algebraic sum of a fairly large number of individual currents and it would become increasingly difficult to maintain the required accuracy. It is preferable, if a range of 2π for θ is needed, to use $-\pi$ to $+\pi$ rather than 0 to 2π, since a second set of diodes, indicated at II in Fig. 7.37, can produce

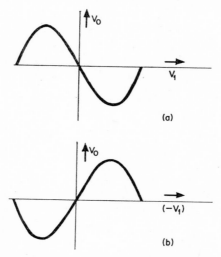

(a)

(b)

FIG. 7.39. Negative-sine and Sine Functions.

the required output voltage for negative values of V_1, with all the diodes of set I in the non-conducting state. The performance of the complete circuit of Fig. 7.37 is represented by

$$V_O = -k \sin(V_1/K) \quad -\pi \leqq V_1/K \leqq \pi,$$

as shown in Fig. 7.39a. If an output of opposite sign is desired, as shown in Fig. 7.39b, this requires only the reversal of signs of the V_1 voltages in Fig. 7.37, giving $-V_1$ into R_1 and $+V_1$ into I and II. Since both $+V_1$ and $-V_1$ are already available, no additional equipment is required.

When a biased-diode arrangement is being used to represent some function involving fairly rapid changes of slope it is sometimes

12*

possible to achieve a useful rounding of the rather sharp discontinuities which appear at the junction of the straight lines by using an artifice suggested by R. N. Kirkness. This requires simply the addition of an alternating potential V_{ac} to the normal "d.c." input voltage V_1. The frequency of this potential should be fairly high, and care must be taken that it has no adverse effect in the succeeding sections of the simulator. The peak-to-peak ampli-

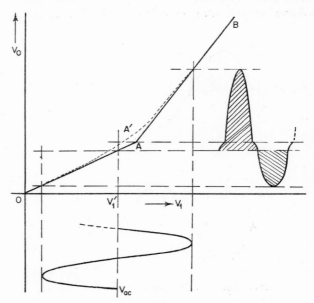

Fig. 7.40. Superimposed Alternating Potential.

tude is best found by experiment, but is generally less than the interval between successive bias voltages. When the value of V_1 is such that the swing of V_{ac} does not extend over more than one straight-line segment the mean value of the output voltage is unchanged, but if part of the positive half-cycle extends, say, to a segment of higher slope the mean output is somewhat higher than if V_{ac} were absent. As V_1 increases, the proportion of the cycle which extends on to the higher slope also increases, until V_1 reaches the bias value, when the increase due to V_{ac} is a maximum. As V_1 increases still further the effect of V_{ac} diminishes until, when the negative peak of V_{ac} does not swing below the bias point, the effect of V_{ac} is again zero.

The effect is illustrated in Fig. 7.40, for a function represented in the absence of V_{ac} by the two lines OA, AB, and for a particular value V_1' of the input voltage V_1. When V_{ac} is present the mean output will be increased by the difference between the two shaded areas, and the characteristic will be as $OA'B$.

Another curve which can be produced without difficulty by means of biased diodes is the upper half of the parabola

$$V_1 = k\, V_O^2.$$

This gives an output voltage proportional to the square-root of the input voltage, so that the arrangement can be used as a square-root device, and it is often preferable to the type described at the end of Section 7.4.

Besides the parabolas and sine functions described, biased-diode arrangements can be used to provide many other curves, using methods similar to those already outlined. The diode circuits are suitable for operation at relatively high frequencies, if required, since there are no moving parts and no reactances except diode and stray capacitances and possibly some small reactance in the resistors and wiring. The advantages of versatility, quick response, and potential accuracy, however, are somewhat offset by the complexity of equipment. Thus, for the highest accuracy a complete multiplier of the type shown in Fig. 7.36 might include 40 or 50 diodes, and 200 resistors; and in order to produce $\pm V_1$, $\pm V_2$, and possibly $\pm V_B$, up to six high-gain d.c. amplifiers may be needed, besides the one shown, the exact number being dependent on whether any of the required voltages are available from low-impedance sources.

7.10. DISCONTINUOUS FUNCTION SIMULATION

Certain elementary non-linear functions can be idealized to simple discontinuous functions which are very easy to simulate with biased-diode arrangements. The best-known of these is probably the limiting circuit, shown in Fig. 7.41a. So long as $-V_B < V_1 < V_B$ neither diode conducts, and $V_O = V_1$. When $V_1 > V_B$ the lower diode conducts, and assuming its impedance and also the impedance of the source of V_B are very low compared

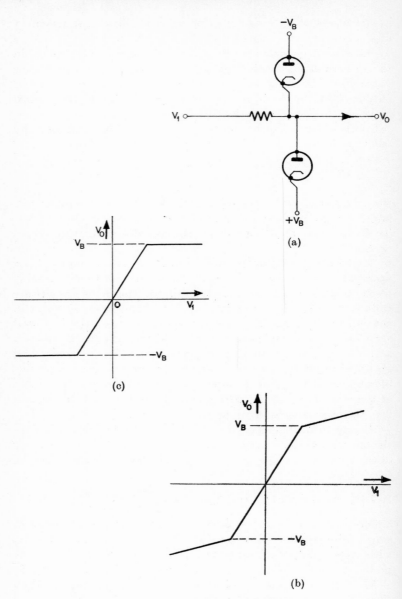

FIG. 7.41 a, b, c. Biased-diode Limiter.

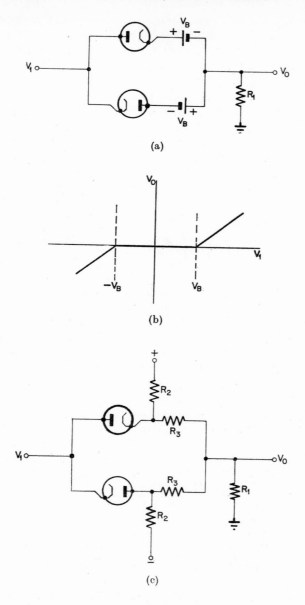

FIG. 7.42 a, b, c. "Dead-space" Generator.

with the resistor, the anode voltage will not rise appreciably above V_B, so that $V_O = V_B$. Similarly, when $V_1 < -V_B$, $V_O = -V_B$. The relation between V_O and V_1 is shown in Fig. 7.41 b. Asymmetrical limiting can easily be achieved by using unequal bias voltages, and the sharpness of the "knees" in the characteristic can be controlled to some extent by altering the value of the resistor. A characteristic of the shape shown in Fig. 7.41 c in which the slopes of the outer parts are not zero, but have particular values, can be achieved by including resistors in series with the diodes.

Another simple arrangement of biased-diodes is the "dead-space" circuit shown in Fig. 7.42 a. If $-V_B < V_1 < V_B$ neither diode conducts, so $V_O = 0$. If $V_1 > V_B$ the upper diode conducts,

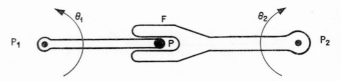

FIG. 7.43. Mechanism with Backlash.

and if its impedance and the impedance of the bias battery are negligibly small, $V_O = V_1 - V_B$. Similarly, if $V_1 < -V_B$, $V_O = V_1 + V_B$, and the complete characteristic is shown in Fig. 7.42 b. The sharpness of the knees will depend on the relative impedances of diode, battery and resistor R_1. The use of batteries may be inconvenient, because the voltage can only be adjusted in steps, and because the value of V_B will change if current flows for appreciable periods; if so the bias voltages can be supplied from other sources via resistors R_2, R_3, as shown in Fig. 7.42 c. This circuit, however, introduces some attenuation, so that when $V_1 > V_B$, for example, $V_O = k(V_1 - V_B)$, where $k < 1$. The circuits of Figs. 7.42 a and 7.42 b can be modified to give a characteristic in which the slope of the centre section is positive instead of zero by adding resistors in parallel with the diodes.

Besides limiting and dead-space effects it is sometimes required to simulate backlash. This is not easy to do in the general case, but the arrangement of Fig. 7.42 can be used in some cases. Suppose, for example, that the system being simulated includes the simple mechanism shown in Fig. 7.43. A pin P at the end of an arm pivoted at P_1 is a loose fit in a fork F at the end of a second arm pivoted at P_2. The pin and fork may be taken as representing gear-wheel teeth. In the position shown, take $\theta_1 = \theta_2 = 0$, and now assume that there is a spring-centring device which always tries to return θ_2 to zero. If θ_1 begins to increase from zero, θ_2 does not change until the pin strikes the upper prong of the fork, and thereafter, assuming the effective lengths of the arms remain equal, $\theta_2 = \theta_1 - \alpha$, where α depends on the diameter of the pin and the spacing of the prongs. When θ_1 begins to decrease, this relation is maintained until $\theta_1 = \alpha$, when $\theta_2 = 0$, and if θ_1 continues to decrease through zero, θ_2 remains zero until $\theta_1 = -\alpha$ and for values of θ_1 less than $-\alpha$, $\theta_2 = \theta_1 + \alpha$.

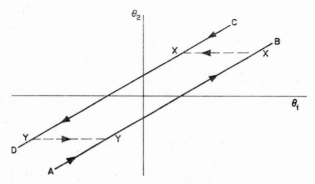

FIG. 7.44. Backlash Characteristic.

The relation between θ_1 and θ_2 is therefore of the form shown in Fig. 7.42 b, so that the mechanism could be simulated by the circuits of Figs. 7.42 a or 7.42 c.

A more usual form of backlash occurs when a frictional force operates at the pivot P_2 so that the fork only moves when it is pushed by the pin. If θ_1 at first increases, θ_2 will not change until the pin hits the upper prong of the fork, and then it will increase steadily with θ_1; and if θ_1 later reverses its direction, the fork will remain stationary while the pin moves from the upper prong of the fork to the lower. This type of motion is represented in Fig. 7.44, where AB gives the relation between θ_1 and θ_2 while θ_1 is increasing, and CD gives the relation while θ_1 is decreasing. This representation applies only while the pin remains continuously in contact with one prong of the fork, and during the change-over from one prong to the other, when θ_2 remains constant, the relation between θ_1 and

θ_2 is represented by a horizontal line, such as XX or YY, between AB and CD. Any electronic device to represent this behaviour requires some sort of "memory" which "remembers" the value of θ_2 during the change-over period, and one such arrangement, which is satisfactory in some cases, is shown in Fig. 7.45. The pair of biased-diodes operates in the same way as those in Fig. 7.42 a, but the resistor is replaced by a capacitor, and the input voltage is applied through a high-gain amplifier with feedback. Suppose initially that the voltages V_1 and V_O are zero, and then V_1 begins to decrease stead'ly. The voltage V_1' increases steadily but V_O remains at zero until V_1' overcomes the bias on the upper diode, and then the diode conducts, so that the capacitor is connected via the

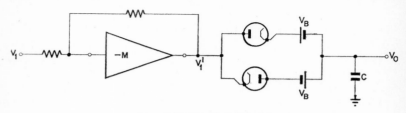

FIG. 7.45. Backlash Circuit.

bias battery to the amplifier output terminal. The object of the amplifier is to provide a source of very low impedance to feed the capacitor so that no appreciable lag is introduced. In practice the resistance of the battery is liable to be greater than the amplifier impedance, but if it is, say, 10 ohms, and the capacitance is $1\cdot0\ \mu$F there will be a lag of 10 microseconds, which will not usually be important. Thus, ignoring the small voltage drop in the conducting diode, $V_O = V_1' - V_B$, and this relation will be maintained so long as V_1' continues to increase. If, however, V_1' begins to decrease, the upper diode will cut off, since there is no means of removing charge from the capacitor, and the output voltage will therefore remain at the value it reached when V_1' reversed. However, when V_1' has fallen by $2V_B$ the lower diode will begin to conduct, and thereafter the output voltage will decrease with V_1' in accordance with $V_O = V_1' + V_B$. The modification which avoids the use of bias batteries is shown in Fig. 7.46, but it may be necessary, in using this circuit to take account of the attenuation introduced by the resistor network.

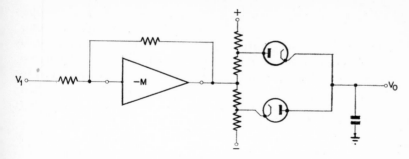

FIG. 7.46. Backlash Circuit without Separate Batteries.

With ideal diodes, a capacitor of infinite leakage resistance, and infinite input impedance for the device into which V_O is fed, this arrangement would give the characteristic of Fig. 7.44; but in practice the diodes do not cut off sharply, they have appreciable forward impedance, and there will be some leakage from the capacitor during the change-over intervals. These effects may be serious if it is required to represent a sharp change from, say, AB to XX, or if the system is expected to spend appreciable periods in the condition where the pin (Fig. 7.43) is not touching either side of the fork. In other cases, however, this arrangement gives a satisfactory simulation of this type of backlash. While the above simple circuits suit many purposes, more accurate simulation of discontinuous functions may be achieved using variations of the so-called feedback bridge limiter. All these variations basically utilize the high d.c. amplifier gain, e.g. as shown in Fig. 7.47. This very accurate limiter circuit was used in early missile simulators at R.A.E., Farnborough, and is probably due to Squires, and is the first of many similar unpublished circuits developed by him some ten years ago for the simulation of Coulomb friction and similar threshold effects. Much of the latest work in this field is by Korn [61, 62].

The action of the bridge-limiter circuit may be considered by assuming that V_1 is a steadily increasing voltage in the positive sense. Before any limiting action takes place there is a linear relationship between V_1 and V_2, and V_2 and V_O, which is ultimately controlled by the feedback resistor R_f. Voltages V_2 and V_O are related by the currents drawn by the diodes through resistors R_6

and R_7 thereby setting up a voltage drop across them. Eventually V_2 becomes so negative that diode c fails to conduct and no further current changes occur in R_6 and R_7 so that V_O cannot become more negative as V_1 continues to increase. This implies that the amplifier feedback via R_f is inoperative and therefore the full gain of the amplifier becomes operative and V_2 increases sharply, rather like a trigger, only to be crudely limited by the "safety" diodes e, f, in the

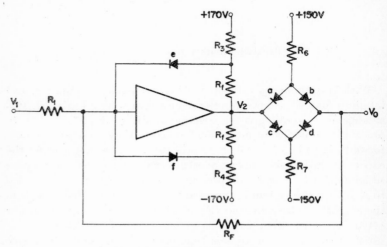

FIG. 7.47. Diode-bridge Limiter.

case considered. The circuit will limit either positively or negatively going signals at potentials determined by the bias conditions applied. The trigger action of V_2 can be utilized to advantage in operating switching relays to provide scale changing or other signal-controlled programme functions if required.

Another more advanced circuit is illustrated in Fig. 7.48, where two operational amplifiers are used, and with which a variety of discontinuous functions may be obtained. This is a dead-space limiter due to G. A. Korn [62], where the two slopes and the breakpoints are separately adjustable. A slight modification to the above circuit forms the so-called dead-space comparator of Fig. 7.49, and other circuit configurations suggested by Korn in [62] provide interesting applications to relay hysteresis and step-wise signal quantization.

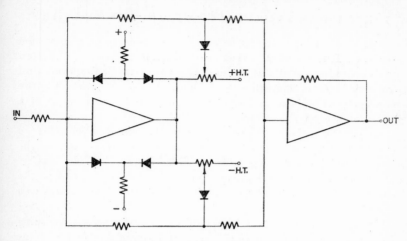

FIG. 7.48. Dead-space Limiter.

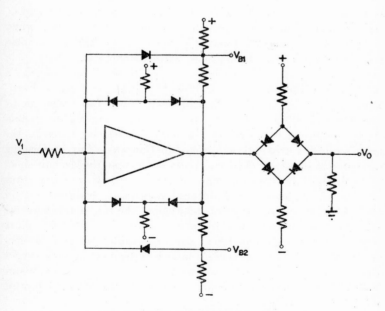

FIG. 7.49. Dead-space Comparator.

7.11. TWO-VARIABLE FUNCTION GENERATORS

It is sometimes necessary to provide functions of more than one variable. This presents considerable difficulties, but some limited success has been achieved in simulating two-variable functions, and some of the more important methods will be described. Usually the two-variable function is artificially constructed in the shape of a physical or electrical model.

One of the earliest successful attempts to construct an arbitrary two-variable function generator was at M.I.T [63]. This took the form of an X–Y plotting table, modified so that the pen was replaced by a stylus mechanism which was servo-positioned to the coordinate (x, y). The area of the plotting table contained a sculptured plaster relief model of the two-variable function, over which the stylus tracked. The height of the model varied according to the value of the function $f(x, y)$ and the stylus followed the variations in height. The variation in stylus height was converted to a voltage by means of a potentiometer such that the output voltage $V_z = f(x, y)$. The obvious limitations were slow X and Y servo responses, and the mechanical difficulty which arose when steep slopes were encountered. The need for a sculptor may also have been a minor embarrassment with this method.

In an attempt to overcome some of these disadvantages, a method was used by Gait and Garvey [64] at R.A.E., Farnborough, in conjunction with Dobbie-McInnes Ltd., who modified a standard X–Y plotting table by inserting a thin carbon sheet containing a matrix of regularly spaced electrodes in the table's working area. The arbitrary function was set up by forming contours at constant electrical potential across the carbon sheet according to the contour map of the arbitrary function, thus eliminating the need for a sculptured model and, to a great extent, the difficulty due to regions of steep slope. The function generation was moderately restricted by power limitations, and by finite resolution of the electrical field due to the finite number of electrodes. The inherently slow performance of the plotting table servos was not overcome by this method. A similar instrument using Teledeltos paper on which contours may be painted in conducting ink is commercially available.

The most recent improvement of the electro-mechanical type has been at the College of Aeronautics, Cranfield, and is an extension

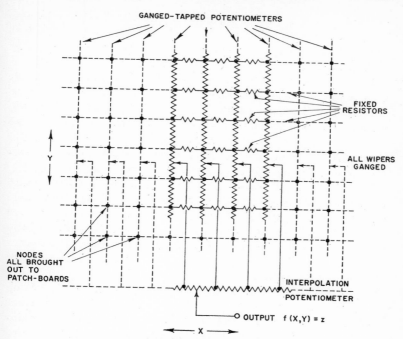

GANGED–TAPPED POTENTIOMETERS

FIXED RESISTORS

ALL WIPERS GANGED

Y

NODES ALL BROUGHT OUT TO PATCH-BOARDS

INTERPOLATION POTENTIOMETER

O OUTPUT f (X,Y) = z

X

Fig. 7.50. Potentiometer Net.

of the tapped potentiometer single-variable function generator mentioned earlier in this chapter. For two-variable functions a group of tapped potentiometers are connected as shown in Fig. 7.50 where adjacent equi-spaced tappings are interconnected by resistors of value equal to the resistance of the potentiometers between tappings. This forms the now classic resistance-net developed by Liebmann and others [65, 66] in the late 1940's which was used for the analogue solution of the Laplace equation. However, the net formed by the potentiometers has the advantage that it can be continuously "explored" in the Y-direction by ganging all the tapped-potentiometer sliders together at the same relative angular position, and by rotating the common shaft. The sliders of all these potentiometers are each connected to respective tappings of another tapped potentiometer which is called the interpolation potentiometer. Motion of the slider of this potentiometer then explores the net in the X-direction. Its resistance is made as high as possible compared with the ganged potentiometers to minimize the loading effect on the net. At some expense, the loading effect can be avoided completely by inserting cathode followers, or better still, d.c. amplifiers in the slider circuits if required.

If for any reason a potential field exists over the area of the net, then a cross-section or "profile" of this field at any arbitrary ordinate y will take the form of a voltage distribution along the interpolation potentiometer when the ganged shaft is rotated to the angular setting representing y. Also the angular position of the interpolation potentiometer slider represents the coordinate setting x, so that the voltage which appears on it will represent z, where $z = f(x, y)$. The arbitrary function is set up in a similar way to the earlier R.A.E. machine by applying a pattern of voltage contours on a specially provided patch-board. This instrument due to Garner [67] largely overcomes most of the difficulties of the earlier devices. The servomotors driving both the X and Y potentiometers can be quite independent and, if necessary, can be hydraulic motors to give rapid response with bandwidth up to 20–30 c/s. Compared with the 1 or 2 c/s response for conventional plotting table servos this represents a considerable improvement. A further merit of the instrument is that only standard commercially obtainable equipment is required. A typical multi-tapped ganged potentiometer unit manufactured by General Controls Ltd. Basildon is illustrated in Fig. 7.51. Other versions of the same basic device show promise in facilitating the solutions of problems based on the Laplace equation [68], and in the solution of complex variable problems associated with the performance of electrical networks and feedback control systems [69–72], all of which are beyond the scope of this present book.

All-electronic methods of generating functions of two variables are so far rare. One due to Meissinger [73] could be considered as the analogue of the potentiometer-net described above. In the linear-segment approximation method using biased-diodes (Section 7.7), it is comparatively easy to set up a single-variable arbitrary function using several circuits of the type shown in Fig. 7.31. In principle, this sets up the "profile" at some arbitrary coordinate y. If to each bias terminal there is connected an individual single-variable function generator, each related to the coordinate y, then the profile can be changed in accordance with y. The variable x is the "normal" input so that the output from the whole circuit

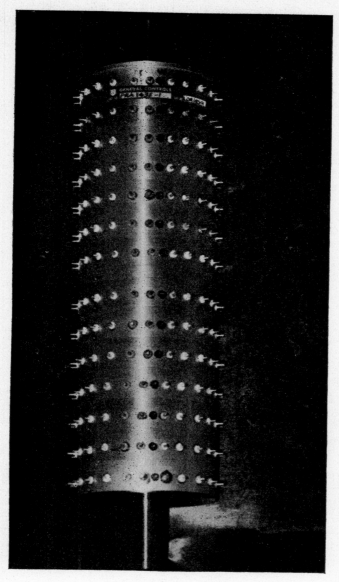

FIG. 7.51. Multi-tapped Ganged Potentiometer
(General Controls Ltd.).

is $z = f(x, y)$. This method, while having a relatively large bandwidth and good accuracy, is extremely difficult to set up, despite its
apparent simplicity.

Some simplification is achieved, however, by connecting the outputs of the set of single-variable diode function generators to the
taps of a multi-tapped potentiometer in order to generate the second
function electro-mechanically. This arrangement is attractive when
one variable changes quickly and the other slowly.

7.12. THE TRIGGER CIRCUIT

A number of different trigger circuits have been designed and
Fig. 7.52 shows a popular arrangement due to Schmitt [74].

In the normal condition, with the input terminal at about earth
potential, V_2 passes a moderate current, and this gives sufficient
potential drop in the variable resistor to bias V_1 almost to cut-off.

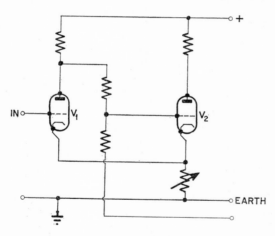

FIG. 7.52. Basic Schmitt Trigger Circuit.

If the input terminal is made more positive, the current through V_1
increases and the grid of V_2 becomes more negative, so that the
cathode of V_1 becomes less positive and there is a further increase
of current through V_1. If the input terminal becomes steadily more
positive, a critical value is reached at which a small change in the
grid potential of the V_2 tends to produce a somewhat larger change,

of the same sign, in the anode potential of V_1. The circuit is then unstable, and the anode current of V_1 increases very rapidly until limited by non-linear effects. At the same time the current through V_2 falls almost to zero.

If the input terminal is now made steadily more negative, another critical point will be found at which the circuit reverts suddenly to its original condition, with moderate current in V_2 and very little in V_1. The difference in voltage between the two triggering points, i.e. hysteresis, may be 20 volts or more, or as little as 0·1 volt, depending on the circuit values, especially the value of the variable resistor. Refinements to this basic circuit are many, and they have been made mainly with the object of achieving accurate repeatability and low hysteresis. A value of 5 mV for the hysteresis is not uncommon.

CHAPTER 8

SETTING UP A SIMULATOR

WHEN a given dynamic system is to be studied by means of a simulator it is convenient to derive a set of equations which describe as far as possible the behaviour of the system, although complete description by means of equations may not be possible because of non-linearities. In the initial stages some of the non-linearities and possibly all of them may be ignored, and some of the less important dynamic effects, such as small time lags, resilience of shafts, etc., can also be omitted. If it is intended that the simulator shall ultimately include actual parts of the real dynamic system (Section 10.3) these should, in the initial stages, be simulated by simple lags or in some other convenient manner. As the work proceeds, more complete and accurate representation may be required, and appropriate changes are made to the equations, and additions to the simulator, so that at least some of the non-linearities and smaller time lags, etc., are included. It is important to remember, however, that however far this procedure is taken, a completely accurate simulation of a dynamic system is not possible. For example, the resilience of a shaft may have been ignored; but if it has been taken into account, it may appear only as an elastic effect, with no account taken of the inertia of the shaft itself, which may or may not be negligible compared with the inertia of an attached gear wheel; and a more realistic representation still would allow for the fact that the mass of the shaft is not "lumped" but "distributed", so that the shaft acts as a mechanical "transmission line". Furthermore, the elastic behaviour of the shaft may be non-linear, and so on, and corresponding imperfections appear in all other practical components.

For some cases, of course, such refinement of representation as these remarks suggest may be quite unneccessary and even undesirable because of the wasteful use of computing elements and the extra computing errors introduced by these elements. For other cases it may be necessary to include a large number of these minor effects. In this respect the simulator method is no different from other computing techniques, but experience has shown that it is rather easy, when using a simulator, to fall into the way of thinking that a particular simulator, especially if it contains many elements, is a true model of the dynamic system being studied. In fact, the simulator is a representation of some other dynamic system, which resembles the real dynamic system more or less closely, but which contains a number of idealizations, omissions, and approximations. The art of using a simulator consists, at least in part, in being able to judge the degree of perfection in simulation which a given dynamic system and a given problem require; in continually remembering that the simulator model is imperfect; and in bearing in mind the imperfections when the results of simulator work are being studied.

Assuming, however, that a decision has been made as to which effects are to be included and which are to be ignored, attention can be given to "setting up" the simulator. In setting up a simulator or analogue computer a dominant requirement is to choose the scale factors in such a way that no overloading occurs, but at the same time the voltages representing variables should always be as large as convenient in order to prevent undue contamination by noise, hum, etc. If the simulator is to be used to represent a given set of linear equations, or a set of equations with a number of nonlinearities of types for which suitable curve followers or function generators are available, the construction of a block diagram is usually not difficult. In some cases there will be more than one possible block diagram, and the choice will depend on the number and types of computing elements available, on the range on variables to be handled, and the accuracy required.

8.1. SCALE FACTORS AND TIME SCALES

When the block diagram has been drawn a list is prepared of the expected or estimated maximum values of quantities which are to be represented as output voltages from computing elements. Generally, of course, the maximum values of all the quantities will not be known, but for those which are known a first estimate of scale factor is made by dividing the output voltage which the element can give without overloading by the maximum value of the corresponding variable. Thus, suppose the expected maximum value of an angle θ is $12°$, and the maximum allowable output voltage is 45 volts. The scale factor will be $K_\theta = 45/12$ volts per degree $= 3.75$ volts per degree. Suppose also that the maximum value of another angle φ is $14°$, with the same maximum of 45 volts, so that the first estimate of scale factor is $K_\varphi = 45/14 = 3.22$ volts per degree. In practice it would usually be preferable not to use these two scale factors, but to use a common factor of 3.0 volts per degree for both variables, because the round number simplifies mental estimates, and the use of a common factor eases comparisons and reduces the chance of errors due to using the wrong scale factor. Using 3.0 volts per degree the θ voltage will only reach 36 volts, compared with the permissible 45, but the gain in convenience will offset the small loss in signal-to-noise ratio. The scale factors thus derived will probably indicate the gains required in some of the amplifiers, so that values of input and feedback resistors can be found. For amplifiers whose gains cannot be found in this way because maximum values of some variables are not known, an estimate is made, based on the broad assumption that the output voltage of one amplifier is the input to another similar amplifier, so that it is reasonable, in the absence of any other indication, to choose a gain of unity for an amplifier with one input, and a rather smaller value if there are two or more inputs. For the time constants of an integrator, there may be some information about expected values and manner of variation of input quantities, but if not an estimate may be made, based on whatever is known of the time scale of the dynamic system being represented.

On the basis of estimates of this kind, and corresponding estimates for multipliers, function generators, etc., the scale factors for the remaining quantities in the problem can be found. The estimates, of course, will often be very rough, but they will enable a complete set of scale factors, gains, time constants, etc., to be written down and entered on the block diagram. It is important at this stage to check for consistency; for example, if a summing amplifier is being used to compute $\theta = \varphi + \psi$, then with the chosen input and feedback resistors an input voltage representing, say, one degree of φ according to the scale factor chosen for φ should give an output voltage representing one degree of θ according to the scale factor for θ, which may or may not be the same as for φ. Similarly for ψ, which may have a different scale factor again, and hence may need a different value of input resistor. Considering Fig. 8.1, if φ is scaled at a degrees/volt to give θ at c degrees/volt and ψ is scaled at b degrees/volt to give θ at c degrees/volt also then $R_1/R_2 = b/a$ since R_f is common.

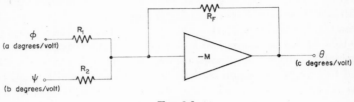

FIG. 8.1.

Further, since both φ and ψ may reach their maximum value simultaneously, then it must be arranged that the resulting maximum value of θ does not saturate the amplifier. This may be determined by considering the particular case when

$$\frac{R_f}{R_1}\left[\frac{\varphi_{max}}{a}\right] + \frac{R_f}{R_2}\left[\frac{\psi_{max}}{b}\right] = \frac{-\theta_{max}}{c}$$

and

$$R_1/R_2 = b/a$$

giving

$$\frac{a\,\theta_{max}}{c(\varphi_{max} + \psi_{max})} = -\frac{R_f}{R_1}$$

which is the maximum permissible value for R_f/R_1, which in turn establishes R_2. Similar reasoning applies for more than two inputs. For an integrator computing θ from $d\theta/dt$, an input voltage representing a step of, say, 1 degree per second according to the scale factor for $d\theta/dt$ must produce an output voltage which rises steadily at a rate of K volts per second, where K is the scale factor associated with θ. For the case of the summing integrator shown in Fig. 8.2, where $R_1 C = T_1$ and $R_2 C = T_2$, consistency is established when $T_1/T_2 = b/a$ since C is common.

When the first block diagram is complete, with resistor and capacitor values, etc., inserted in accordance with the estimates, the simulator elements are adjusted and interconnected to correspond, and the desired disturbing voltages, such as steps or sine waves, are applied. The output voltages from the computing elements are observed by means of voltmeters, recorders, or oscilloscopes, and if any of the elements overload, or if the maximum output voltage from an element is much smaller than the overload value, appropriate changes are made to gains, time constants, etc., and the consequent changes of scale factor are noted. When the changes have been made the simulator will be capable of accepting the required inputs without error due to overload or to excessive noise.

This procedure for setting up the simulator and deciding the scale factors is not difficult to apply to a small machine, but may become tedious when applied to a large machine. However, a large simulator is very often set up in a number of stages, perhaps by beginning with a highly simplified model of the complete dynamic system and making a series of modifications which give a more

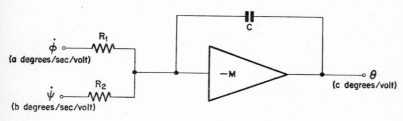

(a degrees/sec/volt)

(b degrees/sec/volt)

(c degrees/volt)

Fig. 8.2.

accurate and complete representation of the system; or alternatively, it may be possible to consider the dynamic system in a number of sections, for which separate small simulators are set up and tested before being connected together to form the complete simulator. Such methods not only simplify the problem of deciding scale factors, but they help the operator to build up a mental picture of the mechanism he is studying; in fact a stage-by-stage procedure is often justified for this reason alone, even though, as is usually the case, the operator of a large machine has had experience in setting up and using smaller machines.

Systematic methods have been devised for setting-up and scale factoring [75, 76], and most manufacturers include adequate procedures in handbooks on their equipment. However, there is no substitute for common sense and experience in this vital aspect of analogue computing, particularly when dealing with highly complicated systems containing non-linearities. The following considerations may be found useful in deciding proper signal levels.

The most common type of input is the "step" voltage, and in systems which contain non-linearities it must be remembered that a change in the amplitude of the input step will not cause a proportional change in the amplitudes of all the other voltages in the simulator. In other cases the amplitude of the step may not be critical, and slight overloading may be removed by using a smaller step. Other input functions are the impulse function, sinusoidal voltages, and random functions such as noise. The impulse function, although important as a mathematical concept, is not often usable in analogue computers because of the probability of overloading. The ideal impulse has an amplitude approaching infinity and lasts for an infinitesimal time, the product of amplitude and duration being finite. The practical impulse has finite amplitude and duration, but to give a reasonably close representation of an ideal impulse the duration must be short compared with the time constant of the system to which it is applied. To satisfy this requirement without using an amplitude so large as to cause overloading usually means that the disturbing effect on the system is small, and the resulting output voltages are also small and difficult to measure accurately. For this reason and also because a practical approximation to an impulse is more difficult to produce than a step function, the impulse function has not found wide application in analogue computers.

Testing with sinusoidal voltages is a useful and generally straightforward technique, though care must be taken to avoid overloading when the frequency is changed, because although the amplitude of the input may be the same the effects of resonance may give unexpectedly large voltages in some parts of the system. Disproportionately large errors can be caused if a sharp peak of voltage draws grid current in an input circuit and allows charge to appear on a capacitor which has only a high-resistance discharge path when the grid current stops. The charge on the capacitor may persist for long enough to give appreciable error, even though the period of true overload is negligibly brief. This effect is particularly important in chopper drift-corrected amplifiers because of the inherent long time constant of the chopper-amplifier filter network, and it may completely paralyze the computation.

The most useful application of sinusoidal voltages is to complex linear systems. The sinusoidal response of simple linear systems can be calculated with relatively little labour by the method developed for communication networks and servo-mechanisms [77,78]. However, the response of non-linear systems to sinusoidal inputs is liable to be misleading unless great care is taken in its interpretation. In the latter case, resort to analytical techniques such as the Describing Function is necessary [79, 80].

With random inputs occasional overloads for very short periods cannot always be avoided. Indeed, if the input voltage has a "normal" distribution there is a finite, though usually small, probability that any finite amplitude, however large, will occur; but in practice the input voltage will have been produced by some equipment which is itself limited in the amplitudes and rates of change of amplitude, etc. which it can handle, so that it is usually necessary to accept an amplitude distribution which falls somewhat short of the ideal. Even so, if the simulator includes any differentiating sections, either as explicit differentiators or as loops in which, for example, an integrator appears as a feedback element, the differentiated random voltage may include large peaks, and there may be danger of overloading.

8.2. INITIAL CONDITIONS

Before a computation on a simulator or differential analyser can be begun all the voltages representing variables must be set to the correct values, in accordance with the set of initial conditions associated with the problem. This applies even for voltages whose

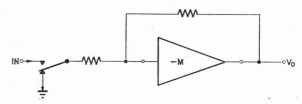

FIG. 8.3. Amplifier with Start-relay Contacts.

initial values are zero, since there may be stray voltages due to residual charges on capacitors, etc. For this purpose, and also to facilitate "zero-setting" in amplifiers not fitted with automatic means for drift correction, it is common practice to provide each computing element with a "start" relay whose prime function is to disconnect the input terminal of the element temporarily from its source of input voltage and connect it to earth. The arrangement for an amplifier is shown in Fig. 8.3, in which the input resistor is earthed so that when zero-setting has been done the output voltage

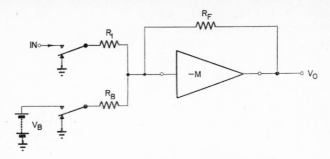

FIG. 8.4. Start-relay for Non-zero Initial Value.

is zero. This condition is maintained for all the amplifiers in the simulator up to the instant when the solution is begun, when the closing of a master switch operates all the relays simultaneously and all the input resistors are connected to their appropriate sources of input voltage. Following the usual practice the relay contacts in the diagrams are all shown in the "unoperated" condition.

Figure 8.3 gives the condition $V_O = 0$ when $t = 0$. For any other initial value the arrangement of Fig. 8.4 is used, the second input resistor R_B being earthed until $t = 0$ when the changeover contact applies a steady voltage V_B, giving an initial value for V_O equal to $-V_B R_F / R_B$. A similar method can be used with other computing elements whose output/input relations are independent of time.

For an integrator a relay is also used, and operated by the same master switch, but for the condition $V_O = 0$ at $t = 0$ there must be no charge on the capacitor at $t = 0$, so the relay is arranged to shunt a low-value resistor across the capacitor as well as earthing

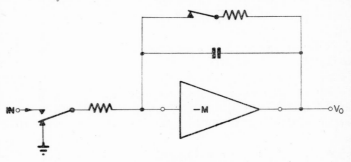

FIG. 8.5. Integrator with Start-relay Contacts.

the input resistor, until $t = 0$, as shown in Fig. 8.5. The low-value resistor is included to limit the capacitor current and to reduce sparking.

If the conditions require that the integrator output voltage V_O has some value other then zero at $t = 0$, i.e. if there is a non-zero constant of integration, the initial value can be introduced by several different methods, most of them depending on producing an appropriate charge on the capacitor at $t = 0$. An obvious way of doing this is shown in Fig. 8.6, where relay contacts are used to

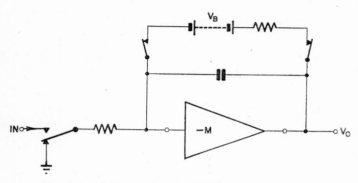

FIG. 8.6. Initital-condition Switching for Integrators.

connect a battery directly to the capacitor. At $t = 0$ the contacts are opened and the capacitor voltage is then V_B. It is easily shown that this gives V_O an initial value equal to $- V_B M/(1 + M)$, which is effectively equal to $- V_B$ if M is large. A limiting resistor of low value is connected in series with the battery.

The arrangement of Fig. 8.6 has the disadvantage that a separate isolated battery must be provided for each integrator. Methods can be devised, as in Fig. 8.7, which allow the capacitors of several integrators to be charged from a common supply, but in the arrangement shown the amplifier has no feedback impedance for $t < 0$, and the very high gain may give rise to undesirable spurious output voltages. Extra relay contacts may be provided to connect a temporary feedback resistor, but careful timing of the switching is necessary to ensure that the capacitor is connected into circuit shortly before the feedback resistor is disconnected, so that there is no interval with no feedback impedance, and also to avoid any

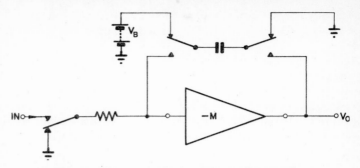

FIG. 8.7. Initial-condition Switching for Integrators.

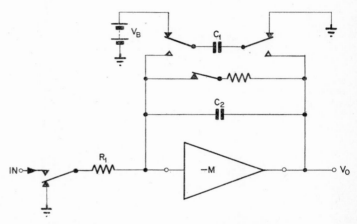

FIG. 8.8. Initial-condition Switching for Integrators.

appreciable discharge of the capacitor via the temporary resistor during the short period when both are connected.

Another method of putting an initial charge on the capacitor is shown in Fig. 8.8. Here the total integrator capacitance is formed of two separate capacitors which are connected in parallel when integration begins. Before $t = 0$, however, one of the capacitors is connected to a source of appropriate voltage and when the relay operates the capacitors are connected in parallel and the charge is shared. If M is very large the initial value of V_O is equal to $- V_B C_1/(C_1 + C_2)$. The usual relay contacts are provided to keep C_2 discharged before $t = 0$, and it is obviously necessary that these

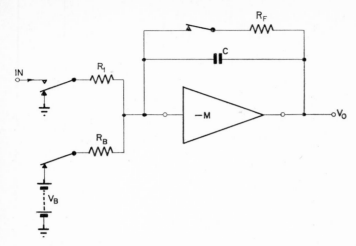

FIG. 8.9. Initital-condition Switching for Integrators.

contacts should open before the changeover contacts connect C_1 to C_2.

A scheme with simpler switching is shown in Fig. 8.9. In the condition shown, the output voltage is equal to

$$V_O = - V_B \frac{R_F}{R_B} \left(\frac{1}{1 + s C R_F} \right)$$

assuming M is very large. Thus the steady-state value of V_O is $- V_B R_F / R_B$, and the capacitor will retain the charge to give this initial value of V_O when the relay is operated at $t = 0$. When a computation is complete the relay will be returned to the unoperated condition, as shown in Fig. 8.9, and it is essential that time be allowed for the capacitor voltage, and hence V_O, to approach sufficiently close to their steady-state values before the relays are operated again. This waiting period may be objectionable, though the values of R_B and R_F can be made fairly low so that the time constant $C R_F$ which governs the approach to the steady value may be only a small fraction of the time constant of the integrator $C R_1$.

A modification of the scheme of Fig. 8.9 is shown in Fig. 8.10, where a second capacitor is shown in parallel with R_B. The relation

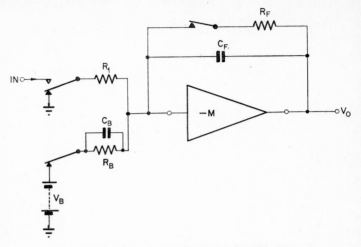

Fig. 8.10. Initial-condition Switching for Integrators.

between V_O and V_B is now

$$\frac{V_O}{V_B} = -\frac{R_F}{R_B}\left(\frac{1 + sT_B}{1 + sT_F}\right) \qquad (8.1)$$

where $T_B = C_B R_B$ and $T_F = C_F R_F$.

Thus if $T_B = T_F$ the output voltage is always proportional to V_B, and there is no time lag between V_B and V_O. In practice the time constants will probably not be exactly equal, and to examine the effect of inequality suppose first that T_B is the greater, so that $T_B = T_F + T'$, where T' is positive. Then from equation (8.1):

$$\frac{V_O}{V_B} = -\frac{R_F}{R_B}\left(1 + \frac{sT'}{1 + sT_F}\right) \qquad (8.2)$$

When V_B is applied suddenly by the release of the relay after a computation, assuming there is then no charge on the capacitors, the value of V_O will rise suddenly to a value equal to

$$-V_B\frac{R_F}{R_B}\left(1 + \frac{T'}{T_F}\right),$$

which is found by setting $s \to \infty$ in equation (8.2). This is greater than the steady value in the ratio $(1 + T'/T_F)$, and V_O will settle exponentially to the steady value with time constant T_F. If, on the other hand, T_F is greater than T_B, let $T_F = T_B + T''$ where T'' is positive. Then

$$\frac{V_O}{V_B} = -\frac{R_F}{R_B}\left\{\frac{1 + s\,T_B}{1 + s(T_B + T'')}\right\}$$

The quantity in curly brackets can be rewritten

$$\frac{T_B}{T_B + T''}\left\{\frac{(T_B + T'')/T_B + s(T_B + T'')}{1 + s(T_B + T'')}\right\}$$

so that

$$V_O = -V_B\frac{R_F}{R_B}\cdot\frac{T_B}{T_F}\left\{1 + \frac{T''}{T_B}\left(\frac{1}{1 + s\,T_F}\right)\right\} \qquad (8.3)$$

Thus when the relays release immediately after a computation, assuming that there is then no charge on the capacitors, V_O will rise suddenly to a value smaller than the steady-state value in the ratio T_B/T_F, and will approach the final value exponentially with time constant T_F.

When T_B and T_F are unequal and T_B is the greater there may be some slight danger of overloading the amplifier if the inequality is large and if V_O is also large. If the inequality is small, whatever the sign, V_O will instantaneously take up a value very near to the final value, and the exponential change is in the nature of a correction. The time for this correction will be much less than the charging time needed for the arrangement of Fig. 8.9, and a rough measure of the improvement is given by the ratio T_F/T' or T_F/T''. The values of R_B and R_F can again be relatively low, so that T_B and T_F are much smaller than the integrator time constant.

If T'' (or T') is zero, i.e. if $T_F = T_B$, equation (8.3) represents the ideal form of the preceding method. If T'' is not zero, then the preceding method aims at hastening the approach of the steady state by making T_B, T_F and T'' all as small as possible. An alternative method is to make us of the initial value of V_O, as given by setting $s \to \infty$ in equation (8.3), instead of the steady-state value. This requires that the value of V_O as given by equation (8.3) does not change appreciably during intervals of time comparable with the time occupied by one computation. This may be achieved by making T''/T_B small, so that the relative change from the initial

state to the steady state is small, and by making T_F large so that
the change is slow. It is therefore desirable to remove the two
resistors R_B and R_F of Fig. 8.10, so that T_B and T_F may be as
large as possible. In addition, instead of connecting V_B at the end
of a computation and allowing the capacitor voltages to "settle"
in the interval before the start of the next computation it is now
desirable that the capacitors should remain uncharged during this
interval, V_B being connected at $t = 0$ or shortly before. This leads
to the arrangement shown in Fig. 8.11, where the two capacitors

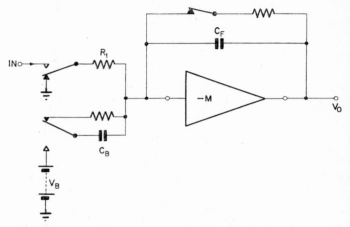

FIG. 8.11. Initial-condition Switching for Integrators.

are shunted through low-value resistors at $t = 0$. If the capacitors
were ideal components, entirely without resistance, then the relation between V_O and V_B would be

$$V_O = - V_B \frac{C_B}{C_F}$$

which is equivalent to equation (8.3) with $T'' = 0$. In any practical
use of this scheme, however, the capacitors will not be perfect and
an estimate must be made to ensure that the last term of equation (8.3) will remain negligible throughout the computation
interval.

A method of adding an integration constant which does not
depend on charging a capacitor is shown in Fig. 8.12. Here the

integrator is arranged as though the initial value of the output voltage were zero, and the integration constant is added subsequently by a summing amplifier. With this method the full output voltage swing is still available in both positive and negative directions. With other methods, in which the initial-condition voltage appears at the integrator output terminals, the available voltage swing due to the integration action is reduced in one direction by the amount of the initial voltage.

In all the cases where relay contacts are connected across an integrator capacitor it is important to check that the insulation

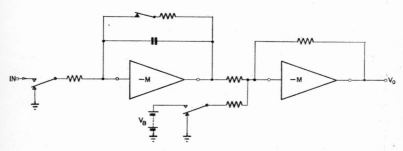

Fig. 8.12. Initial-condition Switching for Integrators.

resistance between the contacts does not appreciably reduce the effective insulation resistance of the capacitor.

For any given simulator the choice of a method of setting initial conditions in the integrators naturally depends on the type and size of the simulator. The most convenient method is undoubtedly that shown in Fig. 8.12. This has no appreciable settling time, gives easy adjustment of the value of the initial voltage, and needs only simple relay contacts with no need for critical timing of the opening and closing of the different contact sets. These advantages are so important that this method has been adopted in a number of medium and large simulators in spite of the cost of extra amplifiers. It is not always necessary to provide each integrator with an additional amplifier exclusively for the addition of the integration constant. It often happens that a summing or reversing amplifier follows an integrator, for some purpose unconnected with initial conditions, and in such cases it can usually be used also for the introduction of the initial condition.

Of the other methods given above some are of little more than academic interest, but one or two are of practical value in some machines when it is desired to avoid the expense of providing additional amplifiers. For a small machine where high precision is not needed Fig. 8.6 may be acceptable, since a few small dry batteries can be used. Figure 8.8 needs no appreciable settling time and is convenient to use if each integrator is provided with a suitable relay and a pair of capacitors of equal value. Figure 8.11 is specially useful in simulators of the repetitive type (Section 10.2) where the length of the computation interval is known and is usually short.

8.3. ECONOMY OF AMPLIFIERS

Only too often in moderate-sized computer installations there comes a time when the complexity of the simulation stretches the amplifier capacity of the computer to the maximum, and it becomes necessary to carry out more than a simple summation or integration across a single operational amplifier, using input or feedback impedances which include more than one resistor or capacitor. Indeed, provided all the derivatives of every variable are considered as implicit and not required to be measured, the use of the circuits described next will always provide some reduction in the number of amplifiers required for a given simulation, and may often improve the overall accuracy of the solution. Many general-purpose computers contain facilities for composing elementary circuits of this kind by arranging for the convenient switching or insertion of passive components around each amplifier, and throughout this section and the next a number of useful networks will be found with their associated transfer functions. In most previous works, the design of complex input and feedback networks for use with d.c. amplifiers is approached in a semi-intuitive way such as is outlined in Section 8.4. It is generally not stated that there are systematic synthesis procedures for deriving any required transfer function.

In fact, it can be stated from network theory concepts that it is theoretically possible to synthesize realizable networks, consisting only of resistive and capacitative elements, which may be used to simulate any rational transfer function representing any linear system, using only one operational amplifier! To obtain a proper

skill at synthesizing such networks necessitates a thorough understanding of network theory [81, 82] and is beyond the terms of
reference of this book to explain, although a brief outline of a
typical method is given in Section 8.5.

Enthusiasm for these more erudite possibilities must be tempered
by the consideration of what is practical, or indeed convenient.
Theory usually assumes ideal elements, i.e. pure resistance, pure
capacitance and ideal amplifier. Thus any predictions as to a
particular network realization must be modified by the knowledge
that such perfect elements cannot be achieved in practice, at least
over an infinite range of frequencies. Nevertheless, over the
frequency band of interest in analogue computing devices, such
components usually can be considered as acceptably close to the
ideal. For this reason, therefore, each network configuration must be
considered according to how sensitive it is to the effects of non-
ideal components. Another consideration of importance is the
spread of component values which may arise from purely automatic
synthesis techniques, and some redesign of the synthesized network
may be necessary in order to utilize "off-the-shelf" values for the
resistors and capacitors. Finally, of course, ease of adjustment of
the network element values must be taken into account in order to
allow for component tolerances, or for subsequent adjustment of
simulation parameters.

Thus providing due consideration is given to these factors and
engineering limitations, there is no reason why the powerful network synthesis techniques should not be used in place of the earlier
cut-and-try methods. All that is required is for a member of a
simulation team to make himself adequately familiar with these
very well established techniques in network theory, and the
references given in the Section 8.5 should provide some suitable
sources. However, before proceeding to this, the older and quite
useful work on implicit simulation will be described.

8.4. COMPLEX OPERATIONAL AMPLIFIER
CONFIGURATIONS

By using more complex input and feedback impedances in place
of plain resistors and capacitors, a single amplifier can be used to
provide more than one elementary operation. As a simple example,

14*

consider the transfer function †

$$V_O = \frac{V_1}{(1 + sT)}$$

In the explicit method of simulation this would first be rewritten

$$V_O + V_O sT = V_1$$

or

$$V_O = \frac{V_1}{sT} - \frac{V_O}{sT} = \frac{1}{sT}(V_1 - V_O)$$

The corresponding computing circuit would need an integrator, a summing amplifier, and a sign-reversing amplifier, making a total of three high-gain amplifiers, arranged as in Fig. 8.13. By contrast with the simple arrangement of Fig. 5.7, which consists only of a series resistor and a shunt capacitor, but has the same transfer

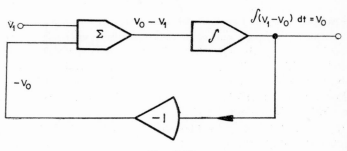

FIG. 8.13.

function, Fig. 8.13 seems very wasteful. However, this latter arrangement provides an output voltage from a low impedance, and both $+V_O$ and $-V_O$ are available; additional signals can be introduced merely by using more resistors at the inputs to any of the three amplifiers; initial conditions can be inserted without difficulty; and in some circumstances it is an advantage to have a resistive input impedance, independent of frequency, which this arrangement provides. By contrast, the input impedance of the simple arrangement varies with frequency, and the current drawn

† Strictly, the use of the "transfer function" requires that s should be redefined as the Laplace variable, but this would not change the form of the expressions.

from the input source may vary with time, as for example when a
step of voltage is applied.

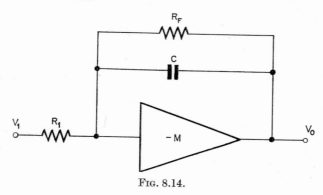

FIG. 8.14.

An intermediate arrangement is shown in Fig. 8.14, and the
corresponding transfer function, assuming a very high amplifier
gain, is

$$\frac{V_O}{V_1} = -\frac{R_F}{R_1}\frac{1}{(1 + sT)} \quad \text{where} \quad T = CR_F$$

This circuit has some of the advantages of the arrangement of Fig.
8.13, and is one of a class represented by Fig. 8.15, which shows an
input impedance Z_1 and a feedback impedance Z_F.

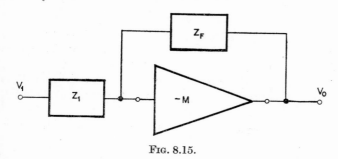

FIG. 8.15.

The transfer function, assuming a very high amplifier gain is

$$\frac{V_O}{V_1} = -\frac{Z_F}{Z_1} \tag{8.4}$$

The simplest forms of impedance apart from single components are a resistor and capacitor in parallel or series. The value of impedance

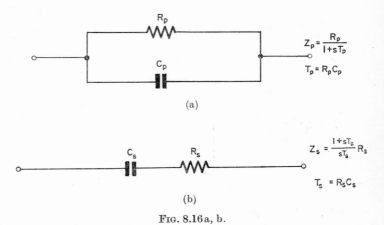

$$Z_p = \frac{R_p}{1+sT_p}$$

$$T_p = R_p C_p$$

(a)

$$Z_s = \frac{1+sT_s}{sT_s} R_s$$

$$T_s = R_s C_s$$

(b)

FIG. 8.16 a, b.

for these combinations are conveniently expressed in the forms:

$$
\left.
\begin{aligned}
Z_P &= \frac{R_P}{1 + sT_P} \\
Z_S &= \frac{(1 + sT_S)\,R_S}{sT_S}
\end{aligned}
\right\}
\tag{8.5}
$$

as shown in Fig. 8.16. Making use of these forms, the transfer functions obtainable by using any combination of single components or pairs of components can be derived directly. In a similar manner combinations of three or more components may be used, though the choice of a circuit to suit a particular transfer function is naturally less simple.

Four-terminal networks and other more complex arrangements can also be used in the input and feedback circuits in place of the usual two-terminal impedances. Figure 8.17 shows a simple two-terminal network as the feedback impedance, but a four-terminal network in the form of a simple T as the input circuit. If the value of M is so large that $1/M$ is negligible, the overall response of this arrangement can easily be found by making the assumption

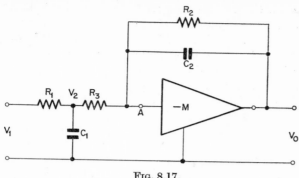

FIG. 8.17.

that the voltage at the amplifier input terminal A is zero. Ignoring grid current, the net current arriving at point A is zero, so that

$$\frac{V_2}{R_3} + \frac{V_O}{R_2} + V_O s C_2 = 0$$

or

$$V_2 = -V_O\left(\frac{R_3}{R_2} + s C_2 R_3\right)$$

The net current arriving at the output terminal is also zero, so that

$$\frac{(V_1 - V_2)}{R_1} - V_2 s C_1 - \frac{V_2}{R_3} = 0$$

or

$$\frac{V_1}{R_1} - V_2\left(\frac{1}{R_1} + \frac{1}{R_3} + s C_1\right) = 0,$$

and substituting for V_2 gives:

$$\frac{V_O}{V_1} = -\frac{R_2}{R_1 + R_3} \cdot \frac{1}{(1 + s T_1)(1 + s T_2)} \qquad (8.6)$$

where

$$T_1 = \frac{C_1 R_1 R_3}{R_1 + R_3}, \quad T_2 = R_2 C_2$$

This result may be compared with the corresponding expression for the arrangement of Fig. 8.18, for which from equations (8.4) and (8.5) it is easily seen that

$$\frac{V_O}{V_1} = -\frac{R_2}{R_1} \cdot \frac{s T_1}{(1 + s T_1)(1 + s T_2)}$$

where

$$T_1 = R_1 C_1, \quad T_2 = R_2 C_2$$

and although the denominator is of the same quadratic form as equation (8.6) the sT_1 term in the numerator is often undesirable.

The arrangement of Fig. 8.17 is a convenient method of producing a second-order function of the low-pass type, but it is limited in its scope because the time constants T_1 and T_2 are necessarily real. It is sometimes required to produce an arrangement giving a response of the form

$$\frac{V_O}{V_1} = -K \frac{1}{1 + 2usT + s^2 T^2} \tag{8.7}$$

which represents a simple second-order "resonance" of undamped natural frequency $1/2\pi T$ and damping ratio u. If u is greater than the "critical" value unity, which means there is no overshoot in the

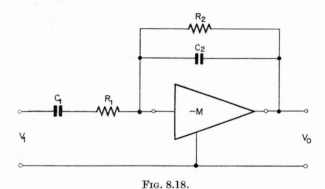

Fig. 8.18.

transient response, the denominator can be factorized into the same form as equation (8.6) and the response can be produced by the arrangement of Fig. 8.17. If, however, u is less than unity, the factors of $(1 + 2usT + s^2 T^2)$ are complex, and the corresponding response cannot be reproduced by Fig. 8.17.

A modification which allows production of responses with less than critical damping is shown in Fig. 8.19. Assuming as before that M is very large,

$$\frac{V_2}{R_3} + V_O s C_2 = 0,$$

or

$$V_2 = -V_O s C_2 R_3$$

and

$$\frac{(V_1 - V_2)}{R_1} - V_2 s C_1 + \frac{V_O - V_2}{R_2} - \frac{V_2}{R_3} = 0$$

Elimination of V_2 gives:

$$\frac{V_O}{V_1} = -\frac{R_2}{R_1}\left\{\frac{1}{1 + sC_2\left(R_2 + R_3 + \dfrac{R_2 R_3}{R_1}\right) + s^2 C_1 C_2 R_2 R_3}\right\} \tag{8.8}$$

Comparing this result with equation (8.7)

$$T^2 = C_1 C_2 R_2 R_3; \quad 2uT = C_2\left(R_2 + R_3 + \frac{R_2 R_3}{R_1}\right)$$

Let $R_2 = R_3 = R$, $R_1 = xR$, and $C_1 = yC_2 = yC$; then

$$T^2 = yC^2 R^2, \quad \text{and} \quad 2uT = CR\left(2 + \frac{1}{x}\right),$$

so that

$$u = \frac{1 + \dfrac{1}{2x}}{\sqrt{y}}$$

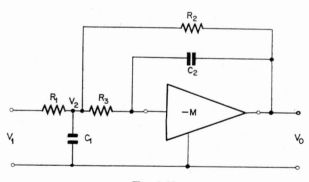

FIG. 8.19.

It is often undesirable to make x and y greater than about 20, and with this value $u = 0.23$. This corresponds to a peak of 6·7 db (2·24 : 1 as voltage ratio) in the frequency response and an over-shoot of about 44 per cent in the transient response to a step function. Most practical servo-systems have heavier damping than this, so their responses can be reproduced by the arrangement of Fig. 8.19 if a second-order linear system is adequate.

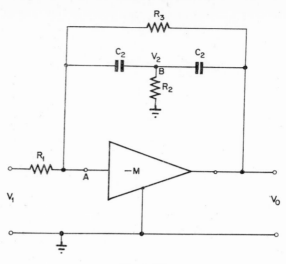

FIG. 8.20.

Another arrangement which gives second-order responses with less than critical damping is shown in Fig. 8.20, which has for its feedback circuit a four-terminal network of the bridged-T type. As before, the transfer function may be derived by equating to zero the net currents arriving at points A and B, i.e.

$$\frac{V_1}{R_1} + V_2 s C_2 + \frac{V_O}{R_3} = 0$$

and

$$-\frac{V_2}{R_2} + (V_O - V_2) s C_2 - V_2 s C_2 = 0$$

Elimination of V_2 gives

$$\frac{V_O}{V_1} = -\frac{R_3}{R_1} \left\{ \frac{1 + 2s C_2 R_2}{1 + 2s C_2 R_2 + s^2 C_2 R_2 R_3} \right\} \tag{8.9}$$

and comparison with equation (8.7) shows that $T = C_2 \sqrt{R_2 R_3}$ and $u = \sqrt{(R_2/R_3)}$. If $R_3 = 20 R_2$, $u = 0.225$, very nearly the same value as for equation (8.8) with $x = y = 20$.

The denominator of equation (8.9) is simpler and rather more convenient for adjustment of values than the denominator of equation (8.8), but the numerator term $(1 + 2s C_2 R_2)$ may not be needed, though it is sometimes useful as a method of introducing pure "phase advance" or derivative of the input voltage. The numerator term could be removed by using another network with a transfer function $1/(1 + 2sC_2R_2)$, connected in such a way that the two transfer functions multiplied without any loading or interaction effects. This would probably involve a buffer amplifier, and a more economical method is to modify the circuit of Fig. 8.19 to that shown in Fig. 8.21, by adding a series resistor and shunt capacitor R_4C_1 in the input circuit. The relation between V_3 and V_1 is given by:

$$\frac{(V_1 - V_3)}{R_4} - V_3 s C_1 - \frac{V_3}{R_1} = 0$$

or

$$\frac{V_1}{R_4} = V_3\left(sC_1 + \frac{1}{R_1} + \frac{1}{R_4}\right)$$

Writing R for R_1 and R_4 in parallel,

$$\frac{1}{R} = \frac{1}{R_1} + \frac{1}{R_4}$$

and

$$\frac{V_3}{V_1} = \frac{R}{R_4}\left(\frac{1}{1 + sC_1R}\right) = \frac{R_1}{(R_1 + R_4)}\left(\frac{1}{1 + sC_1R}\right)$$

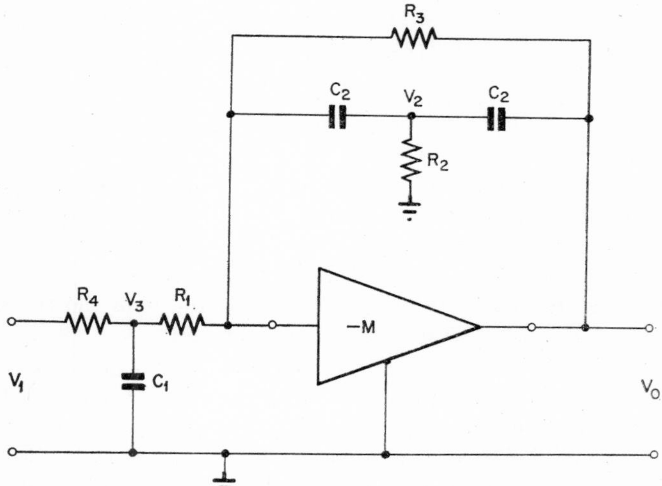

FIG. 8.21.

Now equation (8.9) shows that, for Fig. 8.21,

$$\frac{V_O}{V_3} = -\frac{R_3}{R_1}\left(\frac{1 + 2sC_2R_2}{1 + 2sC_2R_2 + s^2C_2^2R_2R_3}\right)$$

so that

$$\frac{V_O}{V_1} = -\left(\frac{R_3}{R_1 + R_4}\right)\left(\frac{1 + 2sC_2R_2}{1 + sC_1R}\right)\left(\frac{1}{1 + 2sC_2R_2 + s^2C_2R_2R_3}\right)$$

(8.10)

and a pure second-order response may be obtained by setting $C_1R = 2C_2R_2$. Alternatively, of course, the terms $(1 + 2sC_2R_2)$ and $(1 + sC_1R)$ may be retained to produce more complex responses, a particular application being the reproduction of an oscillatory response, represented by the quadratic term, combined with an "impure" phase advance represented by the two linear terms. For this purpose the ratio of time constants $2C_2R_2/C_1R$ would commonly lie between about 3·0 and 20.

There is some scope for ingenuity and skill in devising economical amplifier-plus-network combinations to satisfy particular requirements, and with some practice and experience it is often possible to forecast the nature of the change in the transfer function resulting from a change in the circuit without the labour of solving the equations. As a simple example, suppose it is required to modify the arrangement of Fig. 8.18 whose transfer function is given in equation (8.8), to give a transfer function of the form

$$\frac{V_O}{V_1} = -K\frac{1 + sT_1}{1 + 2usT + s^2T^2}$$

(8.11)

which is similar in form to equation (8.8), except for the additional numerator term. There is no guarantee that this simple modification is possible, but the new expression resembles the original; and there are five component values available for adjustment in the circuit compared with only three parameters T, T_1 and u, in the transfer function, so there is a reasonable hope of success.

Comparison of equations (8.11) and (8.8) shows that (8.11) requires an additional term V_1sT_1, and a means is required of adding such a term in the equations expressing the network currents. One method would be to use another capacitor in parallel with R_1 (Fig. 8.18), giving an extra term $(V_1 - V_2)sC$ in the current equations. Bearing in mind the desire for economy, however, it is worth examin-

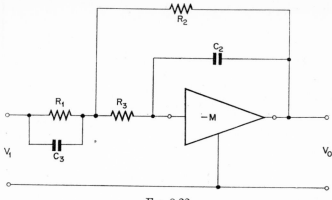

FIG. 8.22.

ing the possibility of using the existing capacitor C_1 in this manner, giving the circuit shown in Fig. 8.22. The transfer function of this arrangement can be derived from equation (8.8), and it is convenient to take two steps. First, it may be imagined that C_1 is removed, so that the coefficient of s^2 in equation (8.8) is now zero. Second, a capacitor C_3 is added in parallel with R_1 and hence in the transfer function R_1 is replaced by the impedance of C_3 and R_1 in parallel, which is $R_1/(1 + s C_3 R_1)$. This gives a numerator term $(1 + s C_3 R_1)$ and introduces a term $s^2 C_2 C_3 R_2 R_3$ into the denominator, the complete transfer function being now:

$$\frac{V_O}{V_1} = -\frac{R_2}{R_1} \cdot \frac{1 + s C_3 R_1}{1 + s C_2 \left(R_2 + R_3 + \dfrac{R_2 R_3}{R_1} \right) + s^2 C_2 C_3 R_2 R_3}$$

This is of the desired form, and is also of the same form as equation (8.9) but without the restriction that the coefficients of s in numerator and denominator are equal.

All the amplifier-plus-network combinations described so far make use of one amplifier only and give transfer functions substantially independent of the gain, provided the gain is very high. Arrangements using more than one amplifier are possible, and one such circuit which has some attractive features has been described by D. V. Blake [4]. The circuit is shown in Fig. 8.23; it makes use of a "mixer", which gives an output equal to the difference between two input voltages, and an amplifier of gain A, together with networks to give the two transfer functions $1/(1 + s\,T_1)$ and $s\,T_2/(1 + s\,T_2)$ (see Figs. 5.6 and 5.4). Then

$$V_O = \left(\frac{1}{1 + s\,T_1}\right)(V_1 - V_2)$$

$$V_2 = A\,\frac{s\,T_2}{1 + s\,T_2}\,V_O$$

whence $\quad \dfrac{V_O}{V_1} = \dfrac{1 + s\,T_2}{1 + s\,\{T_1 + (1 + A)\,T_2\} + s^2\,T_1\,T_2}$

This represents a second-order resonance of undamped frequency $1/2\pi\,\sqrt{T_1\,T_2}$ and damping ratio $\frac{1}{2}\,\{T_1 + (1 + A)\,T_2\}/\sqrt{T_1\,T_2}$; or if $T_1 = T_2$ the damping ratio is $\frac{1}{2}(2 + A)$. Thus, a variation of A

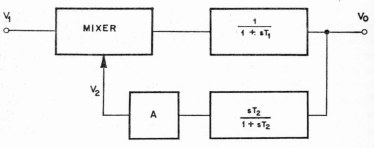

Fig. 8.23.

from zero to -2 gives damping ratios between unity (critical damping) and zero, although when the damping ratio is small it varies rather rapidly with the value of A, and special precautions may be needed to maintain the gain sufficiently constant. Besides the wide range of damping ratios available there is the advantage that the damping can be varied without varying the coefficient of s^2. Negative damping ratios, giving continuous oscillation, can easily be achieved if A is made negative with $|A| > 2$ when $T_2 = T_1$. If T_2 is greater than T_1 a smaller value of $|A|$ will give negative damping.

The numerator term $(1 + s\,T_2)$ may be unwanted in some applications though there is the advantage that the time constant T_2 is not automatically fixed by the frequency and damping of the denominator as in some other circuits. The term could be removed by adding a resistor and capacitor in front of the mixer, to give an additional term $1/(1 + sT_2)$.

A derived form of Blake's circuit, using one high-gain amplifier and one sign-reversing amplifier, is shown in Fig. 8.24. The transfer function is

$$\frac{V_O}{V_1} = -\frac{R_2}{R_1}\left\{\frac{1 + sC_3R_3}{1 + s(C_2R_2 + C_3R_3 - C_3R_2) + s^2C_2C_3R_2R_3}\right\} \quad (8.12)$$

or writing $C_3 = C$, $C_2 = xC$, $R_3 = R$, $R_2 = yR$, $CR = T$;

$$\frac{V_O}{V_1} = -\frac{R_2}{R_1}\left\{\frac{1 + sT}{1 + sT(xy + 1 - y) + s^2T^2xy}\right\}$$

A wide range of damping ratios can be achieved by choosing suitable values for x and y. If $x = (1 - 1/y)$ the damping is zero, and any smaller value of x gives an unstable system. Accurate control of the values of x and y is necessary if a particular damping ratio is to be realized precisely. Also, although it does not appear in an obvious way in the equations, the gain of the sign-reversing amplifier must be accurately controlled at the proper value. A disadvantage of this circuit compared with Blake's arrangement is that the damping ratio cannot be varied in any easy way without varying the frequency also. If this facility is desired it can be arranged by changing the values of the feedback or input resistors

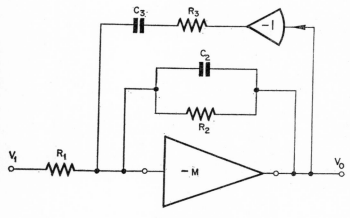

Fig. 8.24.

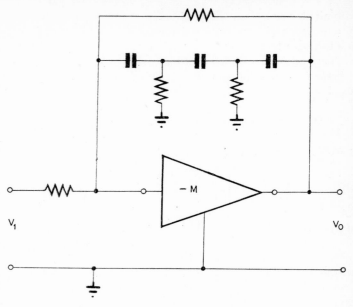

FIG. 8.25 a.

Fig. 8.25 a.

of the sign-reversing amplifier so as to give a gain of value $- N$ instead of $- 1$. The transfer function then becomes:

$$\frac{V_O}{V_1} = - \frac{R_2}{R_1} \left\{ \frac{1 + sT}{1 + sT(xy + 1 - Ny) + s^2 T^2 xy} \right\}$$

and besides the facility of easy adjustment of damping it is now possible to fix independently the values of frequency and damping of the denominator and the coefficient of s in the numerator. An advantage of arrangements of the type shown in Fig. 8.24 compared with Blake's original arrangement is that the output impedance of the circuit is very low, provided the resistors have reasonable values, so that V_O can be fed into another circuit without the need for a buffer amplifier.

If a capacitor C_1 is added in parallel with R_1 in Fig. 8.24 an extra factor $(1 + s C_1 R_1)$ is introduced into the numerator, so that

$$\frac{V_O}{V_1} = - \frac{R_2}{V_1} \left\{ \frac{(1 + sC_1 R_1)(1 + sC_3 R_3)}{1 + s(C_2 R_2 + C_3 R_3 - C_3 R_2) + s^2 C_2 C_3 R_2 R_3} \right\}$$

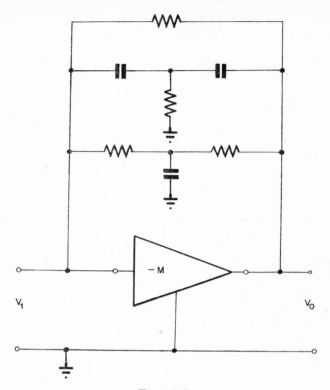

FIG. 8.25 b.

when the sign-reversing amplifier has unity gain. Again, the coefficient of s in the numerator of equation (8.12) may be removed if
desired by adding a series resistor and shunt capacitor in the input
circuit of Fig. 8.24, just as Fig. 8.20 was modified to give Fig. 8.21
(equations 8.9 and 8.10).

Transfer functions representing resonances with light damping
can be achieved with a single amplifier if either a resistance–
capacitance ladder or a pair of resistance–capacitance T-networks
in parallel is used as feedback networks, as shown in Fig. 8.25. The
first of these circuits is basically the same as the ordinary "phase-
shift" type R. C. oscillator, but the loop gain is reduced below the
value necessary for sustained oscillations. The second circuit is
similar, but in this case the corresponding oscillator is of the "Wien-

15 EAC

bridge" type, the double-T arrangement being a transformed version of the standard bridge circuit. These arrangements can give satisfactory performance in certain cases once they are set up to a given frequency and damping, but the expressions for the transfer functions are rather complex, so that adjustment is not easy. For use in a flexible analogue computer these disadvantages are generally sufficient to outweigh the economy in amplifiers compared with Fig. 8.23 or Fig. 8.24.

However, while the above approach, based on an experienced knowledge of the way networks behave, is moderately successful, more systematic methods are desirable to exploit the "implicit" simulation technique fully.

8.5. NETWORK SYNTHESIS OF RATIONAL TRANSFER FUNCTIONS

As stated in Section 8.1, it is possible in theory, by assuming the use of ideal R.C. elements and an ideal operational amplifier, to synthesize a realizable network which conforms to any rational transfer function. The value of this statement to the simulator operator lies in the fact that most simulation circuits can be sub-divided into paths along which only linear operations are performed. Such a path can always be represented by a single rational transfer function even though it may contain several summations, integrations and even local feedback loops around several operational amplifiers. If no individual parameter needs to be adjusted separately, and if no individual variable, excepting the input and output variables need separate measurement, then it may be worthwhile to simulate such a path in the simulation by a single operational amplifier, in association with a somewhat complicated passive network. It should be borne in mind that in the practical case this technique may often improve the overall simulator accuracy by eliminating the noise and drift of the amplifiers made redundant.

In order to deal with this subject effectively, it will now be necessary to introduce some simple network theory concepts. A useful concept is to regard networks, not with wires connected to input and output terminals, but rather as devices having one or more "ports", where a port can be considered as an entrance or exit to or from the network, made by pairs of wires taken

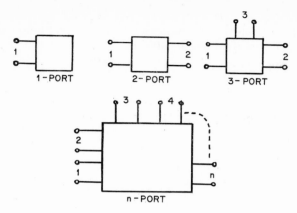

Fig. 8.26.

together to form ports. Figure 8.26 illustrates this idea. It so happens that, especially in computer and control engineering, the 2-port network is the type of special significance, and we shall restrict ourselves to a discussion of this type only. Figure 8.27 shows a 2-port network in a little more detail and from this may be derived the 2-port short circuit admittance parameters. If the 2-port contains no independent energy sources and no initial stored energy it is completely specified by four admittance functions. The first two are defined with the output port short-circuited; thus

$y_{11}(s) \equiv i_1(s)/e_1(s)$ i.e. *the short-circuit input admittance.*

$y_{21}(s) \equiv i_2(s)/e_1(s)$ i.e. *the forward short-circuit transfer admittance.*

The remaining two functions are defined with the input port short-circuited; thus

$y_{22}(s) \equiv i_2(s)/e_2(s)$ i.e. *the short-ctrcuit output admittance.*

$y_{12}(s) \equiv i_1(s)/e_2(s)$ i.e. *the reverse short-circuit transfer admittance.*

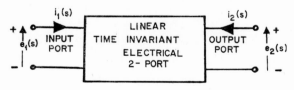

Fig. 8.27.

If the 2-port contains no dependent energy sources (representing active elements such as thermionic valves or transistors) then the forward and reverse transfer admittances are identical, thus,

$$y_{12}(s) \equiv y_{21}(s)$$

Next, the operational amplifier network configuration can be considered. In the sytem of Fig. 8.28, N and N' represent unbalanced 2-ports specified by their short-circuit admittance parameters, and P represents a linear amplifier with voltage gain $-M$ and output admittance $y_0(s)$.

Using Kirchhoff's current law the system can be represented by the three following equations, where for convenience the symbol (s) is consistently omitted from now on.

$$y_{11} e_1 + y_{12} e_2 = i_1$$

$$y_{21} e_1 + (y_{22} + y'_{11}) e_2 + y_{12} e_3 = 0$$

$$(y'_{21} M y_0) e_2 + (y'_{22} + y_0) e_3 = 0$$

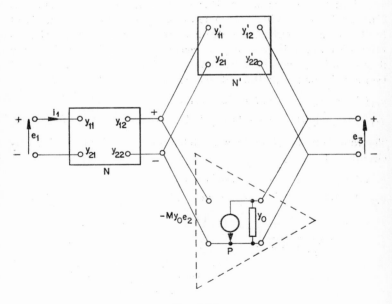

FIG. 8.28.

The solution of which yields

$$\frac{e_3}{e_1} = \frac{\dfrac{y'_{21} - My_0}{y'_{22} + y_0}}{\dfrac{y'_{11} + y_{22}}{y_{21}} - \dfrac{y'_{12}}{y_{21}} \dfrac{y'_{21} - My_0}{y'_{22} + y_0}} = G(s) \qquad (8.13)$$

and

$$\frac{e_3}{e_2} = \frac{y'_{21} - My_0}{y'_{22} + y_0} = -M_1 \qquad (8.14)$$

By substituting (8.14) in (8.13) we obtain the transfer function $G(s)$ of the system of Fig. 8.28 as

$$G(s) = -\frac{y_{21}}{y'_{12}} \frac{1}{1 + \dfrac{y'_{11} + y_{22}}{M_1 y'_{12}}} \qquad (8.15)$$

where M_1 is the voltage gain of the amplifier P with 2-port N' connected. If $M_1 \to \infty$ then (8.15) becomes

$$G(s) \simeq - y_{21}/y'_{12} \qquad (8.16)$$

Thus, if $M_1 \to \infty$, the transfer function $G(s)$ of the system of Fig. 8.28 is given by minus the ratio of the forward short-circuit transfer admittance of 2-port N to the reverse short-circuit transfer admittance of 2-port N'.

In order to demonstrate this, the simplest example to take is shown in Fig. 8.29. Quite obviously the short-circuit transfer ad-

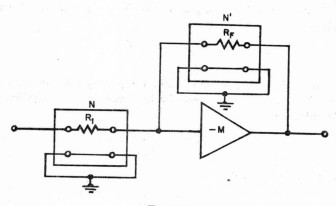

Fig. 8.29.

mittance of the input 2-port N is $y_{21} = -G_1 = -1/R_1$ and similarly 2-port N', $y'_{12} = -G_f = -1/R_f$ so that

$$G(s) \simeq R_f/R_1$$

An example of a more complicated network is shown in Fig. 8.30 where it can be deduced that

$$G(s) \simeq -y_{21}/y'_{12} \simeq -1/s^2 C^2 R^2$$

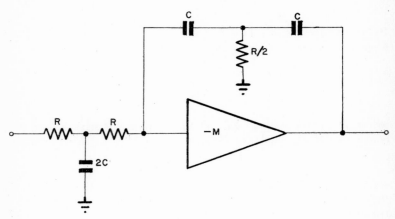

FIG. 8.30.

As far as analogue computer operators are concerned, the problem of synthesis is usually a matter of the practical realization of an operational amplifier network which has a prescribed transfer function of, say, $G(s)$. Let

$$G(s) = -\frac{\varphi(s)}{\psi(s)}$$

be a prescribed (stable and minimum phase) transfer function. If $\delta(s)$ is an arbitrary polynomial in s with simple negative real roots only, we may write

$$G(s) = -\frac{\varphi(s)/\delta(s)}{\psi(s)/\delta(s)}$$

and by (8.16) identify

$$y_{21} = -\frac{\varphi(s)}{\delta(s)}; \quad y'_{12} = -\frac{\psi(s)}{\delta(s)} \qquad (8.17)$$

From the theory of network synthesis it is known that the transfer admittances of equation (8.17) can be realized as unbalanced C. R. 2-ports. In 1955, M. V. Mathews and W. W. Seifert [83] applied Gullemin's ladder network theory [84] to the realization of the transfer admittances of equation (8.17), but S. R. Deards has pointed out† that a simpler and more suitable method is that of J. L. Bower and P. F. Ordnung [85]. As a simple illustration of the use of this method let the prescribed transfer function be the Butterworth function:

$$G(s) = -\frac{\varphi(s)}{\psi(s)} = -\frac{1}{(s+1)(s^2+s+1)}$$

By selecting a convenient $\delta(s)$ such as $(s + 1)(s + 2)$ we write

$$G(s) = -\frac{\varphi(s)/\delta(s)}{\psi(s)/\delta(s)} = -\frac{1}{(s+1)(s+2)} \bigg/ \frac{(s^2+s+1)}{(s+2)}$$

and identifying

$$y_{21} = -\frac{1}{(s+1)(s+2)} \;;\;\; y'_{12} = -\frac{(s^2+s+1)}{(s+2)}$$

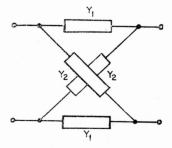

FIG. 8.31. Symmetrical Lattice 2-port.

It can now be shown that if $2y_{21}/s$ is expanded into partial fractions, and each term subsequently multiplied by s, we obtain

$$2y_{21} = 2\frac{s}{(s+1)} - 2\frac{(s+1)}{(s+2)} \tag{8.18}$$

and similarly

$$2y'_{12} = 3\frac{s}{(s+2)} - (1+2s) \tag{8.19}$$

† Private communication to the authors.

Now it is not difficult to show that the symmetrical lattice 2-port of Fig. 8.31 has short-circuit transfer admittances

$$y_{21} = \tfrac{1}{2}(Y_2 - Y_1) = y_{12}$$

so that

$$2y_{21} = Y_2 - Y_1 \tag{8.20}$$

From (8.18) and (8.20) we may write by recognizing the positive and negative terms

$$\frac{1}{Y_1} = \frac{1}{2}\frac{(s+2)}{(s+1)} = \frac{1}{2} + \frac{1}{2}\frac{1}{(s+1)}$$

and

$$\frac{1}{Y_2} = \frac{1}{2}\frac{(s+1)}{s} = \frac{1}{2} + \frac{1}{2s}$$

By noting that a number represents the magnitude of a resistance, and terms in s give values of capacitance, the lattice realization shown in Fig. 8.32a is obtained. By the well-known methods of converting a lattice to unbalanced form (Ref. 81, pp. 86–92) the lattice of Fig. 8.32a is readily converted to the unbalanced 2-port

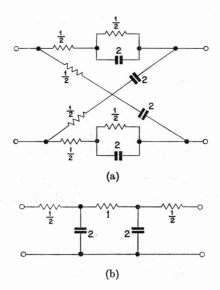

(a)

(b)

FIG. 8.32a, b.

of Fig. 8.32 b. Also from (8.19) and (8.20) we obtain for the network N'

$$Y'_1 = 1 + 2s$$

and

$$Y'_2 = 3\frac{s}{(s+2)}$$

and thus obtain the lattice shown in Fig. 8.33 a and hence the unbalanced equivalent of Fig. 8.33 b. Thus, the final realization is as

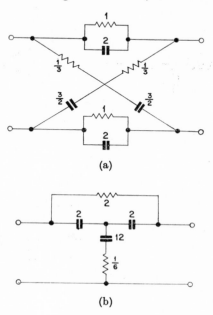

(a)

(b)

Fig. 8.33 a, b.

shown in Fig. 8.34 where the circuit element values are basically in ohms and farads. In order to obtain suitable values for employing real components multiply all the resistance values for both input and feedback 2-ports by a factor until a satisfactory value is obtained and divide the capacitance values for both networks by the same factor. Thus we may select the practical values as indicated in Fig. 8.35.

Summarizing the procedure, therefore, the steps are to regard the prescribed transfer function as the ratio of two polynomials in s,

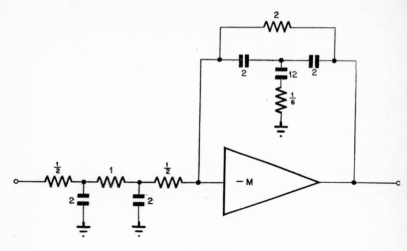

FIG. 8.34.

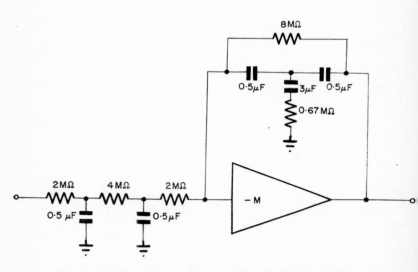

FIG. 8.35. A Practical Realization of a Butterworth Function.

and divide the numerator and denominator by another well-chosen polynomial in s. Having done this, identify the resulting ratio of the numerator and denominator respectively with the transfer admittances y_{21} and y'_{12}. Then by obtaining $2y_{21}/s$ and $2y'_{12}/s$ as partial fractions and multiplying each term by s, equate the resulting positive and negative terms with the short-circuit transfer admittances of the symmetrical lattice network of Fig. 8.31. This

NETWORK	y_{21} $(= -y_{12})$
	$\dfrac{1}{2R} \cdot \dfrac{s^2 C^2 R^2}{(1 + sCR)}$
	$\dfrac{1}{2R} \cdot \dfrac{2sCR}{(1 + sCR)}$
	$\dfrac{1}{2R} \cdot \dfrac{1}{(1 + sCR)}$

TABLE 8.1.

then enables the prescribed transfer function to be realized in this form, from which it is an easy operation to obtain, by standard methods, the unbalanced network equivalent.

This synthesis technique is quite suitable for sections of the simulation which require to remain fixed after set-up, or for the design of special shaping networks in control systems. However, where the ready adjustment of coefficients is an important consideration, such as for networks to be used in adaptive control systems and the simulation of such systems, other approaches are necessary. In recent papers Paul [86, 87] has simulated quadratic functions, with independent control of each coefficient in the

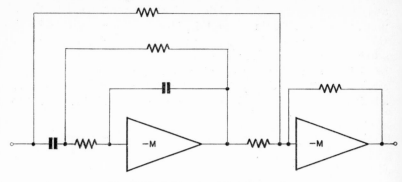

FIG. 8.36. A Transport-lag Network.

transfer function if required. The method is essentially based on a systematic permutation of three basic T-networks shown in Table 8.1, with respective $y_{21}(s)$ and $y_{12}(s)$ functions, and while it is not true synthesis in the network theory sense, a valuable range of networks has been derived from this work, including the single amplifier oscillator mentioned in Section 9.2, simulations of Butterworth, Chebychev and Orthonormal functions of great relevance to adaptive control systems, and equally to the simulation of such systems. Additionally, Paul has provided yet another transport-lag network (Fig. 8.36) similar to those developed earlier by King and Rideout [88]. In another recent paper Taylor [89] also applies the "design by analysis" technique to produce many similar networks.

8.6. SIMULATOR STUDIES

In a complete investigation of a given system the work may be divided broadly into three main parts, although not all of these may be included in any particular study. The first step is to decide whether the system is stable, and in some cases, either because the dynamic system exists and is known to be stable, or because the system is simple enough and sufficiently well understood for a "paper" study to give reliable estimates, no simulator work may be needed to establish stability. In other cases, perhaps because the determination involves the solution of high-order differential equations, a simulator may be used. More commonly, a simulator may be used to determine what sets of values, if any, of the parameters of the system give stability.

For some dynamic systems the simulator work might stop at the first stage, either because there is no further requirement beyond ensuring stability, or because no appreciable adjustment is possible in the value of important parameters of the system. Such a situation might arise if automatic operation or control were being applied to some mechanism or plant which had been designed and built originally for manual operation. Usually, however, when stability has been established, there will be some interest in accuracy, and the second stage of a complete investigation consists in using the simulator to forecast how accurately the dynamic system will perform its task. The errors shown by the simulator will include not only the errors in the system being simulated, but also the errors in the simulator itself. These simulator errors will consist partly of "computing" errors, such as amplifier drift, non-linearity in nominally linear elements, time lag in mechanical elements, etc., and partly of "simulation" errors, due to inaccurate representation of the real system by omission of small resiliences, neglect of small time lags, etc. It is obviously desirable to distinguish the true system errors from computing and simulation errors, but this is not always easy, and sometimes it can only be done by an elaborate series of tests.

When checks of system accuracy are being made by means of a simulator a number of measurements will often be made, using different values of whatever parameters are available for adjustment. This procedure is the beginning of the third stage in the complete investigation, which may be called "optimization". It is obvious that some sets of values of the parameters will give better performance than others, and that one particular set of values will give the best performance. The definition of "best" in this connection is important, and it may refer to the smallest steady-state error; or to the smallest r.m.s. error, especially if there is appreciable "noise" in the system; or to the smallest "dynamic lag" where the input is steadily changing with, say, constant acceleration. Whatever the definition adopted, there will be a "best" set of values for the parameters and the process of optimization includes testing the simulated system with a number of sets of values and deciding which gives the most satisfactory performance. In systems where random signals contribute appreciably to the output voltage the optimization process may take a long time, because the output voltage will be unsteady, and it will be necessary to make observations over a period of time, or to repeat the measurement perhaps dozens of times, before stable mean or r.m.s. errors can be determined for one set of parameters. The whole procedure must be repeated for each set of parameters.

If a sufficiently wide range of values of parameters is tested, the "best" set will inevitably be found, but optimization can sometimes be taken a stage further. To illustrate this, suppose the input voltage to a linear system consists of a continuously-varying legitimate voltage plus some noise, both being "stationary" in the statistical sense [78], so that they may be considered to have fixed spectral distributions. Then according to Wiener's noise theory [91–93] there is a form for the transfer function of the whole system which will give the smallest r.m.s. error in the output voltage, and if the system is required to give the minimum r.m.s. error its transfer function must conform to the Wiener optimum form. It may be, however, that of all the different transfer functions which can be produced by selecting different sets of parameters, none resembles very closely the optimum shape. The remedy is to add additional elements, such as electrical networks, to modify the response suitably.

Regarding the use of a simulator for investigating the errors in a dynamic system, it is obviously desirable to be able to estimate the degree of accuracy with which the simulator is representing the real system. Reference has already been made to the two classes of simulator error, viz. "imperfect simulation" errors and "computing" errors, and to the need for continuous vigilance to ensure that changes in the simulator do not introduce unsuspected new errors. Positive checks on the imperfect simulation errors are generally difficult to devise, and much depends on the skill and experience of the operator. In certain cases, however, checks can be made. Thus if the approximation $\theta = \tan \theta$ is being used to avoid the need for a tangent computer, and if θ is not always so small that the error is clearly negligible, some indication of the magnitude of the error can sometimes be gained by changing either the value of θ or its scale factor by an amount corresponding to the difference between θ and $\tan \theta$ and observing the effect on the output voltage.

Quantitative estimation of the "computing" errors in a simulator is also difficult, and the only thoroughly reliable method is to compare the results given by the simulator with results obtained by accurate step-by-step or analytical solution of the system equations. To some extent, of course, this procedure begs the question, since a simulator is not justified if a paper solution is possible without excessive labour. In practice, however, if large numbers of solutions are required from the simulator it is often quite reasonable to have a few typical cases solved accurately on paper or by means of a digital machine. Another procedure can also be applied when a large number of simulator tests are to be made on a given non-linear dynamic system, with different sets of parameters and perhaps some minor modifications to the system itself. One typical arrangement of the system is selected, with an average set of parameters, and corresponding to this a completely linear system is derived by removing the non-linearities. The equations of motion of this linearized system are written down and a solution is found for the selected set of parameters. The simulator is then set up to represent the linear system, with the selected parameters, and its response is checked against the numerical solution. Any difference will be due to simulator errors, and if these are acceptably small the simulator can then be modified to include the non-linearities with considerable confidence that the results from the non-linear simulator will not be appreciably affected by computing errors. Similar considerations apply to changes of parameters and to modifications of the simulated system, provided these do not depart too much from the original arrangement.

It is, of course, important that the accuracy of individual computing elements should be checked, even when an overall check against a numerical solution is possible. When no numerical solution is available the only method of assessing the accuracy of the simulator results may be to estimate the effect of the errors due to all the elements in the simulator, and often an experienced operator can make a satisfactory estimate. In any case quantitative determination of the error in an element is a necessary procedure, and some reference will be made to it in the next chapter.

In considering the question of the accuracy of the results which a simulator might give, it must be remembered that a set of quantitative answers represents only a part of the useful output of a simulator. Another important part of the output is the understanding or "feeling" for the problem which an operator is able to acquire. The simulator is a more or less complete model of the dynamic system he is studying, with the masses, resiliences, and dampings, etc., under convenient control, and in adjusting these quantities and observing the effects on the behaviour of the system he is able to build up, almost subconsciously, an appreciation of the relations between the various quantities and of their relative importance, in a more complete and direct manner than he could from studying graphs and tables of numbers.

Thus, to extract the maximum benefit from a simulator study the operator should be the man who has been engaged in the preceding theoretical studies.

This ideal can only be achieved completely if the problem is of "one-man" size. However, for bigger problems and bigger simulators the same broad principle may be applied, which means that at least some members of the team concerned should take part in both the theoretical work and the simulator study. In contrast, an important part of the potential value of the study is lost if the so-called "post-box" method is adopted. According to this method, when the theoretical worker has reached a stage where an extension of his studies by paper methods only would be impracticably laborious and he decides that a simulator should be used, he writes down a formal mathematical statement of the problem, with ranges of values of parameters to be tested, and passes these to the simulator operators. The simulator team perform the necessary solutions, using their simulator only as a calculating machine and not at all as a model of a dynamic system; indeed they may have little or no knowledge of the dynamic system involved. The simulator results, in the form of graphs and tables, are then "posted" back to the theoretical group. Although this method will give the solutions which the theoretical group ask for, it excludes the possibility of direct absorption of understanding of the problem which could be achieved if some members of the team took part in both the theoretical work and the simulator exercise. The method does little towards the solution of one of the great problems consequent on the use of a large computing machine—the problem of digestion by human mentalities of the great mass of information which such a machine can provide as the solutions to complex problems.

The post-box method also implies that the theoretical group can decide in advance the necessary "runs" which the simulator should perform. There is a high probability that any such pre-planned programme will give either too few solutions for sets of parameter values in the critical ranges, or too many solutions with uninteresting combinations of values.

It should be emphasized that the use of simulators is no substitute for thinking. On the contrary more thinking may be needed if a simulator is used properly, because a simulator will only be used for problems which are more complex than can be conveniently handled on paper. The simulator can only perform the unintelligent mechanical parts of the solution of problems. It certainly does not automatically solve the problem confronting the operator. Within its limitations of accuracy, etc., it can solve a problem which resembles the real problem more or less closely, but the degree of the resemblance, and the extent to which the simulator answers may be taken as answers to the real problem, are never complete, though often adequate; and the operator must take care to ensure that they remain adequate. In principle, of course, similar considerations apply to "all-paper" solutions, but experience shows that when using a simulator it is rather easy for vigilance to be relaxed.

When a complex problem is to be solved, even if it is quite certain that a simulator will be used, it is nearly always wise for the operator to spend a while on a paper study. Such a study may need such sweeping simplifications that any numerical answers may be almost useless even as rough solutions. Nevertheless, such a study is of value in giving the operator a chance to think about the whole problem, to make some sort of estimate of ranges of values and relative importance of various quantities, and to decide the stages by which the final complex simulator set-up is to be achieved. At this stage also the operator should think carefully and critically about the aim of the study; he should be quite clear as to what he is trying to discover about his system and in what form the answers are likely to emerge. It is easy to plan to select a large number of values for each of the parameters and to run through all the possible combinations, and to make records of all the variables, but except for quite small problems this will result in a vast indigestible mass of results on paper. A better plan is usually to try a small number of runs, with widely separated values, and to examine the results before performing more runs to fill in the interesting areas. It is often justifiable to record only a few of the variables, for although this entails some risk that information may be lost which might have proved useful, the reduction in the volume of records to be handled is very welcome. The problem of transferring the output of a large computer from paper or film to the minds of the human operators is one which can never have enough attention. It is false to assume that the amount of information absorbed is proportional to the volume of records.

8.7. MATRIX PROGRAMMING

Before finally leaving the topic of "using simulators" it is necessary to mention a setting-up procedure proposed by R. E. Horn and P. M. Honnell. In their method [94] the differential equations to be solved are formulated in matrix fashion, which if the simulation is at all complicated, results in a large matrix equation. Despite the size of the matrix equation, and in fact, because of the elegance of matrix methods, the equation can easily be manipulated by multiplication with transformation matrices, which are chosen to bring all the coefficients to near unity, and to minimize the number of negative coefficients. These transformations are carefully noted to preserve the ultimate scale factors, and the resulting modified matrix equation is then "synthesized" as a computer circuit. To simplify the "synthesis" they used a machine which was specially constructed to represent the matrix as a physical layout, although with care this procedure can apply to any computer. For this method it is claimed that because of the formality of the procedure there is less chance of errors in the organization of the simulator set-up and that it usually enables a considerable reduction in the number of necessary sign-reversers. Further, it is claimed that in some problems elimination of extraneous solutions is possible which, by the more ordinary methods of computer setting-up, can in some instances [94, 95] falsify the solution.

CHAPTER 9

AUXILIARY APPARATUS

FOR the operation of an analogue computer, not only are the constituent computing components required, but also equipment for their interconnection and setting-up, and for providing the necessary power supplies. In addition a considerable range of so-called peripheral apparatus for generating input wave-forms, observing and recording output voltages, and monitoring or performance checking instruments are necessary.

With the advent of considerable commercial activity in the production and sale of analogue computers, and the widespread use of these machines, the most notable recent advances have taken place in the development of the auxiliary apparatus. Furthermore, measuring equipments for studying automatic control systems have also made great advances in the last few years, and most of these are directly applicable to use with analogue computers.

The proper design and orientation of this peripheral equipment can make or mar the success of an analogue computer, almost in spite of the inherent computational accuracy which may be achieved from its d.c. amplifiers. Therefore, by implication, this chapter deals with what ergonomists term the "interface" problem, i.e. the effectiveness of the interconnection between the human operator and the machine.

9.1. SIGNAL GENERATION — THE FORCING FUNCTION

Whenever a system is being studied, its dynamic response can only be observed by injecting a disturbance into the system. If the response is being studied analytically by means of its mathematical model, the disturbance is called the forcing function, and the solution can only be obtained if the forcing function can be represented in mathematical form. To study the system's response in reality, or by means of its analogue on a computer, the input

16*   233

disturbance can take any arbitrary form in principle. However, because it is generally advisable to relate experimental results with theory as far as possible, it is desirable that the disturbing signal should have a well-known and relatively simple analytical representation to minimize the mathematical complexity of the theoretical relationships. Thus commonly used input signals are step-functions and ramp-functions to provide aperiodic disturbances, and sinusoidal signals at controlled frequencies for harmonic responses. One further input signal of great importance is random noise, which despite its apparent complexity, is analytically relatively simple to deal with, and is finding more and more application in dynamic system analysis and design [93, 96, 97], particularly in the field of optimization and adaptive control.

The generation of a step of voltage is very simple, requiring basically no more apparatus than a switch with a clean make or break action. The impulse function, which is occasionally used, can be approximated by a pulse of large amplitude and short duration generated by a pair of electro-mechanical relays, or an electronic "flip-flop" or trigger device, operated preferably by impulses from a standard-frequency source so that the length of the impulse is accurately controlled. Ramp-functions are simply obtained by applying a step of voltage to an integrator, the output of which is the ramp function.

9.2. SINE-WAVE GENERATORS AND OSCILLATORS

Sinusoidal voltages can be generated by steady rotation of a sine potentiometer. Function generators of the biased-diode or photo-electric types can also be used over a range $0 \leq V_1 \leq 2\pi/k$ if they are fed with a saw-tooth input voltage. Thus, suppose such a generator gives an output equal to $V_O = K \sin kV_1$. Then if V_1 rises steadily from zero to a value $2\pi/k$, returns suddenly to zero and then begins to rise again, repeating the cycle indefinitely, then V_O will vary sinusoidally. Alternatively, V_1 can increase steadily from 0 to $2\pi/k$, and then decrease at the same rate to zero. If a biased-diode arrangement is used some economy can be achieved by providing only the zero to π range, and reversing the sign of the output voltage for alternate half-cycles. Using a symmetrical input wave, with equal rates of rise and fall it would even be possible to use only a zero to $\pi/2$ range if sign reversing were arranged to give the negative half-cycles. The Servomex Low-Frequency Waveform Generator is typical of this type, and combines a considerable number of combinations of square-wave, saw-tooth and aperiodic waveforms as well, and probably is the most versatile instrument available for computer excitation.

Many successful sine generators have been made using continuously rotated synchros.† If the rotor of a synchro is fed with current at 50 c/s, say, and turned at a constant rate of 1·0 revolution per second, the current induced in a stator coil will be effectively a 50 c/s carrier with a sinusoidal modulation at 1·0 c/s, and a 1·0 c/s sine-wave can be produced by a simple demodulator. Other speeds of rotation give other modulation frequencies, but above a few cycles per second adequate filtering of the 50 c/s carrier becomes difficult, and it may be desirable to use 400 c/s or a still higher frequency for the carrier. An advantage of the synchro method is that a synchro with a pair of stator coils can be used giving two output waves, both of frequency equal to the rotor speed, but in phase quadrature at all frequencies. Nowadays, the most common method of generating slow sine-waves is to use a pair of high-gain Miller integrators, connected as in Fig. 2.6, but with the $\dot{y}$ feedback omitted, so as to give theoretically zero damping. If a step or impulse voltage is applied at x an oscillatory voltage is generated, and with good components the rate of change of amplitude can be made slow enough to give a good approximation to a sine-wave over useful periods. Lange, Lonergan, and Herring used this basic arrangement originally in a successful generator of continuous waves. Their oscillator possessed very light damping. The peak amplitude was compared with a reference voltage, and once per cycle a pulse of height proportional to the difference was injected into the oscillatory circuit. This not only gave a wave of substantially constant amplitude, but when the generator was switched on the pulse was large, so that the amplitude built up rapidly.

One of the most successful low-frequency oscillator circuits is due to Paul and McFadden [98], which forms part of the Short Bros. and Harland Control System Analyzer. The variation with time of the peak-to-peak amplitude of this type of oscillator

† "Synchro" is a universal term applied to any of the various synchronous devices used for data transmission, etc. Trade names for such devices include Magslip, Selsyn, Autosyn.

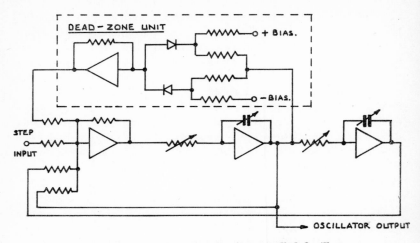

FIG. 9.1. Low-frequency Amplitude-controlled Oscillator.

depends on the quality of the d.c. amplifiers and the network components, which cannot be perfect in practice. Because of this, small phase shifts occur around the feedback loop, which if leading give rise to positive damping, causing the oscillation to decay, and if lagging produce a divergent oscillation. To overcome this a non-linear damping control loop is included in the form of a dead-zone circuit as shown in Fig. 9.1. The feedback gain is adjusted to cause the amplitude to tend to increase by providing just sufficient negative damping. The dead-zone circuit is set to just less than the initiating step voltage, and outside these limits provides a very large positive damping signal. The total harmonic distortion is less than 0·5 per cent, the control of amplitude is better than 1 per cent, and the d.c. content is within 50 microvolts. The designed frequency range is from 0·01 c/s to 110 c/s.

Some further developments are the promising single-amplifier oscillators obtained by using the design techniques of Section 8.5.

It should be apparent from the above discussion that the operational amplifier is the basic component of modern sine-wave generators. It is not surprising, therefore, that the analogue computer should itself be used to form its own test oscillator [99] and in addition, may be used for the measurement of phase at low frequencies by means of the circuit shown in Fig. 9.2.

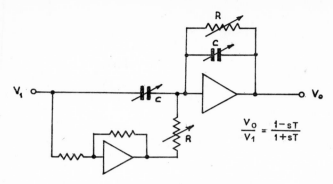

$$\frac{V_0}{V_1} = \frac{1-sT}{1+sT}$$

Fig. 9.2. Phase-shift Network.

Electronic low-frequency oscillators of the ladder-network or Wien-bridge type are not widely used now, although the single-amplifier types mentioned above are, of course, closely related.

9.3. RANDOM VOLTAGES

For the production of random voltages the main methods available are, amplification and filtering of electrical noise generated in a resistor, valve, or gas-filled tube; rapid switching of a bank of preset potentiometers; regeneration from a recording on magnetic tape for example; and a recently-developed digital system.

The first of these methods involves no new principle. To ensure a random variation without flicker it is usually necessary to start in the audio band or higher, and use a frequency changer to produce noise in the "servo" band. Since the servo band is narrow, in terms of cycles per second of bandwidth, high amplification is needed.

The waves produced by this method cannot, of course, be repeated so that to observe the effect of any change in the simulator a large number of runs before and after the change may be needed to give averaged results for which the scatter is small enough for the effect of the change to be detected. Several instruments of the type described are available commercially.

In the switched-potentiometer method the basic arrangement consists of a rotary switch with a large number of contacts, each connected to the slider of a potentiometer fed with a steady voltage. As the switch rotates the voltage on its moving contact jumps from one value to another, depending on the setting of the potentiometers, so that a given wave can be approximated by a stepped wave, the closeness of the approximation depending on the switching rate. Since the output wave is repeatable it cannot truly be called random, but it may be regarded as a section of a longer random wave, and the repeatability is useful, especially in the early stages of an investigation. Different waves can be produced by different sets of settings for the potentiometers.

The voltage waves to be used with these switched devices can be derived from experimental records of noise or other disturbances, or alternatively they may be made up from random number series, with a choice and weighting to give a desired spectrum and amplitude distribution.

Recording devices using magnetic tape, photographic film, or punched paper tape or celluloid film are now well known. With some of these devices, especially those using magnetic tape, the recording of "servo" frequencies cannot be done directly, so that some form of modulation must be used, and this increases the difficulty of achieving accurate reproduction of recorded amplitudes. The input waves to the recorders may be obtained from actual equipment in operation or from a noise generator of any of the types described above. A newer and potentially important noise generator [100] in an advanced stage of development employs a digital shift register which possesses the ability to generate an uncorrelated sequence of binary signals, whose bandwidth is directly proportional to the clock-pulse rate of the system, enabling a random noise of controlled amplitude and bandwidth to be generated, with an accurately delayed identical signal if required for correlation studies.

When using the above programmed techniques with a "repetitive" simulator (Section 10.2), however, the repetition rate of the simulator must not coincide with the noise "replay" rate. It is essential that there should be zero correlation.

9.4. PRESENTATION OF OUTPUTS

For the observation and recording of the simulator output voltages standard equipment can generally be used. Meters may be used if the rates of change are slow, and oscilloscopes of the cathode-ray or reflecting galvanometer (Duddell) type [101, 102]

FIG. 9.3 a. X-Y Plotting Table (Electronic Associates Ltd.).

Fig. 9.3b. X-Y Plotting Table (Bryans).

for faster variations. With modern ultraviolet sensitive recording paper the multi-channel galvanometer-type recorder is a very adaptable instrument. Permanent records may be made by photographing oscilloscope traces or by means of pen recorders, either the usual moving-coil type, or the position-servo type, which in one form (Evershed and Vignoles) has a frequency response extending to well over 20 c/s for amplitudes of 4 inches peak-to-peak.

For the simultaneous recording of two related variables, such as the coordinates of an aeroplane in "eastings" and "northings", a plotting table is commonly used. This is a device in which a pen is carried over a sheet of paper by a carriage which runs on a gantry which in turn runs on a pair of rails fixed to opposite sides of the table. Motion of the pen in two directions at right angles, along the gantry and along the rails, is provided by motors driven from amplifiers. Feedback potentiometers are fitted to the gantry and to the rails so that the coordinates of the pen position are accurately proportional to the input voltages to the amplifiers. Some modern plotting tables are illustrated in Figs. 9.3 a, b.

For measuring the harmonic response of simulated systems, the so-called "transfer function analysers" or "T.F.A.s" can be employed. These instruments are basically sine-wave generators with accurately controlled amplitude and frequency to excite the simulator, and special networks which measure and display the amplitude and phase relationship of the simulator output signal [103].

Typical methods of phase measurement are based upon the following procedure. The harmonic response of any linear system can be expressed as

$$\frac{V_O(j\omega)}{V_i(j\omega)} = R(\omega) + jQ(\omega)$$

where $V_i(j\omega)$ is the input sine wave, $V_O(j,\omega)$ is the output sine wave, and $R(\omega)$ and $j\,Q(\omega)$ are the real and imaginary parts of the system transfer function. Multiplying the output waveform $A\sin(\omega t + \varphi)$, by $\sin\omega t$ and $\cos\omega t$ obtained as reference signals from the oscillator (see Section 9.2), results in two signals $\frac{1}{2}A[\cos\varphi - \cos(2\omega t + \varphi)]$, and $\frac{1}{2}A[\sin\varphi - \sin(2\omega t + \varphi)]$ respectively. Appropriate means of averaging either continuously or by finite integration, depending on the signal frequency, removes the harmonic term and provides a meter presentation of the in-phase and quadrature components of the output signal.

Less specialized methods such as geometrical comparison of two simultaneous input and output signal recordings, and also the Lissajou Figure technique [99], are still effective.

Recently analogue-to-digital conversion equipments have been developed which are similar in principle to the now well-known digital voltmeter. The true digital voltmeter converts stationary analogue voltages into numerical displays representing the magnitude of the voltages in decimal form. Such displays are typically in the form of illuminated numbers or as typewritten print-outs.

Conversion equipment operating on continuously varying signals cannot, except for very slowly changing values, provide a useful numerical display, but has been highly developed for data handling purposes, and also for hybrid computing equipment (Section 10.5).

9.5. ADJUSTMENT OF ELEMENTS

For the testing of individual computing elements the methods and equipment depend on the desired accuracy. Summing amplifiers and integrators are usually the most important items. For summing it may be sufficient, if the gain is high enough, to measure the values of the input and feedback resistors, but this method may

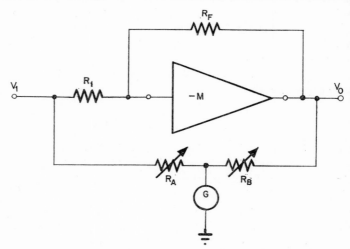

Fig. 9.4. Measurement of Amplifier Gain.

be inconvenient because it requires disconnection of the resistors. An obvious method is to make use of ordinary voltmeters to measure the output voltage produced by a known input voltage. For the highest accuracy, however, ordinary voltmeter methods are not good enough, even though sub-standard meters may be used, and bridge techniques must be used either based on high-grade resistance boxes or on the use of digital voltmeters. A simple and accurate method of measuring and adjusting amplifier gain is illustrated in Fig. 9.4. An input voltage V_1 is applied, and a pair of adjustable resistance boxes R_A, R_B, are connected in series between the input and output, the junction of the two resistances being connected to earth via a galvanometer. R_B is set to some suitable value, which is not critical, but should not be so low as to load the amplifier too heavily, and not so high as to give undue leakage errors. R_A is then adjusted for zero current through the galvanometer, and it is easily shown that $V_O/V_1 = -R_B/R_A$. For adjusting V_O/V_1 to a desired value the ratio R_B/R_A is made equal to this value, and then either R_1 or R_F is altered until the galvanometer current is zero. The alteration of R_1 of R_F may not be easy, and it is useful to remember that an ordinary carbon resistor may be added to increase the total resistance by a few tenths of one per cent without seriously degrading the stability of the whole resistance. Thus, suppose a 1000 ohm carbon resistor is added to a half-megohm wire resistor, giving an increase of 0·2 per cent. If the carbon resistor value changes by as much as 10 per cent the combination changes by 1000 ohms, or 0·2 per cent. In principle the same effect could be obtained by using parallel carbon resistors, but the values required would be inconveniently large.

A more convenient method of adjusting the gain of an amplifier is shown in Fig. 9.5. The high-stability resistors R_F and R_1 have values such that the ratio R_F/R_1 is slightly greater than the desired value of overall gain, and the gain is reduced to the correct value by adjusting the "coefficient" potentiometer P. The amount of adjustment will generally not be more than a few per cent, so the fineness of control can be improved by adding a fixed resistor R_P in series with the potentiometer as shown. This arrangement allows rapid setting of the gain if the method of Fig. 9.4 is used to measure the gain. Care must be taken to ensure that the reduced input impedance of the circuit of Fig. 9.5 does not put too great a load on the preceding element.

The method of Fig. 9.4 can be used with different values of "d.c." input voltage, both positive and negative, so that the departure from linearity, measured by the variations of V_O/V_1, can be checked.

For checking integrators the usual methods are based on the simple principle of applying a known input voltage for a known time and measuring the output voltage at the end of the measured interval. For the most accurate results the input voltage is either derived from standard cells, or is measured by means of an accurate potentiometer using a standard cell as a reference. A very

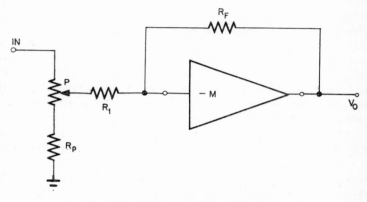

Fig. 9.5. Adjustment of Amplifier Gain.

useful arrangement for such purposes is a high-stability "summing" amplifier with a single input voltage from a battery of standard cells. This gives a source of accurately-known e.m.f. which can be made stable to within a millivolt or less, and which is not damaged when appreciable current is drawn. The measurement of the integration interval is best done automatically by impulses from a standard clock, or from a tuning fork or quartz crystal followed by frequency dividers. Precautions must be taken to ensure that the integrating capacitor is free from charge at the beginning of the test. At the end of the integration interval, when the input voltage is removed, the capacitor will retain its charge for a time, and the voltage to which it has been charged may be measured by connecting a hig-resistance voltmeter across the output terminals. The current drawn by the meter will, of course, hasten the discharge of the capacitor, but because of the very low output impedance of the high-gain amplifier the rate of decay of the voltage will usually be slow enough to allow a measurement to be made. If a meter is not sufficiently accurate, a null method may be used, with the circuit arrangement shown in Fig. 9.6. The potentiometer P is fed from a

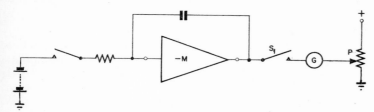

FIG. 9.6. Measurement of Integrator Voltage.

stable source, and is adjusted so that when the switch S_1 is closed after the end of the integration interval no galvanometer kick is caused. Several trials will be needed before the correct setting of P is found, and the galvanometer should be shunted for the first few attempts. The voltage given by P at the null position is found by reference to a standard cell; or alternatively, the voltage V_P and the input voltage can be compared, using two resistors and a galvanometer, as in Fig. 9.4, since it is the ratio of these voltages which is required rather than their absolute values.

Most computing elements other than integrators give an output voltage which is some desired function of an input voltage independent of time, and these can be tested and adjusted by the methods described for amplifiers, i.e. by measuring input and output voltages by means of voltmeters or potentiometers, or by the method fo Fig. 9.4. The remaining elements involve rotation of a shaft or some other mechanical motion for which methods of checking and adjusting are well known.

9.6. AUTOMATIC COEFFICIENT POTENTIOMETER SETTING

A method of setting up coefficient potentiometers automatically is adopted in some commercial machines [104, 105] and is intended to fulfil two important functions. The primary function is to facilitate the adjustment of amplifier gains using a bridge technique whereby the voltage ratio from the input terminal of the input resistance to the output of the amplifier is compared against a single standard potential divider. The basic network arrangement is shown in Fig. 9.7, where it is apparent that this technique avoids the potentiometer loading error problem by adjusting the voltage on the slider while the coefficient potentiometer is connected to its associated amplifier. The second function is to enable coefficient setting to be carried out quickly, often from one central position. Usually this operation is by means of a push-button call station, whereby the individual potentiometer is "dialled" according to its prearranged code number or "address". Subsequently, a further number is dialled which represents the voltage ratio setting required for the coefficient represented by the particular potentiometer. This voltage ratio is obtained by applying the standard reference voltage to the selected coefficient potentiometer and comparing the voltage at the amplifier output with the voltage automatically switched up on the standard reference potentiometer.

In such systems a position servo-mechanism similar to the multiplier of Section 7.3 is used to turn the potentiometer to its required setting. It would, of course, be very wasteful in equipment to have an individual servo for each coefficient potentiometer in a computer, and most machines employ a single servo to operate a batch of potentiometers through clutches which operate only when "addressed", and disengage when the potentiometer setting is completed. For large computers, several coefficient programming units of this type may be installed.

In addition to the manually operated system described above, a punched-tape reader may be provided, which can interpret a preprogrammed list of coefficient addresses and prescribed settings.

The accuracy of the method depends on the stability of the reference voltage and the master potentiometer during the setting-up time for the complete machine, the accuracy of the servo-mechanism, the amount of disturbance, if any, of the releasing clutch, and the noise level of the d.c. amplifier being set up, including its drift-stability.

9.7. PATCHING EQUIPMENT

The connections between the elements of an analogue computer can be made in various ways and the design of the interconnection system is of extreme importance. It can materially affect the

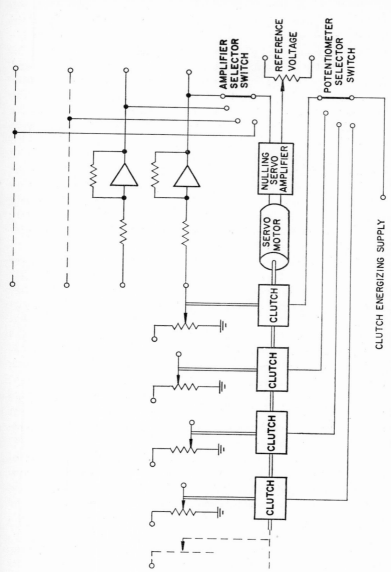

FIG. 9.7. Automatic Coefficient Potentiometer Setting System.

specification for the d.c. amplifier and greatly influence the ultimate accuracy of the computer because of the introduction, to a greater or lesser extent, of wiring capacitance and undesirable leakage currents. At the same time simplicity in patching system design greatly reduces the time to set up, lessens fatigue, and thereby helps to reduce the possibility of human error. There have been many approaches to the design of patching systems. All the past attempts can be divided into two main types; free-routed, or centralized. In the free-routed type each amplifier, which may have several input and output terminals, and may also be provided with its own input and feedback networks, may be connected by patch-cords in any way to any other amplifier, but usually to the next one in the amplifier rack. Such an arrangement places the minimum constraint on amplifier performance, and the system is easily learned. However, such a system often leads to a very-nearly unmanageable tangle of wires, and the resulting set-up cannot readily be removed, stored, or replaced. The time occupied check-ing the interconnections can be excessive. Because of poorer amplifiers the earliest machines were mostly engineered this way, and for quite different reasons, i.e. because they are inherently small, transistor computers are still constructed like this (Fig. 5.14).

Centralized systems are not new and are now almost standard [106]. In these systems it is fairly usual to connect the amplifier grid and output terminals permanently to a central array of sockets. Such an array of sockets is usually referred to as a patch-panel, or patch-board. Also arranged in the same bank of sockets are rows of common sockets (busbars or trunks), and other adjacent sockets are connected to coefficient potentiometers and reference voltage sources.

Each computer designer has his own ideas on the number of summing amplifiers, integrators, coefficient potentiometers, non-linear function units, etc., that will be required by the user, so that the format of these patch-panels varies considerably between one computer and another. In some machines, particularly in Short's General Purpose machine and in their latest SIMLAC computer, great ingenuity has been used to allow the patching to be done solely with rigid interconnecting plugs. Some manufacturers have arranged that the completely programmed patch-panel can be removed as in the example shown in Fig. 9.8. This enables the

FIG. 9.8. Removable Patch-board (Electronic Associates Ltd.).

computer to be changed very quickly to a new problem, simply by removing one patch-panel and substituting another panel already prepared. After removal from the computer, a prepared panel can de stored and then replaced later whenever further work is to be bone on the relevant problem. This is an attractive facility in circumstances where, for example, a single computer is shared by several research groups, even though the cost of additional patch-panels may be appreciable.

9.8. AUTOMATIC PATCHING EQUIPMENT

It has been shown that the technique of automatically programming the coefficient potentiometers is not too difficult. It has long been thought desirable to organize the computer set-up by completely automatic means, from a punched-tape. For a moderate-sized 60 amplifier-machine the "telephone exchange" required to interconnect this number of amplifiers, each with say, five inputs, and a choice of three types of input and feedback impedances, with about 100 coefficient potentiometers, reaches formidable proportions. Although it is not impossible to construct, the simple approach indicates that an excessive cost is involved.

Attempts have been made to rationalize the problem but with little real success in reducing the cost appreciably, or in meeting the reliability problem. Furthermore, there may be undesirable effects from the extra reactive load inevitably attached to the amplifier input and output.

In the final count, it depends on what the customer is prepared to pay, remembering that, in principle, there is little difference between wiring up a modern removable patch-panel and punching out a numerical tape.

9.9. POWER SUPPLIES

In Chapter 5 it was indicated that d.c. amplifiers for use in analogue computers should be designed to be insensitive to variations of supply voltages, but in spite of this it is usually necessary, in all but the smallest and crudest computers, to use "stabilized" or "regulated" high-tension supplies if the equipment is to be operated from the public supply mains or an equivalent source. Any change in the voltage of such a source will cause some change in the h.t. voltage and hence some unwanted changes in the output voltages of the computing amplifiers. These changes of output voltage can be reduced by careful amplifier design, but it is generally economical to pay some attention to the stabilization of the h.t. supply rather than to rely entirely on making the amplifier insensitive.

Another advantage of stabilized h.t. supplies is that the level of ripple due to incomplete smoothing of the power-supply frequency and its harmonics is very small. Contamination of the output voltage of a computing element by ripple voltages of small amplitude is not, in itself, objectionable in some cases, but the system may contain elements such as phase-advancers or differentiators which give appreciable gain at ripple frequencies and there is then a danger that the amplified ripple may cause unsuspected overloads. In computers working with fast time scales (Section 10.2) the variations of output voltage of the computing elements may involve frequencies similar to the ripple frequencies and it is then necessary to keep the ripple level low so that the genuine variations can be properly observed.

A third and very important benefit which a stabilized h.t. supply source offers is a very low internal impedance. When an input voltage is applied to a computing element there is a re-distribution of currents within the element and, in general, there is a change in the total current drawn from the h.t. supply. This causes a change of h.t. voltage and this in turn may mean that the variation of output voltage due to the applied input is not precisely the same as if the h.t. voltage remained absolutely constant. This effect is not usually serious, because it is not difficult to check the overall performance of a computing element connected to its proper h.t. supply source. Suppose, however, that a second computing element is supplied from the same h.t. source. Then an input voltage applied to the first element may cause a variation in the output voltage of the second element; there may, in fact, be an unwanted coupling between the two elements via the internal impedance of the h.t. source, and there will be corresponding couplings between all the elements supplied from the same h.t. source. If there are appreciable gains in any of the elements, and if the h.t. source impedance is not very low the coupling may be sufficient to produce instability, but more usually the effect of the unwanted couplings is to upset the intended quantitative relations between the voltages in the various computing elements so that the computer gives incorrect answers. In principle the presence of coupling effects of the kind can be checked by earthing the input terminal of an element and observing its output voltage while an input voltage is applied to another element supplied from the same h.t. source. This is impracticable as a regular procedure, however, and it is therefore essential that the h.t. source impedance should be low enough to prevent appreciable coupling under all likely conditions. The actual value of tolerable impedance depends on the sensitivity of the computing elements to changes of h.t. voltage, on the type of problem being solved, the accuracy required, and also on the levels of computing voltages at various points in the computer, since a given spurious voltage at the output of a given element will be more serious when the legitimate output voltage is low. The internal impedance of the h.t. supply must be maintained at a low value for at least the whole range of frequencies occupied by the variables in the problem being solved, and preferably over the whole working frequency range of the computing elements.

It is fairly common practice in medium and large analogue computers to use more than one h.t. supply unit. This is done partly for convenience, in using a number of units of existing types rather than a single unit of special design, and it helps to avoid long runs of power-supply wiring. In addition, it greatly reduces unwanted couplings due to common h.t. source impedances. In some machines, there is a common source of "raw" h.t. power, rectified and partially smoothed, which feeds a large number of separate stabilizing or regulating units, each of which feeds a small number of computing elements.

Most elements used in analogue computers need at least two h.t. supplies, at different voltages, and some designs need as many as four. The foregoing remarks on constancy of voltage, ripple content, and internal impedance, apply to all the h.t. supplies, although it cannot be assumed that characteristics which are acceptable for supply at one voltage are adequate or necessary for supplies at other voltages.

The h.t. stabilizer or regulator is normally of the thermionic type [107] in which all the h.t. current flows between anode and cathode of a regulator valve. The output voltage is compared with that of some stable source, such as a gas-discharge tube or battery or zener diode, and the difference is amplified and applied to the

17*

grid of the regulator valve in such sense as to compensate for changes of output voltage.

Unwanted couplings between computing elements can occur not only in the "supply" side of the h.t. circuits but also in the earth-return leads. There is always a small voltage drop due to the return h.t. current flowing along an "earth" conductor back to the h.t. source. If this current changes when an input voltage is applied to the element the voltage drop will change slightly and this slight change may be added to the input and output voltages of other elements which use the same earth-return conductors. To reduce this type of coupling a heavy conductor is used, and some machines use copper bars of up to 0·5 square inch in cross-section. In addition it is sometimes desirable to use more than one earth-return connection, and in some machines there are two distinct sets of "earth" conductors; the return h.t. currents are carried by one set of conductors, while the other set is used exclusively for the "earthy" input and output terminals of computing elements. The conductors of both sets are connected together at a single point. This arrangement is sound in principle, though in practice it is not always easy to distinguish precisely between h.t. return currents and currents associated with computing voltages, since all the computing currents are provided by the h.t. source. Some care is necessary in planning these multiple earth systems to ensure that the desired decoupling will be achieved.

Some attention must also be given to heater supplies for thermionic computing elements. A given variation in the voltage of the public supply mains will give an immediate change of h.t. voltage and hence an immediate change of output voltage from a computing element, though the magnitude of the output change may be negligibly small. The same change in mains voltage will also produce a change of heater voltage, and this may well give a change of output voltage which is not negligibly small. The effect, however, will not be immediate because of the smoothing action of the thermal lags in the valve heaters and cathodes, and for this reason there is a tendency to overlook the effects of heater voltage variation. In most computers, some degree of compensation is desirable, and it is common practice to achieve this by using a constant-voltage transformer. This transformer may be of the saturated-core type, or of one of the types in which the effective ratio is varied automatically, either by means of sliding tap-changing gear or by moving a short-circuited turn along a limb of the core so as to change the field distribution. This transformer may also be used to supply alternating current to the h.t. rectifiers, giving an additional measure of compensation against mains-voltage variations.

CHAPTER 10

OTHER RELATED TYPES OF ANALOGUE COMPUTERS

THE simulators which have been described in the earlier chapters mostly belong to a large and important class which have the following features in common:

1. They are "unity-time-scale" machines; i.e. if a particular event in the real dynamic system occupies a time interval T, then the analogous event in the simulator likewise occupies an interval T. Time constants and frequencies of oscillation have the same numerical values in the simulator as in the real system.

2. They are "d.c." "voltage" machines, which means that the analogous quantity in the simulator which corresponds to a variable in the real dynamic system is a voltage whose instantaneous value is proportional to the instantaneous value of the variable.

10.1. TIME SCALES

There are other important classes of simulator which do not share these features. One of the most important includes machines which have time scales different from the time scales of the system being studied, so that an event which occupies an interval T in the real system occupies in the simulator an interval $k\,T$, where k is a time-scale factor which may have a value greater or less than unity. Suppose, for example, that in Fig. 2.6 or Fig. 2.7 the values of the integrator capacitances are all doubled. For a given charging current the rate of voltage rise on a capacitor is now only half the former value, and as there are no other time-conscious elements events proceed as before, but at half the rate. An event which previously occupied an interval T now occupies $2T$. If the capacitances were all halved instead of being doubled events would proceed twice as fast, and similarly for other changes of capacitance. There is a wide range of time scales in which the computation can be carried out, and depending on the circumstances there are advantages to be gained from computation rates either slower or faster than the one-to-one rate, and there are also some disadvantages in discarding the unity time scale.

The use of "slow" time scales, with a time-scale factor k greater than unity, is obviously valuable when the dynamic system includes rates of change so high that significant alteration in the value of some variable takes place in a time interval comparable with the lags in the simulator. Thus, suppose the dynamic system being studied includes a resonance at 50 c/s, and the simulator includes some computing element having a simple time lag with a time constant of 0·01 second. Such a lag would lead to errors if a real time scale were used, but if the computer were slowed down by using a time-scale factor of 10 the analogous resonance in the simulator would now occur at 5 c/s, and the 0·01 second time lag would be much less important. A larger factor than 10 would reduce the error still further.

As an extreme example of slow time scales it is possible to solve certain problems in geometrical optics by means of an analogue computer. For this purpose a particle may be imagined to move with a speed of, say, a few centimetres per second, its path being a straight line so long as the refractive index of the medium in which it moves is a constant, but changing direction in accordance with the usual laws at a reflecting or refracting surface. Such a dynamic system corresponds to an optical system, with the path of the particle representing a ray of light, and an analogue machine could be used to compute, one after another, the paths taken by different rays, so that the behaviour of the optical system could be examined. By the use of function generators curved surfaces, both spherical and aspherical, could be introduced, and with some additional complication some problems involving a medium with a continuously-varying refractive index, such as arise in electron optics, might be solved. Such a simulation would involve a time-scale factor of the order of 10^9, and would carry with it some implication of a corpuscular theory of light. For this purpose the corpuscular theory is quite acceptable for the optical case, and more obviously so for the electron optics.

10.2. FAST TIME SCALES; REPETITIVE
SIMULATORS

Compared with slow time scales the use of fast time scales, with values of k less than unity has found wider application. An obvious field is in the simulation of systems which have inconveniently slow time scales, notably chemical plants, where events occupy minutes or hours rather than seconds. Another important application of fast time scales is to "repetitive" simulators [108], in which the time scale is chosen so that the whole solution of a problem is completed in a period of, say, one fifth of a second or less. Such a simulator may be used to examine the response of a system to a step function, but instead of a single step the input voltage is a square-wave, which corresponds to alternate positive and negative steps repeated indefinitely. The display of the response of the system to the negative steps is usually suppressed in some way, and the output voltage stimulated by the positive steps is fed to the Y plates of an oscilloscope which has a linear time base, operating at the same frequency as the square-wave, connected to the X plates. Thus, provided the frequency of the wave and the afterglow of the oscilloscope screen are such as to prevent excessive flicker, there appears on the screen a stationary trace representing the step-function response of the system. A repetitive simulator has the advantage that the effects of changes in the parameters of the system are immediately obvious, and a large number of different combinations of parameters can be examined quickly [109]. It has also the advantage that since the voltages in the simulator comprise only the fundamental and harmonics of the square-wave frequency with some sidebands there is no need to use direct-coupled amplifiers, and capacitance-coupled amplifiers may be used, provided they are designed to give negligible phase shifts at the relevant frequencies. This means that troubles due to drift and grid current are reduced, and there is also the possibility of operating from a smaller number of h.t. supply voltages than in the case of d.c. amplifiers.

At the beginning of each positive step there should be no residues of voltages from the response to the previous step, and to ensure this it is desirable to short-circuit the integrator capacitors by relay contacts which close during the negative step. This operation is unnecessary if it is certain that the natural decay of voltages leaves only a negligible residue, but the possibility of an appreciable voltage remaining at some intermediate point, even though the output itself is near zero, must not be overlooked. If the initial conditions for the problem are not all zero the initial-condition voltages are switched synchronously with the input square-wave.

Whether the amplifiers be direct- or capacitance-coupled they have to operate at higher frequencies than the amplifiers for a unity-time-scale simulator, and this leads to stability difficulties if a very high loop gain is used with heavy feedback. Consequently, the amplifiers in a repetitive simulator sometimes have lower gains, and a value of around 2000 is not unusual, compared with 50,000, say, for unity-time-scale amplifiers. This limits the accuracy, of course, but since the output trace is normally observed on a cathode-ray oscilloscope of normal design, which is not a very accurate amplitude indicator, this limitation is often unimportant. The individual computing element errors are often as poor as about 1·0 per cent.

A disadvantage of the repetitive simulator is that it is restricted to the examination of the response of a system to brief stimuli. The usual stimulus is a step, which ideally occupies zero time, but other functions are possible, e.g. a triangular pulse, or a square-topped pulse, or a function which increases linearly from zero to some finite value and then remains constant at that value. It is essential, however, that the function involves changes of voltage only for some period which is less than half the square-wave period and preferably much less if the consequent response is to be observed. The repetitive simulator is not very useful for problems which involve continuous input functions, such as the road vehicle problem of Section 4.3 or any problem in which the input contains continuous noise.

All analogue computers are essentially repetitive machines in so far as a solution to a given problem may be repeated as often as is desired, but if the repetition rate is greater than, say, 12 per second the solution may be displayed on a CRO using a suitable time-base, and it appears as a steady response curve which can be traced or photographed. This in itself has no great merit, particularly when other considerable difficulties arise in order to achieve high-speed repetition, so such a technique requires stronger justification. It is, of course, justified immediately it becomes worthwhile to study a system undergoing parametric variations for, in such cases, the solutions displayed are each slightly different and belong to a family containing multi-dimensional information; and often such information is difficult to absorb unless it becomes "animated" or unfolds before the eye, so to speak. MacKay and Fisher [109] consider that computer repetition frequencies should range between 12,000 and 25,000 solutions per second, and at 25,000 solutions per second the display of 32 times 32 complete permutations of two parameters is permitted at 25 times a second, giving a steady CRO display.

In principle, speed and accuracy are interchangeable, but it has been shown McKay and Fisher that the information content of a group of solutions increases more rapidly by increasing the repetition frequency than by increasing the computational accuracy, which is the significant justification of ultra-high speed developments. Undoubtedly a great deal more development is possible with such machines, but the primary limitation lies not so much in the accuracy of high-speed multipliers and function generators as in the ever-present problem with all computers, the efficacy of the display means. Isometric, stereoscopic, and pseudo-3-dimensional displays are not even enough to transmit to the human mind all the possible information output at the rate at which it can be presented by the computer. However, it should be remembered that usually only a small proportion of information is ever really required, or is indeed significant, the larger volume of solutions being of no permanent consequence. Therefore the display essentially becomes a device with which to make a narrow choice.

It is important to observe that the trace on the screen represents the response to a single occurrence of the stimulating function; the repetition is merely a convenient way of making the response easily and continously visible. If the usual input square-wave is replaced by a sine-wave, $\sin \omega t$, of the same frequency, the output will not represent the frequency response of the system at frequency $\omega/2\pi$, or any simply-related frequency; it will most likely be the response to a function which is identical with $\sin(\omega t/k)$ over the interval 0 to π, but which is zero for all other time, k being the time-scale factor which is less than unity for a fast-time-scale simulator.

The normal frequency response of the real system with continuous sinusoidal inputs can be measured by using the analogous network included in the simulator but omitting the square wave, synchronous switching, etc. The response of the simulator to a wave $\sin(\omega t/k)$ will give the response of the real system to $\sin \omega t$.

10.3. ITERATIVE OPERATION

One important variation of the repetitive mode is iterative operation where, in principle, two or more virtually separate repetitive machines are operated sequentially. Often this is arranged in such a way that the final solution values of one computer section become the initial conditions for a subsequent section, and so on, so that one section is holding its solution values while another section computes. Usually, as soon as the second section commences computation, the former section relaxes from "hold" to a condition ready to accept the next computational step from solution values derived from a second or subsequent section of the computer.

Inherent in the design of such machines is the use of an accurate comparator-trigger circuit in order to accomplish the switching from one computing section to another at predetermined increments of some chosen parameter.

Step-by-step solutions of a large range of non-linear and partial differential equations may be solved in this way, thus greatly extending the scope of conventional analogue computing methods.

10.4. INCLUSION OF COMPONENTS OF THE REAL SYSTEM

A disadvantage of all simulators which have time-scale factors different from unity is that parts of the real system cannot be inserted into the simulator loops. Consider, for example, a simulator for the study of a dynamic system which includes as a part of the system a feedback amplifier supplying a geared motor which drives a potentiometer, the potentiometer pick-off voltage being passed on to the next element. This combination needs an input voltage to operate it and gives another voltage as output, the output being equal to the input, say, in the steady state but lagging when the input varies. In the early stages of an investigation it would be sufficient to represent the whole combination by a simple R.C. lag (Fig. 5.7), but at a later stage it might be necessary to introduce imperfections such as amplifier overload, motor and gearing friction and backlash, motor hysteresis, etc. Simulation of these effects is possible, but a simpler alternative is to connect the actual amplifier and motor combination into the simulator in place of the original R.C. circuit. This is, of course, not always practicable, but when it is it not only puts the imperfections into the simulator but also subjects the combination to realistic input variations.

The use of time-conscious parts of the real system as element of the simulator is only possible, or at least only has any useful meaning, if the time scales of the real and simulated systems are identical.

10.5. A.C. SIMULATORS

There is another class of analogue computing machines which use voltages as the analogue quantities, but which use "a.c." rather than "d.c." [110]. In such machines a carrier wave is used, and the instantaneous amplitude of a variable in the real system is proportional to the instantaneous amplitude of the envelope of the carrier. Thus, a variable in the real system represented by $f(t)$ would appear in the simulator as $f(t) \cdot k \sin(2\pi f_c t)$, where k is a scale factor and f_c is the carrier frequency. The various modulated carriers can be added, subtracted, and multiplied by constants, in capacitance-coupled amplifiers, so that drift and grid-current troubles are unimportant and errors can be kept small. For integration, differentiation, smoothing, and any operation which involves time derivatives or integrals of the envelope of the carrier it is not possible to use the methods which are satisfactory for d.c. machines because these methods operate on the instantaneous value of the input voltage and so give the derivative, etc., of the carrier and not of its envelope. In communication engineering there is a technique of low-pass to band-pass transformation [15] by which the characteristics and circuit arrangement of a band-pass device, say a band-pass filter, can be deduced from the corresponding low-pass device. The use of an alternating carrier instead of "d.c." in an analogue computing machine is effectively a low-pass to band-pass transformation, and using the methods of communication engineering it is possible to derive circuits corresponding to the integrator and other d.c. computing elements. These a.c. circuits will contain, for example, parallel-tuned combinations of inductance and capacitance in place of single capacitors in the d.c. circuits, and although this gives arrangements which will, in theory, provide the required operations on the carrier it is found in practice that it is difficult to keep the anti-resonant frequency of the tuned combinations exactly equal to the carrier frequency and also to realize sufficiently low losses in the components. Some practical work has been done on these lines and also with resistance–capacitance networks equivalent to tuned circuits [111, 112], but the more usual procedure is to demodulate the alternating voltage, perform the desired operation on the demodulated d.c. signal, and remodulate. This procedure introduces d.c. errors during the operation on the demodulated signal and detracts from the benefits of using a carrier wave. Furthermore, in order to preserve the signs of the analogue quantities the demodulators must be of the phase-sensitive type, and the presence of any quadrature component in the demodulating carrier gives an additional error. The attractions of this type of simulator have diminished since the development of satisfactory drift-stabilized d.c. amplifiers.

There is another quite distinct class of analogue computers, using alternating voltages with "synchros", of the types used for data transmission, as the computing elements [113]. Such computers are attractive for some applications, since they enable addition, subtraction, and especially resolution, to be performed conveniently and accurately. However, they suffer from the same disadvantage as other a.c. systems when operations involving integration or differentiation are required, and for automatic operation some of the synchros must be driven by servo-motors, which may introduce undesirable lags.

10.6. DIGITAL DIFFERENTIAL ANALYSERS AND HYBRID MACHINES

The significant features of digital computation of high accuracy, and freedom to integrate with respect to any variable, appear attractive. All digital computers integrate in an approximate manner in a series of incremental steps and the approximation can be made as good as required by reducing the size of the increment. However, the smaller the increment, the greater is the number of computational steps required to cover the same range of integral, and so, for the same pulse-clock rate, the integration time increases with accuracy. Thus, for a digital computer having a central arithmetic unit a problem containing several integrations may take a considerable time to solve as each of the integration operations has to be time-shared on just the one arithmetic unit. A computer arranged to solve a differential equation this way is termed a serial digital differential analyser, or serial DDA. However, in recent years special-purpose digital computers comprising several digital integrators have been constructed, in which each integrator can be interconnected with straightforward adding and arithmetic multipliers with the same flexibility as an analogue computer. These machines are called parallel DDA's [114, 115].

Each integrator uses well-established digital techniques. A typical integration procedure is illustrated in Fig. 10.1 where the relationship $z = \Delta y_1 . \Delta x$ is computed. There are many possible

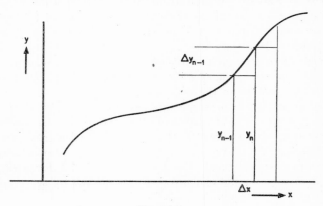

FIG. 10.1.

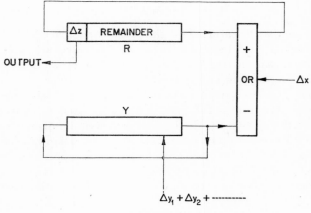

FIG. 10.2.

ways of constructing a digital integrator and one form [116] is shown in block diagram form in Fig. 10.2. R and Y are shift registers where binary numbers are fed in at one end and out at the other in the same sequence as they originally entered. If $\varDelta x$ is always less than the least significant digit it is only necessary to accumulate values of y to obtain z by adding or subtracting y according to the size of $\varDelta x$. From Fig. 10.1

$$y_n = y_{n-1} + \varDelta y_{n-1}$$

indicating that y is computed by adding or subtracting $\varDelta y_{n-1}$ from y_{n-1} according to its sign. Whenever a new $\varDelta x$ is received the up-to-date value of y is entered into R which is one digit longer than the Y register, and changes in the R register are equivalent to the increments or decrements $\varDelta z$, which form the output signal available for connection to a further integrator.

More complicated forms of integrator are necessary in practice in order to overcome many minor problems such as rounding-off errors and zero drift, and there has been considerable development in the construction and use of these machines [116]. One feature in particular is worth mentioning, and that is the relationship between accuracy and speed which is given by Herring and Lamb [116] as

$$f = \frac{p}{2N \cdot 2\pi r q} \; \text{c/s}$$

where p is the clock pulse rate

N is the number of digits in a word

r is the number of digit periods occupied by one iteration

and q is the number of integrators processed in sequence

According to this paper, with a clock pulse rate of 10 Mc/s and an accuracy of approximately $\pm 0\cdot01$ per cent (14 bits), the bandwidth will be at best only 5 c/s. Such a bandwidth is marginal for many real time simulations, especially considering the moderate accuracy achieved. Nevertheless, with development this figure is improving. Despite this only moderate success, the advantages of unrestricted integration make possible, for example, the use of the expression

$$uv = \int u \cdot \mathrm{d}v + \int v \cdot \mathrm{d}u$$

to form an effective multiplier. Also a great many functions can be
generated [117] and of course partial differential equations can be
solved, opening up a whole new range of problems capable of
solution.

In between the pure analogue and pure digital differential
analysers there are a great variety of so-called hybrid systems which
exploit many different modulation techniques. One of the more
promising developments of hybrid computers is that due to
R. J. A. Paul [118] at the College of Aeronautics, Cranfield, which
is based on the use of "Delta-Modulation" [119, 120]. Delta-
modulation is a particular form of pulse-modulation and the basic
computer application uses a modulator shown in Fig. 10.3a which
multiplies a variable y by $\delta x/\delta t$ in the following way. One input
is the variable y, which may be considered to be a normal continuous analogue voltage (Fig. 10.3b). The important feature of this
method is the formation of $\delta x/\delta t$ which is carried out by means of
a constant amplitude, constant repetition frequency pulse generator. The polarity of these pulses is controlled by sampling the other
input, which is the continuous analogue voltage x to form a
staircase waveform, Fig. 10.3c, so that whenever a rising increment
occurs the network generates a positive pulse, and whenever a
falling increment occurs, a negative pulse. This train of pulses
digitally representing $\delta x/\delta t$, Fig. 10.3d, is fed into the modulator,
and the combination waveform, Fig. 10.3e, forms the product term
$y \cdot \delta x/\delta t$. Now if this latter signal is applied to a pure analogue
integrator the result is

$$\int y \cdot \frac{\delta x}{\delta t} \cdot \mathrm{d}t$$

which is an approximation to the desired integration of y with
respect to a variable x, i.e. approximately $\int y \cdot \mathrm{d}x$ which is the
fundamental operation of the DDA. However, the inputs and out-
puts are pure analogue and thus the interconnection flexibility of
the pure analogue computer is preserved. If a digital integrator is
used instead then the signalling can remain in pulse form, enabling
temporary or permanent digital storage systems to be used. The
delta-modulation hybrid computer typically operates at a pulse
repetition frequency of up to 1 Mc/s providing a useful bandwidth, and as in the pure DDA accuracy improves at the expense of
useful frequency range.

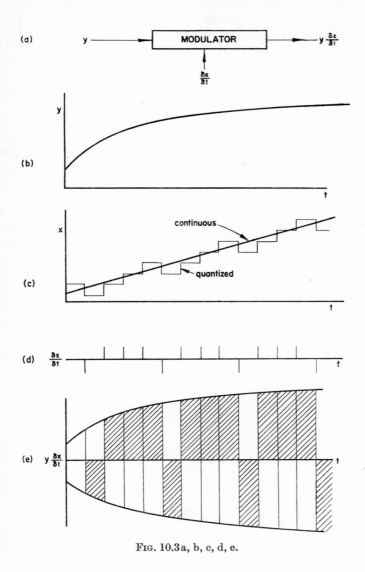

FIG. 10.3a, b, c, d, e.

Using delta-modulation it is possible to generate a wide variety of single-variable functions by various combinations of integrators and multipliers [121] including a transport-lag system with a delay of between 10^{-2} and 10 seconds. The latter facility will enable the development of a correlator to generate auto- and cross-correlation functions [121] which are of great importance in the study of complex signals in control systems, and in the simulation of such systems.

The development of this type of hybrid computer using modulation techniques is really an extension of multipliers of the variable mark-space type (Section 7.1), which if they had provided adequate accuracy, would have solved the problem years ago. However, electronic techniques and components are steadily improving, and so will hybrid computer design.

It should be noted that digital-to-analogue and analogue-to-digital conversion equipment is now available in proliferation enabling pure analogue components to be coupled with pure digital systems so that hybrid systems can be constructed *ad hoc*. Such systems can provide satisfactory facilities in special circumstances, but generally prove to be very expensive and rather inflexible.

CHAPTER 11

ANALOGUE COMPUTERS AT WORK

A VERY large number of analogue computers are manufactured commercially, with practically every major industrial country having its own suppliers. Excellent machines are obtainable, some comprising as little as five operational amplifiers and ranging up to installations containing a hundred or more. It is therefore impossible in the space available to provide a useful description of these commercial equipments, but there are several sources [10, 11, 27] where such information can be obtained. What is perhaps more important is an appreciation of the major role played by analogue computers in modern technology. This becomes most apparent when considering the computing facilities operated by the research departments of industry, public authorities, and ministries in the U.K. alone. For smaller organizations without the capital resources to invest in their own computer facilities, an analogue computer centre has been established in the U.K. by a leading manufacturer, as a service to industry at large.

Another financially important group is formed by the airline companies who install elaborate flight simulators for training crews for each type of aircraft in current operation. Similar machines for training operators in other industries have also been developed.

Finally, because of the existence of analogue computers, it is necessary to instruct engineering students in their use, after which the computer, in the hands of an able teacher, can become a powerful educational aid in the study of the behaviour of the solution of differential equations and of dynamic systems.

11.1. COMPUTERS FOR RESEARCH

The value of analogue computation is well understood by the major research establishments of both government and industry, and there are many examples of considerable-sized installations some of which are reviewed as an illustration of the scale of computer application in the U.K. For a long time the major users of analogue computers were the guided missile industries for which such machines were originally developed. It is not surprising, therefore, to find large machines in each of the major missile firms and at the Royal Aircraft Establishment, Farnborough. As reported in the first edition of this work, the largest such installation was TRIDAC which is still actively engaged on missile and space problems, although its design may now be thought to be somewhat out of date. There are, of course, many smaller computers being used at R.A.E. for solving the continual day-to-day control problems in the space and weapon programmes under consideration. Similarly, each missile company has fairly extensive computational facilities often of their own design and manufacture [122–124]. These same computers also provide similar simulation studies of modern aircraft flight control systems, which, particularly in the military field, are becoming more and more missile-like in character, and pre-flight simulation is essential. Perhaps the most interesting single problem arises in connection with the vertical take-off (V.T.O.) aircraft, which provides an almost classic example of a case where simulation study is essential to ensure the machine's safety before any real flights are undertaken. The total investment in analogue computers in aeronautics is a difficult figure to determine precisely, but it certainly runs into several million pounds by now.

However, the defence industry is not by any means the only user nowadays, and extensive machines are operated by public authorities and the larger industrial organizations [125–128].

11.2. THE COMPUTING CENTRE – A FACILITY FOR INDUSTRY

Large computers are expensive and beyond the reach of many smaller firms and engineering consulting organizations. However, it is often the case that even a small team can have a big problem. To fulfil an obvious need the Computing Centre has arisen where quite large computing facilites in well-designed laboratories can be made available to any customer on a rental basis. The computers are operated by high-grade personnel, backed by a team of systems engineers who can, if required, take the problem at any stage and carry out considerable design work in a consultative capacity. In general, however, their task is to throw the customer's problem into a form suitable for computation on their own machines, and to work in close collaboration with him in order to extract the essential solution data, and to modify the simulation as the design work proceeds. Normally, the customer, or his representative, "sits-in" during the actual runs. This avoids the "post-box" method, which is generally not satisfactory in getting the optimum value from the simulator study.

The flexibility of this arrangement is very great and the machines are well maintained and chosen to suit the magnitude of the customer's problem. Furthermore, the computer team's experience grows from day to day because of the wide range of problems that they meet, so that they are often able to offer very valuable advice to their customers.

Such a centre in the U.K. is operated at Burgess Hill, Surrey, by Electronic Associates Ltd., and at the time of writing it offers four complete computers ranging in size from 160 down to 10 operational amplifiers, with extensive auxiliary equipment. These facilities, which are available to some degree from most of the larger manufacturers, also offer the prospective purchaser a real opportunity to run a trial simulation which can be typical of his future requirements, and to assess the true ability of the computer before a decision to purchase is made.

11.3. TRAINING SIMULATORS

Increasingly, the human control of expensive plant and machinery is becoming more exacting and yet more widespread. More and more complex equipment is becoming controlled by fewer and fewer personnel, and therefore the individual controller's responsibility is becoming greater and greater. The most striking example is the modern passenger aircraft, where in addition to the responsibility of not damaging a vehicle worth over a million pounds, the safety of perhaps a hundred passengers rests in the skill of one man. Not surprisingly, therefore, the airlines require the pilot and his crew to be thoroughly competent at their respective tasks, under all conceivable circumstances. Such circumstances may include almost anything up to the failure of a major aircraft component, but not the least important requirement is that the relatively dull and monotonous routine control and navigational tasks must be thoroughly well performed. Thus, before the pilot and his crew members are allowed to fly the real aircraft, even with no passengers, they are given considerable training under simulated conditions.

The modern flight simulator has come a long way since the early LINK trainers. It now comprises a very realistic mock-up of the flight-deck of the aircraft, complete in every detail, and often a portion of the passenger compartment to increase the environmental realism. Great attention is paid to the simulation of mechanical "feel" of the controls, and to the instrument displays. Fairly recently elaborate projection television systems have been devised to present the pilot with an appropriate scenic display outside the cockpit windscreen, in black and white or in colour.

Connected to the controls and the flight instruments is an extensive simulator comprising a hundred or more operational amplifiers, electro-mechanical multipliers, resolvers, and non-linear function generators, capable of closely simulating the behaviour of the aircraft under all flight conditions, including the kinematics of the flight trajectory. In addition there are circuits to simulate all the fault indicators, and the effects of such faults on the aircraft's behaviour. This section is connected to an instructor's console to enable whatever combination of faults and incidents is required to be applied at the time. Appropriate sounds are also made by ingenious noise generators closely matched to the flight condition. The flight-deck is usually although not always static as it has been found impractical, and luckily not altogether necessary, to provide complete simulation of the acceleration on the pilots body. Figure 11.1, however, shows an advanced "motional" cockpit. Continued practice by an aircrew in such a machine enables routine flights to be dealt with almost automatically, and gives a much greater probability that under stress conditions proper decisions and actions will be carried out.

These machines are extremely expensive, but as with all computers it is the inherent value of the computation they solve that is the measure of their true worth, and in this case there is substantial evidence that the cost is justified.

In the nuclear energy field, simulators have also been devised but have not yet found the same widespread application. In many other fields such as chemical process control the use of simulators will certainly become more general as systems become more difficult to manage.

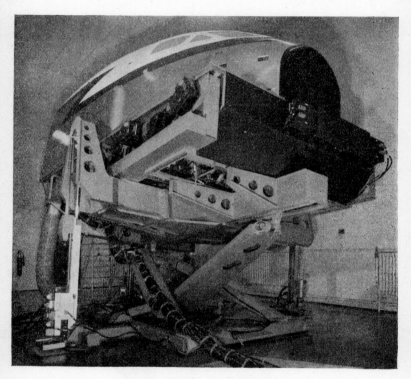

FIG. 11.1. "Motional Cockpit" (General Precision Systems Ltd.).

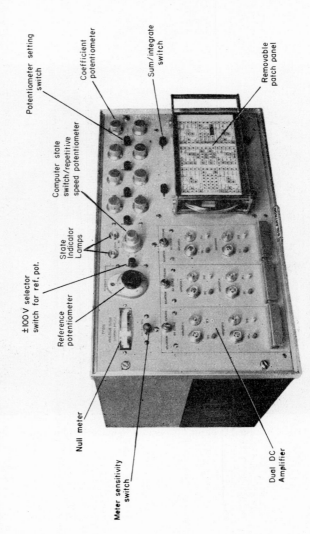

Potentiometer setting switch

Coefficient potentiometer

Sum/integrate switch

Computer state switch/repetitive speed potentiometer

Removable patch panel

State Indicator Lamps

±100 V selector switch for ref. pot.

Reference potentiometer

Null meter

Meter sensitivity switch

Dual DC Amplifier

Fig. 11.2. Desk Computer (Feedback Ltd.).

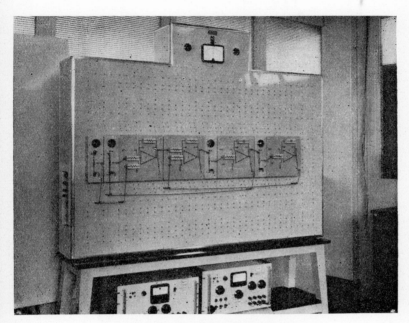

Fig. 11.3. Educational Analogue Computer
(Short Bros. and Harland Ltd.).

11.4. ANALOGUE COMPUTERS IN TECHNOLOGICAL EDUCATION

Because of the widespread use of analogue techniques it has now become necessary to include at least an elementary coverage of the topic in the syllabus of the majority of engineering science courses leading to first degrees or to graduate membership of the engineering institutions. For students who require more specialized knowledge in order to enter such fields as aeronautical engineering and control engineering, post-graduate courses are available at several colleges. To fulfil the special educational requirements, equipment has been developed which is both relatively inexpensive and simple to operate. Such computers are not generally as refined or as accurate as the research machines, but are nevertheless perfectly adequate to verify the theoretical concepts.

There are many 5- or 10- amplifiers machines, available from the leading manufacturers, which are capable of handling quite complex problems within the grasp of the undergraduate. A typical machine is illustrated in Fig. 11.2. One of the most effective eductional analogue computers is that developed by Professor J. C. West of Belfast University and Short Bros. & Harland Ltd., and illustrated in Fig. 11.3. This machine is made in the form of the computing block diagram, with each amplifier in a box with the conventional large triangle on it, and each resistor, and capacitor likewise housed in a large box displaying the circuit symbol. Each element is designed to plug into a large, black-board sized panel in one of many positions, enabling the simulation circuit to be built up by the lecturer in front of his class of students. At the appropriate moment the system can be switched on and the solution displayed on a recorder or demonstration oscilloscope. The students can later operate the machine themselves. There is no need to learn how to use a complicated "chess-board" patch-panel as the layout of the machine is self-evident.

Once a student has appreciated how an analogue computer operates it is found that the awareness of the behaviour of dynamic systems improves, and much of "mystery" of differential equations is eliminated. Furthermore, appreciation of the powerful methods of analogy and duality is enhanced, making the student capable of absorbing the broad, interdisciplinary studies which are becoming increasingly necessary, particularly in fields such as control engineering, cybernetics, and ergonomics.

"ANALYSER" SOLUTION FOR THE COUPLED MASS-SPRING-FRICTION PROBLEM

It was mentioned in Chapter 2 that an "analyser" solution was possible for the coupled system of Fig. 2.11, and two somewhat different methods of setting up an analyser for this purpose will now be described. The equation to be solved is

$$as^4y + bs^3y + cs^2y + dsy + ey = fs^2x + gsx + hx \quad (2.9)$$

where
$$a = m_1 m_2$$
$$b = m_1 m_2 (\mu_1 + \mu_2)$$
$$c = m_1 k_2 + m_2 k_1 + m_2 k_2 + m_1 m_2 \mu_1 \mu_2$$
$$d = m_1 \mu_1 k_2 + m_2 \mu_2 k_1 + m_2 \mu_2 k_2$$
$$e = k_1 k_2$$
$$f = k_1 m_2$$
$$g = k_1 m_2 \mu_2$$
$$h = k_1 k_2$$

Of the two methods available the more obvious, though probably the poorer, removes the derivatives of x by integrating the whole equation twice with respect to time. Assuming that the integration constants are zero this gives:

$$as^2y + bsy + cy + \frac{d}{s}y + \frac{e}{s^2}y = fx + \frac{g}{s}x + \frac{h}{s^2}x \quad (AI.1)$$

To set up the block diagram, assume as before that a voltage is available representing the highest derivative of y, i.e. s^2y. Then the lower derivatives, from sy to y/s^2, are obtained by means of four integrators. The remaining input voltages for the summing amplifier are the three functions of x, and these may be obtained by feeding the x voltage through two integrators. The block diagram (without coefficient multipliers) is shown in Fig. AI.1. This is a

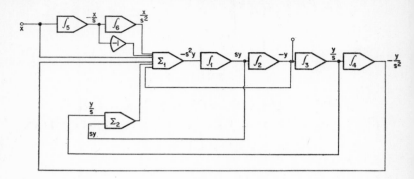

Fig. A I.1.

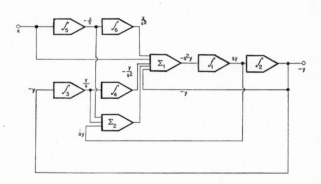

Fig. A I.2.

possible arrangement, and might be employed if the differential
analyser in use had six or more integrators and there was nothing
to be gained by economizing in computer elements. It is, however,
possible to rearrange the block diagram so that the equation (A I.1)
can be solved with only four integrators. The first step in the rearrangement is merely a redrawing of Fig. A I.1, the object being
to show two integrators, numbers 3 and 4, to the left of the summing amplifiers. The new arrangement is shown in Fig. A I.2, in
which one other small change is shown; the x/s voltage is fed into
the second summing amplifier instead of the first so that the reversing amplifier is not needed.

Consider now the two integrators 6 and 4 in Fig. A I.2. Integrator 6 integrates x/s to give x/s^2 and feeds the output to the summing amplifier 1. The same effect can be achieved by omitting integrator 6 and adding a voltage corresponding to x/s to the input voltage to integrator 4. There is now no input of x/s^2 from the output of integrator 6, but an equal voltage appears as part of the output of integrator 4. The use of an integrator to integrate the sum of two voltages has already been described, and it is, of course, necessary

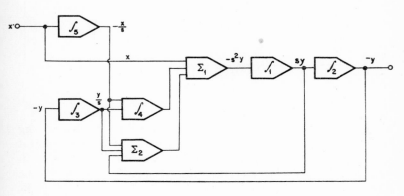

Fig. AI.3.

to select a value of the input resistor for the x/s voltage appropriate to the coefficient of x/s. The new arrangement, using only five integrators, is shown in Fig. A I.3.

Integrator 5 is also unnecessary if an appropriate signal is fed to the input of integrator 3, but the situation is complicated by the "feed-forward" from the output of integrator 3 via summing amplifier 2, and by the need to adjust input resistors to allow for the different coefficients of the x and y terms. Instead of attempting to follow the same procedure as for integrator 6 it is simpler to assume that the arrangement of Fig. A I.4 represents a satisfactory block diagram. Voltages corresponding to x/s are passed to summing amplifier 1 from the output of integrator 4 and also via summing amplifier 2 from integrator 3, and the levels of the x voltages fed into the integrators must therefore be adjusted to ensure that the total x/s voltage has the correct value. To determine the required

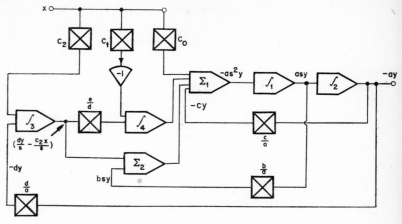

FIG. AI.4.

adjustment quantitatively assume first that the x voltages being fed into summing amplifier 1 and integrators 4 and 3 are multiplied by factors c_0, c_1 and c_2 respectively. The values of these factors, in terms of the coefficients of the original equation (AI.1) can be determined by writing down the sum of the voltages fed into summing amplifier 1 and equating to $s^2 y$. Before this can be done, however, a consistent set of coefficients must be given to the various functions of y, and this has been done in Fig. AI.4. The necessary changes of scale are indicated by multiplying factors c/a, etc.

Before writing the complete equation it is helpful to write down the total output voltages from integrators 3 and 4. These are, for integrator 3:

$$-\frac{1}{s}(c_2 x - dy) = \frac{dy}{s} - \frac{c_2 x}{s}$$

and for integrator 4:

$$-\frac{1}{s}\left\{-c_1 x - \frac{e}{d}\cdot\frac{1}{s}(c_2 x - dy)\right\} = c_1\frac{x}{s} + \frac{e}{d}c_2\frac{x}{s^2} - e\frac{y}{s^2}$$

The full equation is therefore:

$$a s^2 y = c_0 x + c_1\frac{x}{s} + \frac{e}{d}c_2\frac{x}{s^2} - e\frac{y}{s^2} - d\frac{y}{s} + c_2\frac{x}{s} - bsy - cy$$

or,

$$as^2y + bsy + cy + d\frac{y}{s} + e\frac{y}{s^2} = c_0x + (c_1 + c_2)\frac{x}{s} + \frac{ec_2}{d}\frac{x}{s^2}$$

Comparing with equation (AI.1) gives:

$$f = c_0 \qquad g = c_1 + c_2 \qquad h = e\,c_2/d$$

whence

$$\left.\begin{array}{l} c_2 = h\,d/e \\ c_1 = g - h\,d/e \\ c_0 = f \end{array}\right\} \qquad \text{(AI.2)}$$

Thus, Fig. AI.4 represents a practical and economical arrangement for solving equation (2.9).

The arrangement of Fig. AI.4 gives a solution for y only. If a solution is required also for z, this can be obtained by an arrangement like that shown in Fig. 2.7, since by eliminating y from equations (2.7) and (2.8) the relation between z and x is found to be:

$$as^4z + bs^3z + cs^2z + dsz + ez = hx \qquad \text{(AI.3)}$$

which is of the same form as equation (2.5).

It has been assumed so far that y and z and all their derivatives were zero at $t = 0$. If this is not the case the initial conditions can be inserted by one of the methods of Section 8.2.

A difficulty with this arrangement is that the voltages representing y/s and y/s^2 will readily overload the amplifiers unless both

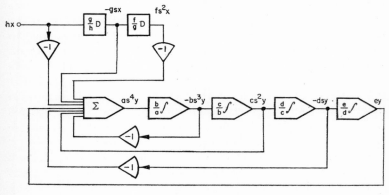

Fig. AI.5.

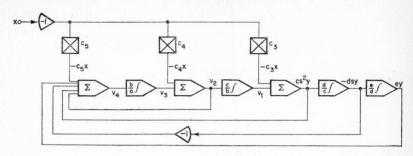

y and y/s have small mean values over the period occupied by the solution.

The difficulty due to the presence of y/s and y/s^2 is removed by using the second method, extended from Section 2.3. A block diagram for the solution of equation (2.9) is first drawn on the assumption that differentiators are available. This can easily be done by the methods given earlier, assuming that a voltage proportional to s^4y is available at the output of a summing amplifier, and the diagram is shown in Fig. AI.5, where for compactness the coefficient multipliers are now included in the integrator, differentiator and amplifier boxes. In this diagram the differential x voltage, $-gsx$, is integrated, together with other voltages, by the b/a integrator; and the voltage fs^2x, which is the result of two differentiations, is integrated by the b/a and c/b integrators, together with other voltages, and with the further complication due the $-bs^3y$ feedback between the two integrators. However, the discussion given earlier suggests that it would be reasonable to examine the arrangement shown in Fig. AI.6, where the differentiators have been removed, and voltages have been added to the input voltages of the second and third integrators to represent c_4x and c_3x, where c_4 and c_3 are constants whose values are to be determined later. The extra summing amplifiers needed for this purpose have introduced sign changes which make one of the reversing amplifiers unnecessary.

If this arrangement is to give the desired solution it must produce a voltage proportional to y, so it is assumed that the output of the fourth integrator represents ey. It follows that the preceding integrators give output voltages proportional to $-sy$ and to s^2y, and it is convenient to label these outputs $-dsy$ and cs^2y. Since the values of c_3, c_4 and c_5 are not yet known, the voltages at points earlier than the output of the c/b integrator cannot be determined by inspection, and they are therefore labelled $v_1, \ldots, v_4$, as shown.

The following relations can be written down immediately:

$$-cs^2y = v_1 - c_3x$$

$$sv_1 = -\frac{c}{b}v_2$$

$$-v_2 = -c_4x + v_3$$

$$sv_3 = -\frac{b}{a}v_4$$

$$-v_4 = -c_ax + ey + dsy + cs^2y + v_2,$$

and elimination of $v_1, \ldots, v_4$ gives:

$$as^4y + bs^3y + cs^2y + dsy + ey =$$
$$= \frac{a}{c}c_3s^2x + \left(\frac{a}{b}c_4 + \frac{b}{c}c_3\right)sx + c_5x$$

This is identical with equation (2.9) if

$$c_3 = \frac{c}{a}f$$

$$c_4 = \left(\frac{b}{a}g - \frac{b^2}{a^2}f\right)$$

$$c_5 = h$$

so that with suitable adjustments of the values of the resistors which fix the values of these three coefficients this arrangement will give the required solution. In practice the reversing amplifier in Fig. AI.6 could be removed and the $-dsy$ feedback could be fed directly into the b/a integrator.

GENERALIZED TAPPED POTENTIO-
METER NETWORKS

THE FOUR BASIC CASES

Figure A II.1 shows the typical circuit of a multi-tapped potentio-meter of resistance R, having $m - 1$ tappings at distances n_1, $n_2, \ldots, n_m$, and with fixed valued resistors $R_1, R_2, \ldots, R_m$ connected

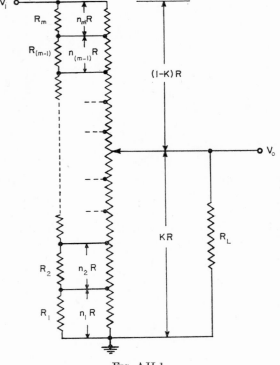

Fig. A II.1.

between them. The slider is at a distance K from the "earthy" end, where K can vary between zero and unity. The input voltage is V_1 and the output voltage is V_O. The output load resistance is R_L.

As K increases from zero to unity an equivalent network can be drawn each time the slider crosses a tapping point and traverses a particular section of the potentiometer. These equivalent networks fall into three fundamental cases as illustrated by Fig. AII.2 a, b, d. A fourth case, shown in Fig. AII.3, is applicable if a shunt resistor has been omitted and the slider traverses this un-shunted section.

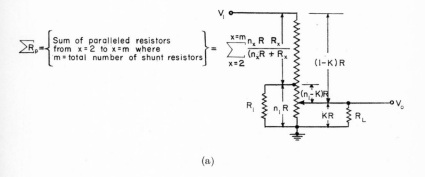

$$\sum R_p = \begin{Bmatrix} \text{Sum of paralleled resistors} \\ \text{from } x=2 \text{ to } x=m \text{ where} \\ m=\text{total number of shunt resistors} \end{Bmatrix} = \sum_{x=2}^{x=m} \frac{n_x R\ R_x}{(n_x R + R_x)}$$

(a)

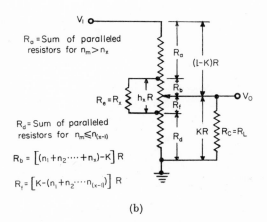

$R_a = $ Sum of paralleled resistors for $n_m > n_x$

$R_e = R_x$

$R_d = $ Sum of paralleled resistors for $n_m \leqslant n_{(x-1)}$

$R_b = \left[(n_1 + n_2 \cdots + n_x) - K\right] R$

$R_f = \left[K - (n_1 + n_2 \cdots n_{(x-1)})\right] R$

(b)

FIG. AII.2 a—b.

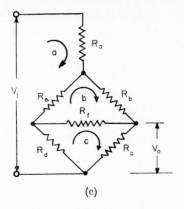

(c)

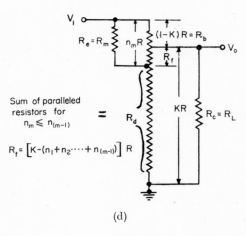

(d)

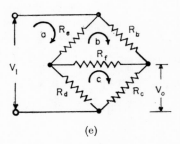

(e)

FIG. A II. 2 c−e.

Case 1 (where $0 \leq K \leq n_1$)

In this case, illustrated by Fig. A II.2, the portion of the potentio-meter between the input and the tapping point at n_1 consists of the sum of all the paralleled resistances and sections of the potentio-meter winding involved.

Case 2 (where $n_1 + n_2 + \ldots + n_{x-1} \leq K \leq n_1 + n_2 + \ldots + n_x$ and where $2 \leq x \leq m - 1$)

Figure A II.2 b shows the circuit for Case 2 where the slider is traversing any section, except for the section connected directly to earth or the section connected directly to the input end.

This circuit can be drawn in an alternative bridge network form as in Fig. A II.2 c where

R_a = Sum of the paralleled resistances for values of n_p where
$\quad m > p > x$

$R_b = [(-n_1 + n_2 + \ldots + n_x) - K] R$

$R_c = R_L$

R_d = Sum of the paralleled resistances for values of n_q where
$\quad 0 < q \leq (x - 1)$

$R_e = R_x$

$R_f = [K - (n_1 + n_2 + \ldots + n_{x-1})] R$

Case 3 (where $n_1 + n_2 + \ldots + n_{m-1} \leq K \leq 1$)

This circuit is given in Fig. A II.2 d and as in Case 2 the alterna-tive bridge network form of the circuit is shown in Fig. A II.2 e.

Case 4 (Slider traversing an un-shunted section)

If one or more fixed-valued shunt resistors are omitted between tappings, a fourth case emerges when the slider traverses such sections. Figure A II.3 a shows a typical example of this case, and Fig. A II.3 b the equivalent circuit.

THE GENERALIZED NETWORK

From further consideration of the circuits it appears that the network of Case 2 is in fact the generalized network, since it is possible to derive cases 1, 3 and 4 from it by making certain

19*

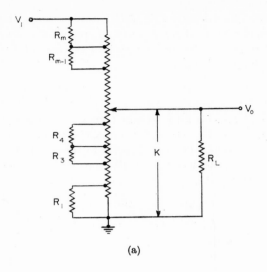

(a)

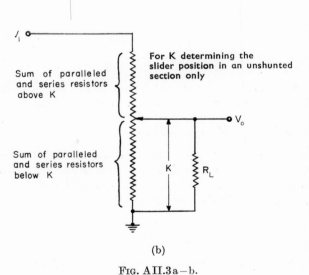

(b)

Fig. AII.3a—b.

resistances zero or infinite. Thus Case 1 may be obtained by considering $R_d = 0$. Case 3 is obtained by letting R_a vanish, and Case 4 by making $R_e \to \infty$.

This approach to the problem enables one general equation, representing the attenuation of the bridge network of Fig. AII.2c to be used for all cases. By compiling the appropriate set of substitutions for each section (which are unique for the section being traversed by the slider), the complete law of the multi-tapped potentiometer may be calculated.

ANALYSIS OF THE GENERALIZED NETWORK

The generalized network is shown in Fig. AII.2c. Let the circulating currents a, b, and c be positive in the sense denoted by the arrows.

By inspection of the figure

$$b(R_b + R_f + R_e) = aR_e + cR_f = bZ_1$$

$$c(R_c + R_d + R_f) = aR_d + bR_f = cZ_2$$

and

$$V_1 = a(R_a + R_e + R_d) - cR_d - bR_e$$

or

$$V_1 = aZ_3 - cR_d - bR_e \qquad (AII.1)$$

from which

$$a = \frac{c(Z_1Z_2 - R_f^2)}{(Z_1R_d + R_eR_f)}$$

$$b = \frac{c(Z_2R_e + R_dR_f)}{(Z_1R_d + R_eR_f)}$$

Putting these values for a and b in equation (AII.1) and rearranging it is found that

$$c = \frac{(Z_1R_d - R_eR_f)}{(Z_1Z_2Z_3 - Z_1R_d^2 - Z_2R_e^2 - Z_3R_f^2 - 2R_dR_eR_f)} V_1$$

and remembering that the output load is represented by R_c one can write

$$V_O/V_1 = cR_c/V_1$$

so that the general equation is

$$V_O/V_1 = \frac{R_c(Z_1 R_d + R_e R_f)}{(Z_1 Z_2 Z_3 - Z_1 R_d^2 - Z_2 R_e^2 - Z_3 R_f^2 - 2R_d R_e R_f)} \quad \text{(AII.2)}$$

where
$$\left.\begin{aligned} Z_1 &= (R_b + R_f + R_e) \\ Z_2 &= (R_c + R_d + R_f) \\ Z_3 &= (R_a + R_e + R_d) \end{aligned}\right\} \quad \text{(AII.3)}$$

ANALYSIS OF EACH OF THE FOUR CASES

Case 1 $(0 \leqq K \leqq n_1)$

As stated above, Case 1 is obtained by making R_d vanish in equation (AII.2) with the result that the equation then represents the network of Fig. AII.2a with the appropriate values substituted. Thus the characteristic is derived from

$$V_O/V_1 = \frac{R_c(Z_1 R_d + R_e R_f)}{(Z_1 Z_2 Z_3 - Z_1 R_d^2 - Z_2 R_e^2 - Z_3 R_f^2 - 2R_d R_e R_f)}$$

by putting
$$Z_1 = (R_b + R_f + R_e) = (n_1 - K)R + KR + R_1 = (n_1 R + R_1)$$
$$Z_2 = (R_c + R_d + R_f) = (R_L + KR)$$
$$Z_3 = (R_a + R_e + R_d) = (\textstyle\sum R_p + R_1)$$

$R_a = \sum R_p =$ Sum of paralleled resistances above tapping at n_1
    (i.e. for values of n_p where $m \geqq p > 1$)
$$R_b = (n_1 - K)R$$
$$R_c = R_L$$
$$R_d = 0$$
$$R_e = R_1$$
$$R_f = KR$$

Case 2 $(n_1 + n_2 + \cdots + n_{x-1} \leqq K \leqq n_1 + n_2 + \cdots + n_x)$ and
    where $(2 \leqq x \leqq m - 1)$

This case has been illustrated in Fig. AII.2b, but for the purposes of analysis it is preferable to consider Fig. AII.2c. The relationship already obtained is

$$V_O/V_1 = \frac{R_c(Z_1 R_d + R_e R_f)}{(Z_1 Z_2 Z_3 - Z_1 R_d^2 - Z_2 R_e^2 - Z_3 R_f^2 - 2R_d R_e R_f)}$$

with the following substitutions

$R_a = $ Sum of the paralleled resistances for values of n_p where $m \geq p > x$

$R_b = [(n_1 + n_2 + \cdots + n_x) - K] R$

$R_c = R_L$

$R_d = $ Sum of the paralleled resistances for values of n_q where $0 < q \leq (x - 1)$

$R_e = R_x$

$R_f = [K - (n_1 + n_2 + \cdots + n_{x-1})] R$

and Z_1, Z_2, Z_3 are as given in equations (A II.3)

Case 3 $(n_1 + n_2 + \cdots + n_{m-1} \leq K \leq 1)$

Case 3 is given in Fig. A II.2 d and the bridge form shown in Fig. A II.2 e. Again the network attenuation is obtained using the generalized equation (A II.2) but with the following substitutions in this case:

$R_a = 0$

$R_b = (1 - K) R$

$R_c = R_L$

$R_d = $ Sum of the paralleled resistances for values of n_q where $0 < q \leq (m - 1)$

$R_e = R_m$

$R_f = [K - (n_1 + n_2 + \cdots + n_{m-1})] R$

and again Z_1, Z_2 and Z_3 are as given in equations (A II.3)

Case 4 (when shunt resistors are omitted between tappings, and the slider is traversing an un-shunted section)

Figure A II.3 b illustrates this case, and it is evident that the same general equation holds good provided that $R_e \to \infty$. Thus

$$V_O/V_1 = \frac{R_c(Z_1 R_d + R_e R_f)}{(Z_1 Z_2 Z_3 - Z_1 R_d^2 - Z_2 R_e^2 - Z_3 R_f^2 - 2 R_d R_e R_f)}$$

and Z_1, Z_2 and Z_3 are as before
and $R \to \infty$
so that neglecting all terms except those containing R_e

$$V_O/V_1 = \frac{(R_d + R_f) R_c R_e}{(R_a + R_b)(R_c + R_d + R_f) R_e + (R_d + R_f) R_c R_e}$$

19 a*

or

$$V_O/V_1 = \frac{(R_d + R_f)\, R_c}{(R_a + R_b)\,(R_c + R_d + R_f) + (R_d + R_f)\, R_c}$$

where

$R_a =$ Sum of the paralleled and series resistances for values of n_p where $m \geq p > x$

$R_b = [(n_1 + n_2 + \cdots + n_x) - K]\, R$

$R_c = R_L$

$R_d =$ Sum of the paralleled and series resistances for values of n_q where $0 < q \leq (x - 1)$

$R_f = [K - (n_1 + n_2 + \cdots + n_{x-1})]\, R$

From the relationships derived above, all the arrangements of multi-tapped potentiometers of the type shown in Fig. A II.1 can be evaluated by choosing suitable values for R_a, R_b, R_c, R_d, R_e and R_f. In the more simple arrangements it is probably more convenient, analytically, to derive the characteristic from first principles. However, when direct numerical substitutions are made in the generalized equation calculation is quite simple.

REFERENCES

[1] QUARMBY, R. B., Electronic analogue computing. *Wireless World* **60**, No. 3, 113–118 (1954).

[2] GOMPERTS, R. J., Computing applications where analogue methods appear to be superior to digital. *J. Brit. I.R.E.* (1957).

[3] KARPLUS, W., *Analog Simulation.* McGraw-Hill 1958.

[4] TUSTIN, A. (Editor), *Automatic and Manual Control* (Papers contributed to the Cranfield Conference, 1951). Butterworths 1952.

[5] BURNS, D. O., A useful theorem in linear differential theory. *Trans. Soc. Instr. Technology* **4**, No. 4, 173–176 (1952).

[6] LANGE, A., and J. DUTE, *Electronic Simulation as an Aid to the Design of Vehicle Suspension Systems.* Willow Run Research Centre, University of Michigan; presented at a meeting of the Society of Automobile Engineers, March 1952.

[7] BAIRSTOW, L., *Applied Aerodynamics.* Longmans, Green.

[8] DUNCAN, *Control and Stability of Aircraft.* Cambridge University Press 1952.

[9] JEANS, J. H., *Electricity and Magnetism.* Cambridge University Press.

[10] CLULEY, J. C., D.C. amplifiers for computers. *Control* **3**, No. 27, 111–113 (1960).

[11] PAUL, R. J. A., Control Survey No. 22: Electronic computers. *Control* (1961).

[12] VALLEY, G. E., and H. WALLMAN, *Vacuum Tube Amplifiers.* M.I.T. Radiation Laboratory series, No. 18. McGraw-Hill 1948.

[13] NYQUIST, H., Regeneration theory, *Bell System Tech. J.* **11**, No. 1, 126–147 (1932).

[14] BLACK, H. S., Stabilized feedback amplifiers. *Electrical Engineering* (U.S.A.) **53**, 114 (1934). Also in *Bell System Tec. J.* **13**, No. 1, 1–18 (1934).

[15] BODE, H. W., *Network Analysis and Feedback Amplifier Design.* D. Van Nostrand Co. 1945.

[16] TERMAN, F. E. *Radio Engineers Handbook.* McGraw-Hill 1943.

[17] LANGFORD-SMITH F. (Editor), *Radio Designers Handbook.* Iliffe and Sons.

[18] WASS, C. A. A., *Introduction to Electronic Analogue Computers.* 1st ed. Pergamon Press 1955.

[19] MACNEE, A. B., Some limitations on the accuracy of electronic differential analysers. *Proc. I.R.E.* **40**, No. 3, 303–308 (1952).

[20] MILLER, K. S., and F. J. MURRAY, A mathematical basis for an error analysis of differential analysers. *J. Math. and Phys.* **XXXII**, Nos. 2–3, 136–163 (1953).

[21] WILLIAMS, A. J., R. E. TARPLEY and W. R. CLARK, D.C. amplifier stabilized for zero and gain. *Trans. Amer. I.E.E.* **67**, 47–57 (1948).

[22] WILLIAMS, A. J., W. G. AMERY and W. McADAM, Wide-band d.c. amplifier stabilized for gain and for zero. *Trans. Amer. I.E.E.* **68**, Pt. II, 811–815 (1949).

[23] PRINZ, D. G., D.C. amplifiers with automatic zero adjustment and input current compensation. *J. Sci. Inst.* **24**, No. 12, 328 (1947).

[24] GOLDBERG, E. A., The stabilization of wide-band direct current amplifiers for zero and gain. *R.C.A. Review* **11**, No. 2, 296–300 (1950).

[25] SUMMERLIN, F. A., The automatic compensation of zero-drift errors in direct-coupled feedback systems. *Proc. I.E.E.* **98**, Pt. II, 59 (1951).

[26] PAUL, R. J. A., and E. LLOYD-THOMAS, The design and applications of a general purpose analogue computer. *J. Brit. I.R.E.* **17**, 1 (1957).

[27] ERNST, D., *Elektronische Analogrechner.* Verlag R. Oldenbourg, Munich 1960.

[28] BENETEAU, P. J., L. BASER and R. Q. LANE, *Transistor Operational Amplifiers.* I.R.E. Convention Record, Pt. 9 (1962).

[29] GREGORY, R. O., *Design Considerations in a Chopper-stabilized Transistor Amplifier.* Presented at I.R.E. Maecon. Kansas City, Mo. November 15–16 (1960).

[30] FISHER, J. E., and H. B. GATLAND, *Electronics—From Theory into Practice.* Pergamon Press (1965).

[31] GRIFFIN, D. J., Some design techniques for low drift d.c. amplifiers using silicon transistors. *Texas Inst. Semiconductor Application Report* **1**, No. 5 (1960).
KEMHADJIAN, H., Transistor amplifiers for d.c. signals. *Mullard Tech. Pubs.* **4**, No. 36 (1958).

[32] GRABBE, E. M., S. RAMO and E. D. WOOLDRIDGE, *Handbook of Automation, Computation, and Control.* Vol. 3. Systems and Components. Chap. 27. Wiley 1961.

[33] OKADA, R. H., Stable transistor wideband d.c. amplifiers. *Trans. Amer. Inst. Elect. Engrs.*, p. 26 (1960).

[34] MILLER, J. M., Dependence of the input impedance of a three-electrode vacuum tube upon the load in the plate circuit. *U.S.A. Bureau of Standards Scientific Paper* 351.

[35] BLUMLEIN, A. D., Improvements in or relating to electric circuit arrangements for effecting integration and applications thereof. British Patent 580527 (Application date 1942).

[36] PUCKLE, O. S., *Time Bases.* Chapman & Hall 1951.

[37] CHENG, D. K., *Analysis of Linear Systems.* Addison-Wesley 1959.

[38] DE BACKER, W., Error analysis of a d.c. integrator. *Ann. Assoc. Internal. Calcul. Analogique* **2**, No. 1, 13–23 (1960).

[39] KLEY, A., Die Fehlerwirkung des Operationsverstärkers im Analogrechner. *Telefunken Ztg.* **116**, 136–41 (1957).

[40] PAUL, R. J. A., Some factors affecting the accuracy of electronic analogue computers. *Proc. 1st International Analogue Computation Meeting*, pp. 232–238 (1956).

[41] *Catalogue of the Thirty-Second Annual Exhibition of Scientific Instruments and Apparatus.* The Physical Society, p. 279 (1948).

[42] MORRILL, C. D., and R. V. BAUM, A stabilized electronic multiplier. *Trans. I.R.E.* Professional Group on Electronic Computers. PGEC 1, December 1952. See also *Electronics*, December 1952.

[43] JIEWERTZ, B., An electronic multiplier. *Proc. 2nd International Analogue Computation Meeting*, pp. 103–109 (1959).

[44] FERRARO, A. J., An economical multiplier for analog computers. *Electronics* (USA) **33**, No. 45, 73–4 (1960).

[45] MACNEE, A. B., An electronic differential analyser. *Proc. I.E.E.* **37**, No. 11, 1315–1324 (1949).

[46] GRUNDLACH, F. W., A new electron-beam multiplier with an electrostatic hyperbolic field. *Proc. 1st International Analogue Computation Meeting*, pp. 101–103 (1956).

[47] SCHMIDT, W., Die Hyperfeldrohre eine Elektronenstrahlrohre zum Multiplizieren in Analogie-Rechengeräten. *Zeit. Aagewandte Phys.* **8**, 2, 69–75 (1956).

[48] LOFGREN, L., *Analog Multiplier based on the Hall Effect*. Proc. of International Analogue Computation Meeting, pp. 111–115 (1955) and Ibid. *J. Appl. Phys.* **29**, 158–166 (1958).

[49] CHASMAR, R. P., and E. COHEN, An electrical multiplier utilizing the Hall effect in indium arsenide. *Electronic Engng.*, p. 661 (1958) and *Control* **3**, No. 21, 125–126 (1960).

[50] MYNALL, D. J., Electronic function generator. *Nature* **159**, No. 4048, 743 (1947).

[51] MACKAY, D. M., A high-speed electronic function generator. *Nature* **159**, No. 4038, 406 (1947).

[52] *Handbook of Scientific Instruments and Apparatus*, 1950. As shown at the 34th Physical Society Exhibition, p. 250.

[53] *Handbook of Scientific Instruments and Apparatus*, 1954. 34th Physical Society Exhibition.

[54] SHEN, D. W., Approximating non-linear functions. *Electronic Engng.* **29**, 434 (1957).

[55] GARNER, K. C., Linear multi-tapped potentiometers with loaded outputs. *Electronic Engng.* **31**, 192 (1959).

[56] GARNER, K. C., Multi-tapped potentiometers as accurate linear transducers. *Electronic Engng.* **33**, No. 395, 32–35 (1961).

[57] GARNER, K. C., Elimination of loading errors. *Control* **4**, No. 31, 107–108 (1961).

[58] DEELEY, E. M., and D. M. MACKAY, Multiplication and division by electronic analogue methods. *Nature* **163**, No. 4147, 650 (1949).

[59] SPRAGUE, C. A., U.S. Patent No. 1711658, May 1919.

[60] BURT, E. G. C., and O. H. LANGE, Function generators based on linear interpolation with application to analogue computing. *Proc. I.E.E.*, Pt. C, No. 3, 51–57 (1956).

[61] KOERNER, H., and G. A. KORN, Function generation with operational amplifiers. *Electronics* **32**, No. 45, 66–70 (1959).

[62] KORN, G. A., Control applications for a new deadspace limiter. *Control Engng.*, March 1962.

[63] BLACKBURN, J. F., G. REETHOF and J. L. SHEARER, *Fluid Power Control*, p. 624. Wiley 1960.

[64] TOOTILL, G. C., A proposed electromechánical generator of functions of two variables. *Proc. 2nd International Analogue Computation Meeting*, pp. 129–134 (1959).

[65] DE PACKH, D. C., A resistor network for the approximate solution of the Laplace equation. *Rev. Sci. Inst.* **18**, 798 (1947).

[66] LIEBMAN, G., Solution of partial differential equations with a resistance network analogue. *Brit. J. Applied Phys.* **1**, 92 (1950).

[67] GARNER, K. C., The potentiometer-net: the basis of a new form of computer. *Control* **6**, No. 97, 97–98 (1963).

[68] GARNER, K. C., AFAC—The automatic field analogue computer. *Process Control and Automation* **10**, No. 2, 51–54 (1963).

[69] GARNER, K. C., A resistance-net analogue using a ganged multitapped potentiometer. *Electronic Engng.* **34**, 728–732 (1962).

[70] BOOTHROYD, A. R., E. C. CHERRY and R. MAKAR, An electrolytic tank for the measurement of steady state response transient response and allied properties of networks. *Proc. I.E.E.* **96**, 163–177 (1949).

[71] MORGAN, M. L., Algebraic function calculations using potential analog pairs. *Proc. I.R.E.* **49**, 276–282 (1961).

[72] GARNER, K. C., Multi-tap pots find frequency response from root locus. *Control Engng.* (June 1963).

[73] MEISSINGER, H. F., An electronic circuit for the generation of functions of several variables. *I.R.E. Nat. Convention Record* P. 4, 150–161 (1955).

[74] SCHMITT, O. H., A thermionic trigger. *J. Sci. Inst.* **15**, 24 (1939).

[75] LANE, L. J., A method of scaling and checking computer circuits. *Trans. Amer. Inst. Elec. Engrs.* **77**, 67–70 (1958). *Applic. & Industr.*, No. 36 (1958).

[76] MURPHY, B., A recommended preparation programming and verification procedure of universal applicability to general purpose electronic analog computers. *Proc. 2nd International Analogue Computation Meeting*, pp. 200–204 (1959).

[77] GREENWOOD, I. A., J. V. HOLDAM and D. MACRAE, *Electronic Instruments*, M.I.T. Radiation Laboratory Series, No. 21. McGraw-Hill 1948.

[78] JAMES, H. J., N. B. NICHOLS and R. S. PHILLIPS, *Theory of Servomechanisms*. M.I.T. Radiation Laboratory Series No. 25. McGraw-Hill 1948.

[79] WEST, J. C., *Analytical Techniques for Non-Linear Control Systems*. English Universities Press.

[80] MACMILLAN, R. H., (Ed.) *Progress in Control Engineering*. Heywood 1962.

[81] WEINBERG, L., *Network Analysis and Synthesis*. McGraw-Hill 1962.

[82] VAN VALKENBURG, M. E., *Introduction to Modern Network Synthesis*. Wiley 1959.

[83] MATHEWS, M. V., and W. W. SEIFERT, Transfer function synthesis with computer amplifiers and passive networks. *Western Joint Computer Conference. I.R.E.*, pp. 7–12 (1955).

[84] GUILLEMIN, E. A., Synthesis of R. C. networks. *J. Maths. and Phys.* **28**, 22–42 (1949).

[85] BOWER, J. L., and P. F. ORDNUNG, The synthesis of resistor-capacitor networks. *Proc. I.R.E.* **38**, 263–269 (1950).

[86] PAUL, R. J. A., Simulation of rational transfer functions with adjustable coefficients. *Proc. I.E.E.* **110**, 4, 673–679 (1963).

[87] PAUL, R. J. A., *The Realization of Fourth order Rational Transfer Functions with Adjustable Coefficients*. College of Aeronautics, Tech. Note No. 126.

[88] KING and RIDEOUT, Improved transport delay circuits for analogue computer use. *Proc. 3rd International Analogue Computation Meeting*, 1961.

[89] TAYLOR, P. L., Flexible design method for active RC two-ports. *J. I.E.E.* 110, No. 9, 1607–1616.

[90] TRUXAL, J. G., *Control Engineers Handbook*. McGraw-Hill.

[91] WIENER, N., *The Interpolation, Extrapolation and Smoothing of Stationary Time Series*. Wiley 1949.

[92] BODE, H. W., and C. E. SHANNON, A simplified derivation of linear least square smoothing and prediction theory. *Proc. I.R.E.* **38**, No. 4, 417–425 (1950).

[93] LEE, Y. W., *Statistical Theory of Communication*. Wiley 1960.

[94] HORN, R. E., and P. M. HONNELL, Matrix programming of electronic analogue computers. *Trans. Amer. Inst. Elect. Engrs.* I, 77, 420–428 (1958). *Commun. & Electronics*, No. 38 (1958).

[95] CEDERBAUM, I., and A. FUCHS, On the stability of linear algebraic equation solvers. *Proc. 2nd International Analogue Computation Meeting*, pp. 174–178 (1959).

[96] NEWTON, G. C., L. A. GOULD and J. F. KAISER, *Analytical Design of Linear Feedback Control*. Wiley 1957.

[97] ROBERTS, A. P., Application of Pontryagin's maximum principle to the design of control systems with randomly varying inputs. *Trans. Soc. Inst. Tech.* **15**, No. 2, 155–160 (1963).

[98] PAUL, J. R. A., and M. H. McFADDEN, Measurement of phase and amplitude at low frequencies. *Electronic Engng.* **31**, No. 373 (1959).

[99] GARNER, K. C., Use your analogue computer as a transfer function analyser. *British Commun. and Electronics.* 6, No. 11, 764–766 (1959).

[100] HAMPTON, R., G. A. KORN and B. MITCHELL, Hybrid analog–digital random-noise generation. *Trans. I.E.E.E. on Electronic Computers*, pp. 412–413 (1963).

[101] CHIESA, A., and G. TANGORRA, Circuits formateurs d'images pour la visualisation en oscillographe de l'allure des solutions d'un calculateur analogique. *Proc. 2nd International Analogue Computation Meeting*, pp. 88–94 (1959).

[102] GARNER, K. C., Survey of galvanometer recorders. *Control* 2, No. 10, 80–83 (1959), and IEA Buyers Guide & Year Book, 1965.

[103] DUDGEON, D. R., and D. McLEAN, Control System Analysers. *Control* 5, No. 46 (1962).

[104] BECKMAN, *Ease Computer Handbooks*. Berkeley Division, California.

[105] GORDON, L. L., Keyboard system makes pot setting simple. *Control Engng.* October 1954.

[106] HERRMANN, H., Beiträge zur Programmiertechnik für elektronische Analogie-Rechenmaschinen. *Abhandl. Braunschw. Wiss. Gesell.* **10**, 117–149 (1958).

[107] PATCHETT, G. H., *Automatic Voltage Regulators and Stabilizers*. 2nd ed. Pitman.

[108] WILLIAMS, F. C., and F. J. U. RITSON, Electronic servo simulators. *J. I.E.E.* **94**, Pt. II A, No. 1, 112–129 (1947). (Proceedings of the Convention on Automatic Regulators and Servomechanisms, May 1947.)

[109] MACKAY, D. M., and M. E. FISHER, *Analogue Computing at Ultra-High Speed*. Chapman & Hall 1962.

[110] SIMPKIN, K. H., The relative merits of a.c. and d.c. as a signal source in analogue computers. *Electronic Engng.* **25**, No. 304, 230–233 (1953).

[111] SOBCZYK, A., Stabilization of carrier frequency servomechanisms. *J. Franklin Inst.* **246**, Nos. 1, 2 and 3 (1948).

[112] McDONALD, D., Improvements in the characteristics of a.c. lead networks for servo-mechanisms. *Trans. Amer. I.E.E.* **69**, Pt. I, 293–300 (1950).

[113] AHRENDT, W. R., *Servomechanism Practice*. McGraw-Hill 1954.

[114] PALEVSKY, M., *An Approach to Digital Simulation*. National Simulation Conf. Proc., Jan. 1956, Dept. of Elec. Engng., Southern Methodist Univ. Dallas, Texas.

[115] ROWLEY, G. C., Digital differential analysers. *Brit. Communications and Electronics.* **5**, No. 12, 934–938 (1958).

[116] HERRING, G. J., and D. LAMB, The digital differential analyser as a general analogue computer. *Proc. 2nd Int. Analogue Comp. Meeting*, pp. 392–396 (1959).

[117] PAUL, R. J. A., and M. E. MAXWELL, Digital and hybrid simulation techniques. *Control* **3**, No. 22, 120–124 (1960).

[118] PAUL, R. J. A., and M. E. MAXWELL, The general trend towards digital analogue technique. *Proc. 2nd Int. Analogue Comp. Meeting*, pp. 403–406 (1959).

[119] SCHOUTEN, J. F., F. DE JA JAGER and J. A. GREEFKES, "Delta modulation", a new modulation system for telecommunication techniques. *Philips Technical Review* **13**, 237 (1952).

[120] Delta modulation. *Wireless World*, p. 427 (1952).

[121] PAUL, R. J. A., *Hybrid Methods for Function Generation*. College of Aeronautics Report No. 153, Nov. 1961 and Ibid, *Proc. 3rd Int. Analogue Comp. Meeting*, 1961.

[122] HODGES, P. L., System assessment and initial design. *Control* **2**, No. 15, 91–95 (1959).

[123] CRONIN, D. E., Simulators for missiles and space vehicles. *Brit. Commun. and Electronics* **7**, No. 10, 742–745 (1960).

[124] HARTLEY, M. G., Versatile analogue computer for g.w. studies. *Control* **4**, 98–101 and 103–104 (1961).

[125] ROTTENBURG, P. A. (Hon. Editor), *Proceedings of the Joint Symposium on Instrumentation* and *Computation in Process Development and Plant Design*, May 1959.

[126] KING, R. E., Optimization studies on an analogue of a simple still. *Trans. Soc. Instr. Tech.* **15**, No. 1, 59–70 (1963).

[127] DOVETON, A. H., The simulation of a large chemical plant on an electronic analogue computer. *Trans. Soc. Instr. Tech.* **12**, No. 4, 180–190 (1960).

[128] Training Devices, *Index Aeronauticus*, Annual Index, Vol. 19, Nos. 1–12, p. 87 (1963).

[129] BEKEY, G. A., M. J. MERRITT and M. S. ASSALI, Synthesis of a model of cardiovascular dynamics with an analogue computer. *Proc. 4th International Analogue Computation Meeting*, 1964.

INDEX

OTHER TITLES PUBLISHED IN THIS SERIES

MADE IN GREAT BRITAIN